STIMULUS AND SENSATION

STIMULUS AND SENSATION

Readings in Sensory Psychology

EDITED BY

WILLIAM S. CAIN
LAWRENCE E. MARKS

John B. Pierce Foundation Laboratory
and Yale University School of Medicine

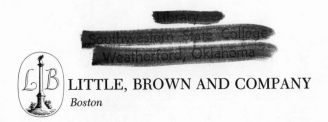

LITTLE, BROWN AND COMPANY
Boston

FIRST PRINTING

*Published simultaneously in Canada
by Little, Brown & Company (Canada) Limited*

PRINTED IN THE UNITED STATES OF AMERICA

ACKNOWLEDGMENTS

We wish to express our gratitude to the authors and publishers of the selections reprinted in this volume. The knowledge that they have accumulated and transmitted forms much of the foundation of the psychology of sensation. This collection of readings belongs truly to them.

We thank in particular Dr. Joseph C. Stevens, whose excellent advice and keen editorial abilities helped to guide us through all phases of this project.

Mrs. Carol Mikalavicius organized our correspondence and gave us invaluable assistance in preparing the manuscript.

W. S. C.
L. E. M.

CONTENTS

INTRODUCTION

The study of sensation is probably the oldest field of experimental psychology. The relatively early origin of experimental sensory psychology was derived, at least in large measure, from philosophy, where interest in sensation has a long history. This history was particularly evident in epistemology. For surely it is the senses that provide information about the world, that form the source of our knowledge of our selves and our environment. In fact, it has even been claimed that sense data comprise all that we know — *nihil in intellectu quod non fuerit in sensu*. Such a position was taken, for instance, by Locke and Hume, and it forms the basis for the viewpoint generally named "empiricist": the mind is at birth a *tabula rasa* upon which experience (via the senses) writes. In contrast is the nativist or rationalist viewpoint, such as that espoused by Leibniz: rather than homogeneous granite, the mind is like a block of veined marble. The veins in the marble can direct, guide, and thereby contribute to the constituents of mind.

Our subject here, of course, is the psychology of sensation, an interest more modest than the origin of the constituents of mind. But the Leibnizian simile is relevant to sensory systems, for sensory systems may be thought of as analogous to the veins in marble. It is clear that the senses do not merely provide eidola of the patterns of stimulus energies in the world. The activity of sensory systems does not merely reflect the external (or internal) environment. The senses are selective. We cannot see very far into the infrared, we cannot hear in the ultrasonic, and, apparently, we cannot at all sense levels or changes in level of magnetic flux. Nor do the senses seem always to respond in a linear manner: the cricket's chirp is clear against the silence of night, but becomes imperceptible when a jet airplane forms the background.

So the questions we ask are "How do the senses attenuate, select, transform external stimuli? What are the functional relations between

1

attributes of sensations and attributes of stimuli?" These questions un-
derlie the area of inquiry known as sensory psychophysics.

It is unfortunate that psychophysics is traditionally considered to be
one of the more dreary topics in experimental psychology. Perhaps
more unfortunate still, there is justification for that attitude, for often
psychophysics is presented as if it is concerned primarily with details
of methodology. We have tried to avoid emphasizing methodology in
this collection of readings. In a basic sense, of course, methodology
cannot be avoided. Assuming that one is interested in measuring sensory reactions, the first question asked is "How can these sensory reactions be measured?" Nevertheless, details of methodology are not
emphasized. Rather, the emphasis has been placed on more general
issues, such as the different types of question that can be answered by
the use of different experimental procedures. But although on the one
hand the readings do not emphasize methodological and procedural
detail, neither on the other hand do they emphasize the content of
sensory psychology. Rather, we have tried to select papers that ex-
emplify significant viewpoints and positions that have been taken with
regard to the measurement of sensory responses.

The first reading in this collection (by J. C. Stevens) provides a brief,
general overview of sensory psychology and sensory measurement. The
readings that follow are arranged in three major topics (Sections 2 to 4).
These three topics may be thought of as representative of three successive, though overlapping, stages in the study of sensation. The first
topic derives from certain features of our most immediate, phenomenological encounter with the world, its stimuli, and their resultant sensations. It is obvious that sensations vary along several dimensions:
sensations have attributes, viz., the loudness and pitch of a sound, the
intensity and quality of an odor, etc. How many attributes exist for a
particular sensory modality and how many stimuli we can identify
when their sensations vary in one or more attributes are the subject
of the readings in Section 2.

Closely allied to the problem of the number of stimuli we can identify in a sensory modality is the second topic, discrimination. (In a
most basic sense, of course, all the readings, indeed all of sensory psychophysics, involves the problem of discrimination. Every type of
psychophysical judgment requires the experimental observer to make
some sort of discrimination between conditions of stimulation.) Primary here is how much two stimuli must differ along some physical
dimension in order for an experimental observer to distinguish between

them. Our capacity for making fine discriminations is often remarkable; our discriminatory precision was remarked upon by William James:

> That "practice makes perfect" is notorious in the field of motor accomplishments. But motor accomplishments depend in part on sensory discrimination. Billiard-playing, rifle-shooting, tight-rope dancing demand the most delicate appreciation of minute disparities of sensation, as well as the power to make accurately graduated muscular responses thereto. In the purely sensorial field we have the well-known virtuosity displayed by the professional buyers and testers of goods. One man will distinguish by taste between the upper and the lower half of a bottle of old Madeira. Another will recognize, by feeling the flour in a barrel, whether the wheat was grown in Iowa or Tennessee. The blind deaf-mute, Laura Bridgman, so improved her touch as to recognize, after a year's interval, the hand of a person who had once shaken hers; and her sister in misfortune, Julia Brace, is said to have been employed in the Hartford Asylum to sort the linen of its multitudinous inmates, after it came from the wash, by her wonderfully educated sense of smell.°

The reader may notice that James' statement bears as well on the topic of stimulus identification as it does on the topic of discrimination.

The final group of readings deals with the measurement of magnitudes of sensation. It is a salient feature of sensations that they vary in intensity: from soft to loud, from dim to bright, from warm to hot. A passing locomotive sounds louder than a ticking wristwatch, and under normal conditions these two sounds will be discriminated all the time. The question raised in the last group of readings, however, is not how *often* the locomotive appears louder but rather how *much* louder it appears. We can, of course, by means of suitable instruments measure the sound pressures of the corresponding acoustical events. But though such measurements can tell us something about the physical magnitudes of the two sounds, they cannot tell us anything about their psychological magnitudes. Thus the readings appearing under the last topic are about whether and how *magnitudes of sensation* can be measured.

° William James, *Psychology: Briefer Course*, 1892, p. 252.

Three broad principles served as guides to the selection and arrangement of the readings. One was to select readings that trace the various lines of development within each topic. An example, under the topic of discrimination, is the emphasis by Cattell and by Crozier and Holway on the relationship between variability and discrimination and the subsequent exposition by Swets, Tanner, and Birdsall of the central role of variability in the theory of signal detection. Not all the developments within one topic have been represented in proportion to their significance for sensory psychology, however. We have included a relatively small amount of material on the theory of signal detection, even though its concepts and procedures play a large role in current research in sensory psychophysics. However, a collection of readings dealing with signal detection is available elsewhere.[1] Notice also that, because of difficulty and complexity, some areas of research, such as multidimensional scaling, are treated only at a rather simple level.

A second principle that guided organization of the readings was the juxtaposition of differing or opposing viewpoints, such as the approaches to the measurement of sensation taken by S. S. Stevens and by W. R. Garner. The reader will discover that nothing like unanimity is to be found among students of sensation on some of the basic issues in topics like the measurement of sensory magnitudes.

Finally, and perhaps most important, even though many of the authors of these readings examine sensory behavior in one modality or another, most of the readings were selected with a view toward general problems in sensation. These readings reflect, we hope, the opinion that much can be learned and understood about how sensory systems operate if one takes an encompassing look at all the senses. To be sure, the different sensory systems have in many respects vastly different anatomical structures and physiological mechanisms, and the mechanisms by which one sense operates must be considered purely by themselves. Yet it is also true that many of the broad principles that describe the input-output relations of sensory systems show marked similarities from one sense to another. The readings in this volume were, therefore, selected in large measure to help make apparent some of the general principles underlying sensory behavior.

[1] J. A. Swets (editor), *Signal Detection and Recognition by Human Observers*, 1964.

1. PSYCHOPHYSICAL PROBLEMS AND PROCEDURES

"Psychophysics" by J. C. Stevens is a comprehensive and readable introduction to general problems and methods in sensory measurement. We hope this article will serve both as an overview of psychophysics and as a reference whose relevant sections will be reread as the reader begins each successive chapter of this volume.

PSYCHOPHYSICS

Joseph C. Stevens

Psychophysics is the study of physical stimuli and their relation to sensory reactions. Of the energy that strikes the sensory surfaces of man and the animals, only a restricted fraction is capable of eliciting a reaction. Thus, visual responses in man are triggered by a narrow band of the vast electromagnetic spectrum (wavelengths between about 400 and 750 millimicrons); and auditory responses result from periodic displacements of the eardrum in the frequency range from about 20 to 20,000 cycles per second (cps). Over these stimulus ranges, neither the

Reprinted with permission of the Publisher from the *International Encyclopedia of the Social Sciences*, David L. Sills, editor, Volume 13, pages 120–126. Copyright © 1968 by Crowell Collier and Macmillan, Inc.

eye nor the ear is uniformly responsive: to produce a sensation may require thousands of times more energy at one wavelength or frequency than at another. It is the goal of psychophysics to map out the relations between the physical events and the psychological responses of organisms, and thus to provide a basic, over-all description of the function of the senses.

Major Problems

The traditional questions posed by psychophysics fall into four groups. For a given sense modality we may ask about (1) the smallest detectable energy (the measurement of *sensitivity*); (2) the smallest detectable change in energy (the measurement of *resolving power*); (3) the configurations of energy that produce an invariant sensory effect, such as a constant loudness or color (the measurement of *static invariances*); (4) the way in which the magnitude of a sensory effect depends functionally on the stimulus (the measurement of *dynamic properties*).

SENSITIVITY

The problem of sensitivity involves the determination of the smallest detectable intensity of a stimulus (called the *absolute threshold*), often as a function of another stimulus dimension, such as wavelength, frequency, duration, or areal extent. The threshold of audibility, for example, depends on the frequency of the tone; sensitivity is greatest to frequencies between about 2,000 and 3,000 cps. In the vicinity of 20 and 20,000 cps (which are conveniently but arbitrarily called the "limits" of hearing), the threshold energy may rise to roughly 10^8 times the minimal value. A similar relation exists between the threshold of visibility and the wavelength of the stimulating light, except that the shape of the visibility curve depends on what part of the sensory surface is stimulated; foveal (cone) vision has maximum sensitivity at about 555 millimicrons; peripheral (rod) vision, at about 505 millimicrons; and the "limits" of visibility are also different for the two populations of receptors.

Variation in Sensitivity

The absolute threshold is not a rigidly fixed value. Sensitivity fluctuates irregularly, so that a given stimulus level may trigger a response at one time but not at another. The threshold is usually defined statistically, e.g., as the energy level that is detected as often as not over a series of presentations.

Sensitivity is also subject to systematic variation, either of the permanent kind encountered in aging or in pathology of the sensory tissues, or of a temporary kind observed, for example, in the relatively rapid decline of visual sensitivity under exposure to light (light adaptation) and the subsequent gradual recovery of sensitivity in the dark (dark adaptation). These and many other systematic changes in sensitivity are frequently expressed as alterations of the absolute threshold.

The study of absolute thresholds reveals the exquisite sensitivity of the sense organs under optimal conditions. A periodic displacement of the eardrum through a distance equal to the diameter of a hydrogen molecule may suffice to produce an audible sound, and a couple of quanta of light absorbed at the retina may suffice to arouse a faint visual sensation.

Methods of Measurement

Because it fluctuates, the threshold is difficult to measure, and the various methods that have been tried do not always yield the same value. The method of *adjustment* provides a rapid approximation; the observer is required to set the level of the stimulus so that it is just perceptible. The threshold may be defined as the average of several settings. In the method of limits, either the stimuli are presented in order of increasing magnitude until the observer reverses his response from "imperceptible" to "perceptible," or they are presented in order of decreasing magnitude until the observer reverses his response from "perceptible" to "imperceptible." The threshold may be defined as the average value that marks the reversal in response over several ascending and descending series. In the method of *constant stimuli,* fixed stimulus levels are presented several times, each in irregular order. The threshold may be defined as the stimulus value that is perceived on half the presentations. This value is interpolated from a plot relating the percentage of positive responses to the stimulus magnitude.

The methods of adjustment, limits, and constant stimuli are known as the *classical psychophysical methods* because they have continued in widespread use ever since G. T. Fechner described them in his *Elemente der Psychophysik* (1860), the monumental work that marks the establishment of psychophysics. (Reviews of the classical methods are given by Urban 1908; Titchener 1905; and Boring 1942.)

One of the difficulties inherent in these methods is the observer's awareness that a stimulus event actually takes place on each trial. When a "catch trial" (a feigned presentation of a stimulus) is given, observers will occasionally give an affirmative response (a "false alarm"). The knowledge that the observer's expectations and motivations come into play has stimulated the invention of new methods that offer the hope of better understanding and controlling the observer's response biases. An example is the *forced choice* method, in which at regular intervals a stimulus is presented or withheld and the observer must decide each time whether or not he detected it. Results obtained under this procedure reveal that detection may depend not only on the magnitude of the stimulus but also on the prearranged probability of a stimulus event. A high proportion of "no-stimulus" trials causes a relatively high incidence of "false alarms"; a low proportion of "no-stimulus" trials, on the other hand, causes a lower incidence of correct detections of actual stimulus events. The probability of a "Yes" or "No" response can also be systematically influenced by rewarding correct detections and punishing the false alarms.

The forced-choice experiments have done much to underscore and clarify the role of response variables in the measurement of thresholds. It is sometimes suggested that the "detection" model may actually do away with the conception of the threshold as a simple, determinable value marking the critical terminus of sensory experience. According to this view, the detection of a stimulus (the "signal") has much in common with the mathematical process of statistical decision. The observer is confronted with two distributions: that of the persistent background noise and that of the signal added to the noise. He decides from which of the two distributions a sample is taken in much the way that a statistician tests a statistical hypothesis. The decision will depend on the overlap of the distributions and also on the "pay-off matrix" — the consequences of false detections and failures of detection (see Swets 1964; Luce et al. 1963).

Interesting technological advances have recently been made in the field of threshold measurement. The Békésy audiometer, for example, uses the method of *tracking* for the efficient measurement of the just-audible intensity as a function of tonal frequency (Von Békésy 1928–1958). The observer "tracks" his threshold by pressing a key whenever the tone is audible and releasing it whenever the tone becomes inaudible. While the key is pressed, the level of the tone steadily decreases; while the key is not pressed, the level steadily increases. The observer may continue to track the threshold while the tonal frequency changes from one end of the audible spectrum to the other. On a moving paper chart, the stimulus level, which weaves back and forth across the threshold, is recorded continuously as a function of the frequency.

The tracking method has also been used to determine the visual thresholds of human observers and has been adapted to mapping the sensitivity functions of animals.

RESOLVING POWER

The second major concern of psychophysics is to measure the smallest detectable change in a stimulus (the so-called *difference threshold*). The problem may be to measure the just-noticeable differences in *intensity*, e.g., in the brightness of a light or in the concentration of a sweet solution, or in *quality*, e.g., in the hue of a colored light.

The capacity for resolving stimulus differences is expressed in terms of the Weber fraction, $\Delta I/I$, where ΔI stands for the increment that produces a just-noticeable change when added to the stimulus level I. The smaller the value of ΔI, the keener is the ability to discriminate.

Methods of Measurement

Like the absolute threshold, the difference threshold is a fluctuating quantity, so that ΔI must be assessed by a statistical treatment of a series of measurements. Most of the methods used are versions of those used to measure absolute thresholds. In the method of *adjustment*, for example, the observer sets a comparison stimulus to match a standard fixed stimulus. The threshold, ΔI, may be defined as the average error or the standard deviation of several settings. The greater the variability of the settings, the grosser the discrimination and the larger the Weber fraction. A difference threshold may be regarded either as a measure of the precision or as a measure of the variability or "noisiness" of the sensory process.

In the method of *constant stimuli*, the observer judges whether each of a set of fixed discrete stimulus levels appears greater or smaller than a standard stimulus (a judgment of "equal" is also permitted by some experimenters). The difference threshold may be defined as the difference between a standard stimulus and a comparison stimulus that is perceived as being greater (or smaller) than the standard stimulus on a certain percentage of the trials. This value can be interpolated from a *poikilitic* (scatter) *function*.

In Figure 1 the ordinate represents the relative frequency with which the comparison stimulus is judged greater than the standard.

The threshold, ΔI, is the difference between the stimulus magnitude that is perceived as being greater than the standard on 75 per cent of the trials (L) and the stimulus magnitude that is so perceived on 50 per cent of the trials (E), i.e., the stimulus that appears to match the standard stimulus. Often there is a small difference, called the time error, between the standard stimulus (S) and the stimulus value associated with the 50 per cent point. Urban (1908) provides a detailed discussion of poikilitic functions.

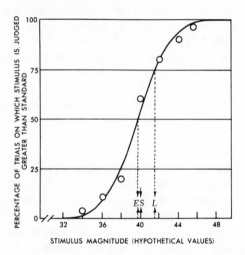

FIGURE 1   *A poikilitic (scatter) function determined by the method of constant stimuli.*

The nature of the difference threshold has often been studied by the method of *quantal increments*. From time to time, a small increment, ΔI, is added briefly to a steady stimulus, I. The task is to indicate whether the increment was detected. Of theoretical concern is the mathematical form of the poikilitic function that relates the proportion of detections to the size of the increment. If the precision were ultimately limited by nothing but the random "noisiness" of the sensory process, then the function would be expected to have the sigmoid shape (the integral of a bell-shaped distribution) that is predicted by the theory of random error. The usual result approximates this form. When pains are taken to aid the attention and to eliminate the extraneous sources of error, the obtained function may assume a linear rather than a sigmoid form and conform to a predictable slope. According to the *neural-quantum hypothesis,* a linear function of the appropriate slope demonstrates that discrimination is basically all-or-none and that sensation grows by the addition of minute but finite (or quantal) steps (see Von Békésy 1928–1958; S. S. Stevens 1961; Luce et al. 1963; Swets 1964).

Weber's Law

A major aim in threshold measurement has been to test the famous generalization, credited to Ernst H. Weber but formalized and promoted by Fechner, that the Weber fraction is constant along a given sensory continuum, or that $\Delta I/I = k$. In other words, a just-noticeable change should occur when a constant fractional increment is added to a stimulus of any magnitude. Under good conditions the increment is about 1 per cent for brightness, 2 per cent for loudness, and 20 per cent for saltiness. The sensory systems differ greatly in their resolving power, but for any one system it is the percentage change that matters most.

On most continua Weber's law holds over a substantial portion of the stimulus range (for loudness and brightness over at least 99.9 per cent of the range), but the law fails near the absolute threshold, where discrimination is relatively gross. Nevertheless, Weber's law stands as one of the oldest and broadest empirical generalizations of psychophysics — psychology's "law of relativity," as one writer put it (S. S. Stevens 1951).

Fechner's Law

If discrimination has seemed to receive more than reasonable attention among students of the senses, the explanation is likely to be found in the significance that the founder of psychophysics attached to the subject. For Fechner, discrimination provided the key to the measurement of sensory magnitude. He began with the postulate that on a given sensory continuum all just-noticeable differences *(jnd)* represent subjectively equal units. Subjective equality of *jnds* is a powerful (if questionable) assumption, because the integration of such units would provide a true scale of subjective magnitude. Since by Weber's law a *jnd* corresponds to a constant fractional increase in the stimulus, it follows that the number of *jnds* grows in an arithmetic series when the stimulus intensity grows in a geometric series. Fechner concluded, therefore, that the magnitude of sensation is a logarithmic function of the stimulus. The logarithmic function implies that equal *ratios* of stimulus magnitude give rise to equal *differences* in subjective magnitude.

Plateau's Power Function

In contrast to the indirectness of the Fechnerian approach to the measurement of sensory magnitudes was an early experiment by the Belgian physicist Joseph A. F. Plateau, who asked a group of artists each to paint a gray that seemed to lie midway between a white sample and a gray sample (a version of a scaling method later termed *equisection*). Of historical interest is Plateau's conclusion that sensation grows as a power function rather than a logarithmic function of the stimulus. But the power function was subsequently given up by Plateau and virtually forgotten until the 1950s. With new techniques for the direct assessment of sensory magnitude, it was shown that Plateau's early conjecture about the form of the psychophysical function happened to be correct. The current approach to the problem is generally to regard as separate properties the resolving capacity of the sensory system and the functional dependence of sensory magnitude on the stimulus.

THE STATIC INVARIANCES
OF SENSORY SYSTEMS

A third major problem of psychophysics is to determine those arrangements of stimuli that produce responses that are equivalent in some respect. The goal of this kind of measurement is to specify all the energy configurations in the environment that produce an invariant or equivalent sensory response.

For example, the goal may be to determine the combinations of intensity and duration of a flash target that produce the same apparent brightness. The level or the duration of a comparison flash is adjusted to match the brightness of a standard flash of fixed intensity and duration. The judgment requires a degree of abstraction because the task is to match for brightness without regard to a difference in apparent duration. A plot relating the duration and intensity that produce a constant (standard) brightness provides an example of an *equal sensation function*. Usually it is desirable to map the family of these equal sensation functions for a pair of parameters. In the present example this means that a function is obtained for each of a set of representative standard brightnesses along the brightness continuum. We learn from this family that, up to a critical duration (roughly 150 milliseconds), a decrease in the stimulus level can be offset by lengthening the flash. Moreover, the critical duration gets systematically shorter as the brightness is increased.

Measurement of the static invariances is common in psychophysics. Examples include the equal brightness functions relating energy and wavelength, the equal loudness functions relating sound pressure and tonal frequency, the equal pitch functions relating frequency and sound pressure (within limits, the apparent pitch of a tone can be altered by a change in sound pressure level), and the equal hue functions relating wavelength and light intensity. (The change in hue when intensity is altered has long been known as the Bezold-Brücke phenomenon.)

The measurement of invariance may call for complete equivalence. An example is the concept of metamerism in color vision. The measurement of metameric pairs (sample lights of identical appearance but different wavelength compositions) has made it possible to state the laws of color mixtures and to predict the color of a sample of any spectral composition.

Methods of Measurement

Because of its speed and immediacy, the method of adjustment usually recommends itself for the mapping of equivalents. Other usable procedures, however, include constant stimuli, limits, and tracking. The measurement of equivalence is straightforward in principle, but any procedure is usually beset by constant errors, such as the "time error" (see Figure 1).

DYNAMIC PROPERTIES
OF SENSORY SYSTEMS

It is one thing to know the stimulus conditions that produce an invariant sensory effect and another thing to know how much larger one sensory effect is than another — e.g., how much brighter one luminance level appears than another or how much two tones seem to differ in pitch. A major problem of psychophysics is to learn how much the magnitude of the sensory response grows when the stimulus intensity increases.

The Direct Scaling Methods

In the 1930s it became apparent to students of hearing that the logarithmic function fails to agree with the reports of observers who are asked to judge the relative loudness of stimuli. Attempts were made to measure the loudness function by a variety of direct methods. Subsequently, the direct methods were expanded and refined and finally applied to the study of all the major sensory continua.

The main feature of the direct methods is the attempt to match segments of the number continuum directly to segments of the sensory continuum. In the method of *magnitude estimation,* various fixed levels of the stimulus are presented one by one in irregular order, and the observer attempts to assign numbers to these levels in proportion to their subjective magnitude. The inverse of this procedure is *magnitude production:* a set of numbers is called out one by one to the observer, who adjusts the level of the stimulus so as to produce subjective magnitudes that are proportional to the numbers. In *ratio production,* a comparison stimulus is adjusted to appear in some fractional or multiplicative relation to a standard stimulus, and in *ratio estimation,* the observer estimates numerically the apparent ratio that corresponds to a pair of stimulus magnitudes. Variations on these procedures are numerous (S. S. Stevens 1958).

Two Classes of Continua

For a few continua, of which pitch is a noteworthy example, a scale of integrated *jnds* turns out to agree well with direct judgment. S. S. Stevens (1957) called these continua *metathetic* and distinguished them from the large class of *prothetic* continua on all of which the *jnd* does not afford a constant unit of subjective magnitude. (Table 1 provides a partial list of prothetic continua.)

The Psychophysical Power Functions

S. S. Stevens has also proposed a general psychophysical relation pertaining to all prothetic continua (1957). Equal stimulus ratios are held to correspond to equal sensation *ratios* (rather than to equal sensation *differences,* as Fechner had conjectured). In other words, the apparent magnitude ψ grows as a power function of the stimulus magnitude, or $\psi = k\phi^\beta$, where k is a constant proportionality and β is the exponent. The size of β varies from one continuum to another. In Figure 2A are plotted the power functions in linear coordinates for three continua: apparent length ($\beta = 1$), brightness ($\beta = 0.33$), and the apparent intensity of an electric current passed through the fingers ($\beta = 3.5$). When plotted in log–log coordinates, as in Figure 2B, these same functions become straight lines whose slopes equal the values of the ex-

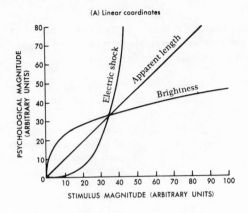

(A) Linear coordinates

PSYCHOLOGICAL MAGNITUDE (ARBITRARY UNITS)

Electric shock

Apparent length

Brightness

STIMULUS MAGNITUDE (ARBITRARY UNITS)

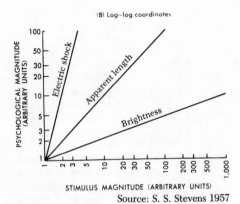

(B) Log–log coordinates

PSYCHOLOGICAL MAGNITUDE (ARBITRARY UNITS)

Electric shock

Apparent length

Brightness

STIMULUS MAGNITUDE (ARBITRARY UNITS)

Source: S. S. Stevens 1957

FIGURE 2 *The power function for three prothetic continua plotted in (A) linear coordinates and (B) log–log coordinates.*

ponents. This is true because the logarithmic form of the power function is $\log \psi = \log k + \beta \log \phi$.

Table 1 shows that the size of the exponent may depend not only on the sense organ stimulated but also on the conditions of the stimulation. Note the difference between the monaural and the binaural loudness functions and the exponent's dependence on frequency for vibration magnitude.

Although the simple equation $\psi = k\phi^{\beta}$ holds for large stimulus values, in the neighborhood of the absolute threshold a more precise form is needed. The power equation can be written as $\psi = k(\phi - \phi_0)^{\beta}$,

TABLE 1

REPRESENTATIVE EXPONENTS OF THE POWER FUNCTIONS
RELATING PSYCHOLOGICAL MAGNITUDE TO STIMULUS
MAGNITUDE ON PROTHETIC CONTINUA

Continuum	Exponent	Stimulus condition
Loudness	0.6	binaural
Loudness	0.54	monaural
Brightness	0.33	5° target — dark-adapted eye
Brightness	0.5	point source — dark-adapted eye
Lightness	1.2	reflectance of gray papers
Smell	0.55	coffee odor
Smell	0.6	heptane
Taste	0.8	saccharine
Taste	1.3	sucrose
Taste	1.3	salt
Temperature	1.0	cold — on arm
Temperature	1.5	warmth — on arm
Vibration	0.95	60 cps — on finger
Vibration	0.6	250 cps — on finger
Duration	1.1	white-noise stimulus
Repetition rate	1.0	light, sound, touch, and shocks
Finger span	1.3	thickness of wood blocks
Pressure on palm	1.1	static force on skin
Heaviness	1.45	lifted weights
Force of handgrip	1.7	precision hand dynamometer
Vocal effort	1.1	sound pressure of vocalization
Electric shock	3.5	60 cps — through fingers
Tactual roughness	1.5	felt diameter of emery grits
Tactual hardness	0.8	rubber squeezed between fingers
Viscosity	0.5	stirring silicone fluids
Visual velocity	1.2	moving spot of light
Visual length	1.0	projected line of light
Visual area	0.7	projected square of light

Source: Adapted from S. S. Stevens 1957.

where ϕ_0 approximates the absolute threshold. The correction for threshold brings into coincidence the zero of the stimulus scale and the zero of the sensation scale (Luce et al. 1963).

The properties of sensory systems may reveal themselves as parametric shifts in the values of ϕ, k, and β. The changes in visual sensitivity that occur under light adaptation provide an example (Stevens and Stevens 1963). Light adaptation causes (1) an elevation in the absolute threshold (i.e., ϕ_0 increases), (2) an increase in the luminance necessary to produce a given subjective brightness (i.e., k decreases), and (3) a slight increase in the exponent β. The mapping of these parametric changes has made it possible to write the power function that pertains to any given level of adaptation and consequently to predict the subjective brightness produced by any luminance level when viewed by an eye adapted to any other luminance level.

Cross-Modality Validations

A method has been devised that circumvents the need for the observer to make numerical estimates of his sensation but leads to the same psychophysical power function (see S. S. Stevens 1961; and Luce et al. 1963). In *cross-modality matching* the task is to make the sensations in two different sense modalities appear equal in strength. The pairs of physical intensities that produce equal apparent intensities can be plotted as an equal sensation function. It turns out that the equal sensation function relating any two prothetic continua a and b is itself a power function of the form $\phi_a = k\phi_b{}^\gamma$, where ϕ_a and ϕ_b stand for physical intensity. The size of the exponent γ depends on which two continua are matched. Within the experimental error, γ is predictable from the psychophysical function governing the two continua. Given that $\psi_a = \phi_a{}^\alpha$ and $\psi_b = \phi_b{}^\beta$ (with suitable units of measurement), and given that $\psi_a = \psi_b$, the equation of the equal sensation function becomes $\phi_a = \phi_b{}^{\beta/\alpha}$. The exponent γ thus turns out to be the ratio of the exponents α and β.

Any continuum could be substituted for the number continuum and used as a "yardstick" to measure sensory magnitudes on all of the other sensory continua. In one set of experiments, for example, force of handgrip as registered on a dynamometer was used to assess subjective magnitudes on nine other prothetic continua (S. S. Stevens 1961). Many other examples could be cited to show that the psychophysical power law is able to predict both the form and the exponent of the equal sensation function obtained by cross-modality matching.

BIBLIOGRAPHY

Boring, Edwin G. 1942. *Sensation and Perception in the History of Experimental Psychology.* New York: Appleton.

Fechner, Gustav T. (1860) 1907. *Elemente der Psychophysik.* 3d ed. 2 vols. Leipzig: Breitkopf & Härtel.

Luce, R. Duncan, Bush, Robert R., and Galanter, Eugene (editors). 1963. *Handbook of Mathematical Psychology.* Volume 1. New York: Wiley.

Piéron, Henri (1945) 1952. *The Sensations: Their Functions, Processes, and Mechanisms.*
New Haven: Yale Univ. Press; London: Müller. First published as *Aux sources de la
connaissance: La sensation, guide de vie.*

Stevens, J. C. and Stevens, S. S. 1963. "Brightness Function: Effects of Adaptation." *Journal of the Optical Society of America* 53:375–385.

Stevens, S. S. (editor). 1951. *Handbook of Experimental Psychology.* New York: Wiley.

Stevens, S. S. 1957. "On the Psychophysical Law." *Psychological Review* 64:153–181.

Stevens, S. S. 1958. "Problems and Methods of Psychophysics." *Psychological Bulletin* 55:
177–196.

Stevens, S. S. 1961. "To Honor Fechner and Repeal His Law." *Science* 133:80–86.

Stevens, S. S. 1966. "A Metric for the Social Consensus." *Science* 151:530–541.

Stevens, S. S. and Galanter, Eugene 1957. "Ratio Scales and Category Scales for a Dozen
Perceptual Continua." *Journal of Experimental Psychology* 54:377–411.

Swets, John A. (editor) 1964. *Signal Detection and Recognition by Human Observers: Contemporary Readings.* New York: Wiley.

Symposium on Principles of Sensory Communication, Endicott House, *1959*. 1961. *Sensory
Communication: Contributions.* Cambridge, Mass.: M.I.T. Press.

Titchener, Edward B. 1905. *Experimental Psychology: A Manual of Laboratory Practice.*
Volume 2: Quantitative Experiments. London and New York: Macmillan.

Urban, Friedrich M. 1908. *The Application of Statistical Methods to the Problems of Psychophysics.* Philadelphia: Psychological Clinic Press.

Von Békésy, Georg (1928–1958) 1960. *Experiments in Hearing.* New York: McGraw-Hill.

2. ATTRIBUTES OF SENSATION AND IDENTIFICATION OF STIMULI

The authors of the two readings in this section investigate in a fundamental manner dimensions or attributes of sensory experience. If we examine introspectively a "simple" visual perception, we are able to identify several sensory attributes, viz., the brightness, hue, and saturation. (We might want to add apparent size and duration.) Now, it is often true that one dimension of the stimulus appears to provide a clear correlate to some sensory attribute. Galileo demonstrated a relationship, for example, between the frequency of a sound and its pitch. The loudness of a sound, on the other hand, correlates highly with the sound's physical intensity, and analogous correlations can be found in the other sensory modalities. Unfortunately, individual attributes of sensation cannot always be specified completely in terms of single physical dimensions of their stimuli. In "The Attributes of Tones" S. S. Stevens demonstrated that four psychological attributes of tone (pitch, loudness, volume, and density) all depend upon both the frequency and the sound pressure of the corresponding acoustical event. The nature of the dependence on sound frequency and pressure differs, however, among all four of the sensory attributes. In fact, Stevens' paper suggests that the criterion for a sensory attribute be independent constancy. That is, in order to maintain constant the level of pitch, as when sound frequency is varied, it is necessary also to vary sound pressure, and to permit all other tonal attributes to vary as well.

In order to distinguish one stimulus in our environment from another, it is obviously necessary that the sensations aroused by these stimuli differ in one or more attribute. How

19

much two stimuli must differ along some physical dimension in order for a person to distinguish them falls into the general subject of discrimination. Although the readings in the next section deal with the topic of discrimination at some length, George Miller's article in the present section also is about discrimination, but in a somewhat different way. In "The Magical Number Seven, Plus or Minus Two: Some Limits on Our Capacity for Processing Information" Miller deals with our ability not merely to say whether some difference can be detected between stimuli but also to identify these stimuli on an absolute basis. Instead of measuring the increase in the sound pressure of a tone that is necessary for a person to say that it sounds louder than another tone, we measure the number of tones of different sound pressures that a person can consistently identify as tone A, tone B, etc. It turns out that the number of stimuli, differing along one dimension, which a person can "keep straight" usually is surprisingly small.

THE ATTRIBUTES OF TONES

S. S. Stevens

It has long been known that the interaction of a sound stimulus with the human auditory mechanism gives rise to the two discriminatory responses known as pitch and loudness. In addition to these two responses we must recognize tonal volume, first studied by Rich[1] in 1916, and tonal density. These four discriminable attributes are all functions of the two dimensions of the stimulus, frequency and energy. It is the purpose of this paper to discuss the nature of these functions as experimentally determined.

The method used by Kingsbury[2] to determine the well-known equal loudness contours was employed to determine similar isophonic con-

From *Proceedings of the National Academy of Sciences*, 1934, 20, 457–459. Reprinted with permission of the author and the National Academy of Sciences.

[1] G. J. Rich, *J. Exper. Psychol.*, 1, 13–22 (1916).

[2] B. A. Kingsbury, *Phys. Rev.*, 29, 588–600 (1927).

tours for pitch, volume and density. Two tones of different frequency were presented alternately to an observer who was allowed to vary the energy of one of the tones until the two tones sounded equal in respect of the attribute in question. This procedure yields, in the case of loudness, contours having a minimum near the middle of the audible range. A part of one of these contours is shown in Figure 1.

When the observer is asked to make two tones of different frequency sound equal in volume (meaning "bigness" or spread), he increases the intensity of the higher tone by an amount which depends upon the intensity level of the standard tone. The results of a series of equations of this type are shown by the curve marked "volume" in Figure 1. This curve is the smoothed average of the results obtained from four observers by having them match each tone to a standard ten times. The average percentage variation of these equations, as measured in terms of the voltage across the output of the audio-oscillator, was 7.9.

When instructions are given for the observer to make the two tones equal in density, the procedure is reversed. The lower tone has to be made more intense, as is shown in Figure 1. The observers were able to

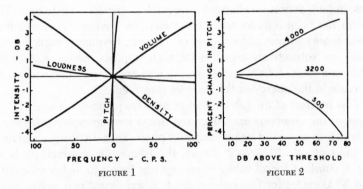

FIGURE 1   FIGURE 2

FIGURE 1   *Isophonic contours representing equal pitch, loudness, volume and density of tones equated to a standard tone of 500 cycles and 60 db. Thus 0 frequency = 500 cycles; 0 intensity = 60 db above the auditory threshold. The pitch contour almost coincides with the 0 vertical when plotted to this scale; but see Figure 2 for the magnitude of its deviation.*

FIGURE 2   *Change in pitch of tones at 500, 3200, and 4000 cycles as a function of intensity of the tones. Intensity is in db above the auditory threshold. The change of pitch is measured by the percentage change in frequency that must be made in order to counteract the change of pitch.*

make these judgments with a percentage variation of 8.8. Furthermore, the introspective reports show that both volume and density are judged with a high degree of subjective certainty. Some observers insisted that no greater certainty attended their judgments of loudness itself. However, the percentage variation obtained from a series of equations for loudness was 6.9, a value which is slightly lower than those cited above for volume and density.

It should be noted that it is a very simple matter to convey to a naive observer what is meant by volume and density by presenting him with a high tone at about 4000 cycles and asking him to note its "smallness" (volume) and its "compactness" or "concentration" (density) and to contrast these characteristics with those of a low tone at about 200 cycles. The difference is at once obvious.

It has generally been supposed that pitch is dependent solely upon the frequency of the stimulus, although several investigators have reported slight changes in pitch as the energy of the stimulus is altered. A systematic study of this effect was made by Zurmühl[3] for frequencies ranging between 256 and 3072 cycles. Zurmühl found that an increase in the intensity of the stimulus caused a drop in the pitch. The percentage of decrease was more for low tones than for high. There was, in fact, almost no change in the pitch of the 3072 cycle tone. The writer has been able to verify these facts by having observers adjust the intensity of one of two tones of different frequency until the two tones are subjectively equal in pitch. It appears, however, that the pitch of a tone of 4000 cycles goes up and not down when there is an increase in the energy of the stimulus (see Figure 2).

This reversal of the pitch effect at high frequencies occurred for all three of the observers and suggested that a frequency could be found at which there would be no change of pitch. Thus, by using a variation of the method of constant stimuli, the frequency at which pitch remains constant for all values of energy was found to lie between 3100 and 3300 cycles for these observers. It is significant that in this range of frequencies the sensitivity of the ear is maximal.[4] In other words, the pitch of a tone is shifted away from the region of greatest sensitivity when the intensity of the tone is increased and toward the region of greatest sensitivity when the intensity is decreased.

We have, then, four distinct types of discriminatory response, all of

[3] G. Zurmühl, Z. f. Sinnesphysiol., 61, 40–86 (1930).
[4] L. J. Sivian and S. D. White, J. Acous. Soc. Amer., 4, 288–321 (1933).

which arise from the interaction of a two-dimensional acoustic stimulus with a multi-dimensional nervous system. With the method employed in these experiments the observer performs a rôle analogous to that of a null instrument. He is "set" or "tuned" by the experimenter's instructions to respond to a difference in a certain aspect of his experience and then the stimulus is adjusted until he ceases to notice a difference. The important point is that the observer can be "tuned" in four different ways. The fact that each type of instruction leads to a response which is a function of the two stimulus variables means that the system can be thought of as bidimensional, but the fact that there are four different types of response means that it should be possible to discover at least four distinguishing characteristics in the neural pattern emanating from the cochlea by the auditory nerve. There is evidence to show that two separate auditory excitations can differ in respect of their position on the basilar membrane, the number of fibres excited, the spread of this excitation and the ratio of active to inactive fibres within the area excited. If these factors could be correlated with pitch, loudness, volume and density, respectively, the solution of the problem of hearing would be greatly furthered.

THE MAGICAL NUMBER SEVEN, PLUS OR MINUS TWO: SOME LIMITS ON OUR CAPACITY FOR PROCESSING INFORMATION

George A. Miller

My problem is that I have been persecuted by an integer. For seven years this number has followed me around, has intruded in my most private data, and has assaulted me from the pages of our most public

From *Psychological Review*, 1956, 63, 81–97. Reprinted with permission of the author and the American Psychological Association.

This paper was first read as an Invited Address before the Eastern Psychological Association in Philadelphia on April 15, 1955. Preparation of the paper was supported by the Harvard Psycho-Acoustic Laboratory under Contract N5ori-76 between Harvard University and the Office of Naval Research, U. S. Navy (Project NR142-201, Report PNR-174).

journals. This number assumes a variety of disguises, being sometimes a little larger and sometimes a little smaller than usual, but never changing so much as to be unrecognizable. The persistence with which this number plagues me is far more than a random accident. There is, to quote a famous senator, a design behind it, some pattern governing its appearances. Either there really is something unusual about the number or else I am suffering from delusions of persecution.

I shall begin my case history by telling you about some experiments that tested how accurately people can assign numbers to the magnitudes of various aspects of a stimulus. In the traditional language of psychology these would be called experiments in absolute judgment. Historical accident, however, has decreed that they should have another name. We now call them experiments on the capacity of people to transmit information. Since these experiments would not have been done without the appearance of information theory on the psychological scene, and since the results are analyzed in terms of the concepts of information theory, I shall have to preface my discussion with a few remarks about this theory.

INFORMATION MEASUREMENT

The "amount of information" is exactly the same concept that we have talked about for years under the name of "variance." The equations are different, but if we hold tight to the idea that anything that increases the variance also increases the amount of information we cannot go far astray.

The advantages of this new way of talking about variance are simple enough. Variance is always stated in terms of the unit of measurement — inches, pounds, volts, etc. — whereas the amount of information is a dimensionless quantity. Since the information in a discrete statistical distribution does not depend upon the unit of measurement, we can extend the concept to situations where we have no metric and we would not ordinarily think of using the variance. And it also enables us to compare results obtained in quite different experimental situations where it would be meaningless to compare variances based on different metrics. So there are some good reasons for adopting the newer concept.

The similarity of variance and amount of information might be explained this way: When we have a large variance, we are very ignorant about what is going to happen. If we are very ignorant, then when we make the observation it gives us a lot of information. On the other hand, if the variance is very small, we know in advance how our observation must come out, so we get little information from making the observation.

If you will now imagine a communication system, you will realize that there is a great deal of variability about what goes into the system and also a great deal of variability about what comes out. The input and the output can therefore be described in terms of their variance (or their information). If it is a good communication system, however, there must be some systematic relation between what goes in and what comes out. That is to say, the output will depend upon the input, or will be correlated with the input. If we measure this correlation, then we can say how much of the output variance is attributable to the input and how much is due to random fluctuations or "noise" introduced by the system during transmission. So we see that the measure of transmitted information is simply a measure of the input-output correlation.

There are two simple rules to follow. Whenever I refer to "amount of information," you will understand "variance." And whenever I refer to "amount of transmitted information," you will understand "covariance" or "correlation."

The situation can be described graphically by two partially overlapping circles. Then the left circle can be taken to represent the variance of the input, the right circle the variance of the output, and the overlap the covariance of input and output. I shall speak of the left circle as the amount of input information, the right circle as the amount of output information and the overlap as the amount of transmitted information.

In the experiments on absolute judgment, the observer is considered to be a communication channel. Then the left circle would represent the amount of information in the stimuli, the right circle the amount of information in his responses, and the overlap the stimulus-response correlation as measured by the amount of transmitted information. The experimental problem is to increase the amount of input information and to measure the amount of transmitted information. If the observer's absolute judgments are quite accurate, then nearly all of the input information will be transmitted and will be recoverable from his responses. If he makes errors, then the transmitted information may be considerably less than the input. We expect that, as we increase the amount of input information, the observer will begin to make more and more errors; we can test the limits of accuracy of his absolute judgments. If the human observer is a reasonable kind of communication system, then when we increase the amount of input information the transmitted information will increase at first and will eventually level off at some asymptotic value. This asymptotic value we take to be the *channel capacity* of the observer: it represents the greatest amount of information that he can give us about the stimulus on the basis of an absolute judgment. The channel capacity is the upper limit on the extent to which the observer can match his responses to the stimuli we give him.

Now just a brief word about the *bit* and we can begin to look at some data. One bit of information is the amount of information that we need to make a decision between two equally likely alternatives. If we must decide whether a man is less than six feet tall or more than six feet tall and if we know that the chances are 50–50, then we need one bit of information. Notice that this unit of information does not refer in any way to the unit of length that we use—feet, inches, centimeters, etc. However you measure the man's height, we still need just one bit of information.

Two bits of information enable us to decide among four equally likely alternatives. Three bits of information enable us to decide among eight equally likely alternatives. Four bits of information decide among 16 alternatives, five among 32, and so on. That is to say, if there are 32 equally likely alternatives, we must make five successive binary decisions, worth one bit each, before we know which alternative is correct. So the general rule is simple: every time the number of alternatives is increased by a factor of two, one bit of information is added.

There are two ways we might increase the amount of input information. We could increase the rate at which we give information to the observer, so that the amount of information per unit time would increase. Or we could ignore the time variable completely and increase the amount of input information by increasing the number of alternative stimuli. In the absolute judgment experiment we are interested in the second alternative. We give the observer as much time as he wants to make his response; we simply increase the number of alternative stimuli among which he must discriminate and look to see where confusions begin to occur. Confusions will appear near the point that we are calling his "channel capacity."

ABSOLUTE JUDGMENTS
OF UNIDIMENSIONAL STIMULI

Now let us consider what happens when we make absolute judgments of tones. Pollack (17) asked listeners to identify tones by assigning numerals to them. The tones were different with respect to frequency, and covered the range from 100 to 8000 cps in equal logarithmic steps. A tone was sounded and the listener responded by giving a numeral. After the listener had made his response he was told the correct identification of the tone.

When only two or three tones were used the listeners never confused them. With four different tones confusions were quite rare, but with five or more tones confusions were frequent. With fourteen different tones the listeners made many mistakes.

These data are plotted in Fig. 1. Along the bottom is the amount of input information in bits per stimulus. As the number of alternative tones was increased from 2 to 14, the input information increased from 1 to 3.8 bits. On the ordinate is plotted the amount of transmitted information. The amount of transmitted information behaves in much the way we would expect a communication channel to behave; the transmitted information increases linearly up to about 2 bits and then bends off toward an asymptote at about 2.5 bits. This value, 2.5 bits, therefore, is what we are calling the channel capacity of the listener for absolute judgments of pitch.

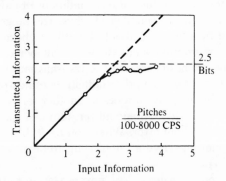

FIGURE 1 *Data from Pollack (17, 18) on the amount of information that is transmitted by listeners who make absolute judgments of auditory pitch. As the amount of input information is increased by increasing from 2 to 14 the number of different pitches to be judged, the amount of transmitted information approaches as its upper limit a channel capacity of about 2.5 bits per judgment.*

So now we have the number 2.5 bits. What does it mean? First, note that 2.5 bits corresponds to about six equally likely alternatives. The result means that we cannot pick more than six different pitches that the listener will never confuse. Or, stated slightly differently, no matter how many alternative tones we ask him to judge, the best we can expect him to do is to assign them to about six different classes without error. Or, again, if we know that there were N alternative stimuli, then his judgment enables us to narrow down the particular stimulus to one out of $N/6$.

Most people are surprised that the number is as small as six. Of course, there is evidence that a musically sophisticated person with absolute pitch can identify accurately any one of 50 or 60 different pitches. Fortunately, I do not have time to discuss these remarkable exceptions. I say it is fortunate because I do not know how to explain their superior performance. So I shall stick to the more pedestrian fact that most of us can identify about one out of only five or six pitches before we begin to get confused.

It is interesting to consider that psychologists have been using seven-point rating scales for a long time, on the intuitive basis that trying to rate into finer categories does not really add much to the usefulness of the ratings. Pollack's results indicate that, at least for pitches, this intuition is fairly sound.

Next you can ask how reproducible this result is. Does it depend on the spacing of the tones or the various conditions of judgment? Pollack varied these conditions in a number of ways. The range of frequencies can be changed by a factor of about 20 without changing the amount of information transmitted more than a small percentage. Different groupings of the pitches decreased the transmission, but the loss was small. For example, if you can discriminate five high-pitched tones in one series and five low-pitched tones in another series, it is reasonable to expect that you could combine all ten into a single series and still tell them all apart without error. When you try it, however, it does not work. The channel capacity for pitch seems to be about six and that is the best you can do.

While we are on tones, let us look next at Garner's (7) work on loudness. Garner's data for loudness are summarized in Fig. 2. Garner went to some trouble to get the best possible spacing of his tones over the intensity range from 15 to 110 db. He used 4, 5, 6, 7, 10, and 20 different stimulus intensities. The results shown in Fig. 2 take into account the differences among subjects and the sequential influence of the immediately preceding judgment. Again we find that there seems to be a limit. The channel capacity for absolute judgments of loudness is 2.3 bits, or about five perfectly discriminable alternatives.

Since these two studies were done in different laboratories with slightly different techniques and methods of analysis, we are not in a

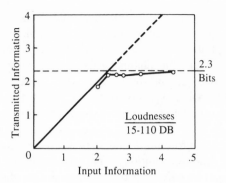

FIGURE 2   *Data from Garner (7) on the channel capacity for absolute judgments of auditory loudness.*

good position to argue whether five loudnesses is significantly different from six pitches. Probably the difference is in the right direction, and absolute judgments of pitch are slightly more accurate than absolute judgments of loudness. The important point, however, is that the two answers are of the same order of magnitude.

The experiment has also been done for taste intensities. In Fig. 3 are the results obtained by Beebe-Center, Rogers, and O'Connell (1) for absolute judgments of the concentration of salt solutions. The concentrations ranged from 0.3 to 34.7 gm. NaCl per 100 cc. tap water in equal subjective steps. They used 3, 5, 9, and 17 different concentra-

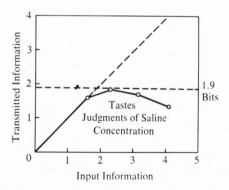

FIGURE 3   *Data from Beebe-Center, Rogers, and O'Connell (1) on the channel capacity for absolute judgments of saltiness.*

tions. The channel capacity is 1.9 bits, which is about four distinct concentrations. Thus taste intensities seem a little less distinctive than auditory stimuli, but again the order of magnitude is not far off.

On the other hand, the channel capacity for judgments of visual position seems to be significantly larger. Hake and Garner (8) asked observers to interpolate visually between two scale markers. Their results are shown in Fig. 4. They did the experiment in two ways. In one version they let the observer use any number between zero and 100 to describe the position, although they presented stimuli at only 5, 10, 20, or 50 different positions. The results with this unlimited response technique are shown by the filled circles on the graph. In the other version the observers were limited in their responses to reporting just those stimulus values that were possible. That is to say, in the second version the number of different responses that the observer could make was exactly the same as the number of different stimuli that the experimenter might present. The results with this limited response technique are shown by the open circles on the graph. The two functions are so similar that it seems fair to conclude that the number of responses available to the observer had nothing to do with the channel capacity of 3.25 bits.

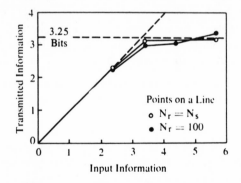

FIGURE 4   *Data from Hake and Garner (8) on the channel capacity for absolute judgments of the position of a pointer in a linear interval.*

The Hake-Garner experiment has been repeated by Coonan and Klemmer. Although they have not yet published their results, they have given me permission to say that they obtained channel capacities ranging from 3.2 bits for very short exposures of the pointer position to 3.9 bits for longer exposures. These values are slightly higher than Hake and Garner's, so we must conclude that there are between 10 and 15 distinct positions along a linear interval. This is the largest channel capacity that has been measured for any unidimensional variable.

At the present time these four experiments on absolute judgments of simple, unidimensional stimuli are all that have appeared in the psychological journals. However, a great deal of work on other stimulus variables has not yet appeared in the journals. For example, Eriksen and Hake (6) have found that the channel capacity for judging the sizes of squares is 2.2 bits, or about five categories, under a wide range of experimental conditions. In a separate experiment Eriksen (5) found 2.8 bits for size, 3.1 bits for hue, and 2.3 bits for brightness. Geldard has measured the channel capacity for the skin by placing vibrators on the chest region. A good observer can identify about four intensities, about five durations, and about seven locations.

One of the most active groups in this area has been the Air Force Operational Applications Laboratory. Pollack has been kind enough to furnish me with the results of their measurements for several aspects of visual displays. They made measurements for area and for the curvature, length, and direction of lines. In one set of experiments they used a very short exposure of the stimulus — ¼₀ second — and then they repeated the measurements with a 5 second exposure. For area they got 2.6 bits with the short exposure and 2.7 bits with the long exposure. For the length of a line they got about 2.6 bits with the short exposure and about 3.0 bits with the long exposure. Direction, or angle of inclination, gave 2.8 bits for the short exposure and 3.3 bits for the long exposure. Curvature was apparently harder to judge. When the length of the arc was constant, the result at the short exposure duration was 2.2 bits, but when the length of the chord was constant, the result was only 1.6 bits. This last value is the lowest that anyone has measured to date. I should add, however, that these values are apt to be slightly too low because the data from all subjects were pooled before the transmitted information was computed.

Now let us see where we are. First, the channel capacity does seem to be a valid notion for describing human observers. Second, the channel capacities measured for these unidimensional variables range from 1.6 bits for curvature to 3.9 bits for positions in an interval. Although there is no question that the differences among the variables are real and meaningful, the more impressive fact to me is their considerable similarity. If I take the best estimates I can get of the channel capacities for all the stimulus variables I have mentioned, the mean is 2.6 bits and the standard deviation is only 0.6 bit. In terms of distinguishable alternatives, this mean corresponds to about 6.5 categories, one standard deviation includes from 4 to 10 categories, and the total range is from 3 to 15 categories. Considering the wide variety of different variables that have been studied, I find this to be a remarkably narrow range.

There seems to be some limitation built into us either by learning or by the design of our nervous systems, a limit that keeps our channel capacities in this general range. On the basis of the present evidence it seems safe to say that we possess a finite and rather small capacity for making such unidimensional judgments and that this capacity does not vary a great deal from one simple sensory attribute to another.

ABSOLUTE JUDGMENTS
OF MULTIDIMENSIONAL STIMULI

You may have noticed that I have been careful to say that this magical number seven applies to one-dimensional judgments. Everyday experience teaches us that we can identify accurately any one of several hundred faces, any one of several thousand words, any one of several thousand objects, etc. The story certainly would not be complete if we stopped at this point. We must have some understanding of why the one-dimensional variables we judge in the laboratory give results so far out of line with what we do constantly in our behavior outside the laboratory. A possible explanation lies in the number of independently variable attributes of the stimuli that are being judged. Objects, faces, words, and the like differ from one another in many ways, whereas the simple stimuli we have considered thus far differ from one another in only one respect.

Fortunately, there are a few data on what happens when we make absolute judgments of stimuli that differ from one another in several ways. Let us look first at the results Klemmer and Frick (13) have reported for the absolute judgment of the position of a dot in a square. In Fig. 5 we see their results. Now the channel capacity seems to have increased to 4.6 bits, which means that people can identify accurately any one of 24 positions in the square.

The position of a dot in a square is clearly a two-dimensional proposition. Both its horizontal and its vertical position must be identified. Thus it seems natural to compare the 4.6-bit capacity for a square with the 3.25-bit capacity for the position of a point in an interval. The point in the square requires two judgments of the interval type. If we have

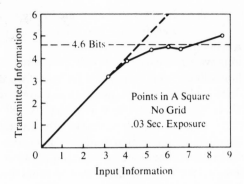

FIGURE 5   *Data from Klemmer and Frick (13) on the channel capacity for absolute judgments of the position of a dot in a square.*

a capacity of 3.25 bits for estimating intervals and we do this twice, we should get 6.5 bits as our capacity for locating points in a square. Adding the second independent dimension gives us an increase from 3.25 to 4.6, but it falls short of the perfect addition that would give 6.5 bits.

Another example is provided by Beebe-Center, Rogers, and O'Connell. When they asked people to identify both the saltiness and the sweetness of solutions containing various concentrations of salt and sucrose, they found that the channel capacity was 2.3 bits. Since the capacity for salt alone was 1.9, we might expect about 3.8 bits if the two aspects of the compound stimuli were judged independently. As with spatial locations, the second dimension adds a little to the capacity but not as much as it conceivably might.

A third example is provided by Pollack (18), who asked listeners to judge both the loudness and the pitch of pure tones. Since pitch gives 2.5 bits and loudness gives 2.3 bits, we might hope to get as much as 4.8 bits for pitch and loudness together. Pollack obtained 3.1 bits, which again indicates that the second dimension augments the channel capacity but not so much as it might.

A fourth example can be drawn from the work of Halsey and Chapanis (9) on confusions among colors of equal luminance. Although they did not analyze their results in informational terms, they estimate that there are about 11 to 15 identifiable colors, or, in our terms, about 3.6 bits. Since these colors varied in both hue and saturation, it is probably correct to regard this as a two-dimensional judgment. If we compare this with Eriksen's 3.1 bits for hue (which is a questionable comparison to draw), we again have something less than perfect addition when a second dimension is added.

It is still a long way, however, from these two-dimensional examples to the multidimensional stimuli provided by faces, words, etc. To fill this gap we have only one experiment, an auditory study done by Pollack and Ficks (19). They managed to get six different acoustic variables that they could change: frequency, intensity, rate of interruption, on-time fraction, total duration, and spatial location. Each one of these six variables could assume any one of five different values, so altogether there were 5^6, or 15,625 different tones that they could present. The listeners made a separate rating for each one of these six dimensions. Under these conditions the transmitted information was 7.2 bits, which corresponds to about 150 different categories that could be absolutely identified without error. Now we are beginning to get up into the range that ordinary experience would lead us to expect.

Suppose that we plot these data, fragmentary as they are, and make a guess about how the channel capacity changes with the dimensionality of the stimuli. The result is given in Fig. 6. In a moment of considerable daring I sketched the dotted line to indicate roughly the trend that the data seemed to be taking.

Clearly, the addition of independently variable attributes to the stimulus increases the channel capacity, but at a decreasing rate. It is interesting to note that the channel capacity is increased even when

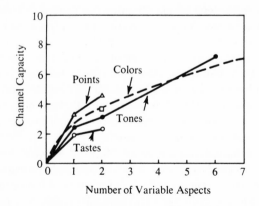

FIGURE 6   *The general form of the relation between channel capacity and the number of independently variable attributes of the stimuli.*

the several variables are not independent. Eriksen (5) reports that, when size, brightness, and hue all vary together in perfect correlation, the transmitted information is 4.1 bits as compared with an average of about 2.7 bits when these attributes are varied one at a time. By confounding three attributes, Eriksen increased the dimensionality of the input without increasing the amount of input information; the result was an increase in channel capacity of about the amount that the dotted function in Fig. 6 would lead us to expect.

The point seems to be that, as we add more variables to the display, we increase the total capacity, but we decrease the accuracy for any particular variable. In other words, we can make relatively crude judgments of several things simultaneously.

We might argue that in the course of evolution those organisms were most successful that were responsive to the widest range of stimulus energies in their environment. In order to survive in a constantly fluctuating world, it was better to have a little information about a lot of things than to have a lot of information about a small segment of the environment. If a compromise was necessary, the one we seem to have made is clearly the more adaptive.

Pollack and Ficks' results are very strongly suggestive of an argument that linguists and phoneticians have been making for some time (11). According to the linguistic analysis of the sounds of human speech, there are about eight or ten dimensions — the linguists call them *distinctive features* — that distinguish one phoneme from another. These distinctive features are usually binary, or at most ternary, in nature. For example, a binary distinction is made between vowels and consonants, a binary decision is made between oral and nasal consonants, a ternary decision is made among front, middle, and back phonemes, etc. This approach gives us quite a different picture of speech perception than we might otherwise obtain from our studies of the speech spectrum and of the ear's ability to discriminate relative differences among pure tones. I am personally much interested in this new approach (15), and I regret that there is not time to discuss it here.

It was probably with this linguistic theory in mind that Pollack and Ficks conducted a test on a set of tonal stimuli that varied in eight dimensions, but required only a binary decision on each dimension. With these tones they measured the transmitted information at 6.9 bits, or about 120 recognizable kinds of sounds. It is an intriguing question, as yet unexplored, whether one can go on adding dimensions indefinitely in this way.

In human speech there is clearly a limit to the number of dimensions that we use. In this instance, however, it is not known whether the limit is imposed by the nature of the perceptual machinery that must recognize the sounds or by the nature of the speech machinery that must produce them. Somebody will have to do the experiment to find out. There is a limit, however, at about eight or nine distinctive features in every language that has been studied, and so when we talk we must resort to still another trick for increasing our channel capacity. Language uses sequences of phonemes, so we make several judgments successively when we listen to words and sentences. That is to say, we use both simultaneous and successive discriminations in order to expand the rather rigid limits imposed by the inaccuracy of our absolute judgments of simple magnitudes.

These multidimensional judgments are strongly reminiscent of the abstraction experiment of Külpe (14). As you may remember, Külpe showed that observers report more accurately on an attribute for which they are set than on attributes for which they are not set. For example, Chapman (4) used three different attributes and compared the results obtained when the observers were instructed before the tachistoscopic presentation with the results obtained when they were not told until after the presentation which one of the three attributes was to be reported. When the instruction was given in advance, the judgments were more accurate. When the instruction was given afterwards, the subjects presumably had to judge all three attributes in order to report on any one of them and the accuracy was correspondingly lower. This is in complete accord with the results we have just been considering, where the accuracy of judgment on each attribute decreased as more dimensions were added. The point is probably obvious, but I shall make it anyhow, that the abstraction experiments did *not* demonstrate that people can judge only one attribute at a time. They merely showed what seems quite reasonable, that people are less accurate if they must judge more than one attribute simultaneously.

SUBITIZING

I cannot leave this general area without mentioning, however briefly, the experiments conducted at Mount Holyoke College on the discrimination of number (12). In experiments by Kaufman, Lord, Reese, and Volkmann random patterns of dots were flashed on a screen for ⅕ of a second. Anywhere from 1 to more than 200 dots could appear in the pattern. The subject's task was to report how many dots there were.

The first point to note is that on patterns containing up to five or six dots the subjects simply did not make errors. The performance on these small numbers of dots was so different from the performance with more dots that it was given a special name. Below seven the subjects were said to *subitize;* above seven they were said to *estimate.* This is, as you will recognize, what we once optimistically called "the span of attention."

This discontinuity at seven is, of course, suggestive. Is this the same basic process that limits our unidimensional judgments to about seven categories? The generalization is tempting, but not sound in my opinion. The data on number estimates have not been analyzed in informational terms; but on the basis of the published data I would guess that the subjects transmitted something more than four bits of information about the number of dots. Using the same arguments as before, we would conclude that there are about 20 or 30 distinguishable categories of numerousness. This is considerably more information than we would expect to get from a unidimensional display. It is, as a matter of fact, very much like a two-dimensional display. Although the dimensionality of the random dot patterns is not entirely clear, these results are in the same range as Klemmer and Frick's for their two-dimensional display of dots in a square. Perhaps the two dimensions of numerousness are area and density. When the subject can subitize, area and density may not be the significant variables, but when the subject must estimate perhaps they are significant. In any event, the comparison is not so simple as it might seem at first thought.

This is one of the ways in which the magical number seven has persecuted me. Here we have two closely related kinds of experiments, both of which point to the significance of the number seven as a limit on our capacities. And yet when we examine the matter more closely, there seems to be a reasonable suspicion that it is nothing more than a coincidence.

THE SPAN OF IMMEDIATE MEMORY

Let me summarize the situation in this way. There is a clear and definite limit to the accuracy with which we can identify absolutely the magnitude of a unidimensional stimulus variable. I would propose to call this limit the *span of absolute judgment,* and I maintain that for unidimensional judgments this span is usually somewhere in the neighborhood of seven. We are not completely at the mercy of this limited span, however, because we have a variety of techniques for getting around it and increasing the accuracy of our judgments. The three most important of these devices are (1) to make relative rather than absolute judgments; or, if that is not possible, (2) to increase the number of dimensions along which the stimuli can differ; or (3) to arrange the task in such a way that we make a sequence of several absolute judgments in a row.

The study of relative judgments is one of the oldest topics in experimental psychology, and I will not pause to review it now. The second device, increasing the dimensionality, we have just considered. It seems that by adding more dimensions and requiring crude, binary, yes-no judgments on each attribute we can extend the span of absolute judgment from seven to at least 150. Judging from our everyday behavior, the limit is probably in the thousands, if indeed there is a limit. In my opinion, we cannot go on compounding dimensions indefinitely. I suspect that there is also a *span of perceptual dimensionality* and that this span is somewhere in the neighborhood of ten, but I must add at once that there is no objective evidence to support this suspicion. This is a question sadly needing experimental exploration.

Concerning the third device, the use of successive judgments, I have quite a bit to say because this device introduces memory as the handmaiden of discrimination. And, since mnemonic processes are at least as complex as are perceptual processes, we can anticipate that their interactions will not be easily disentangled.

Suppose that we start by simply extending slightly the experimental procedure that we have been using. Up to this point we have presented a single stimulus and asked the observer to name it immediately thereafter. We can extend this procedure by requiring the observer to withhold his response until we have given him several stimuli in succession. At the end of the sequence of stimuli he then makes his response. We still have the same sort of input-output situation that is required for the measurement of transmitted information. But now we have passed from an experiment on absolute judgment to what is traditionally called an experiment on immediate memory.

Before we look at any data on this topic I feel I must give you a word of warning to help you avoid some obvious associations that can be confusing. Everybody knows that there is a finite span of immediate memory and that for a lot of different kinds of test materials this span is about seven items in length. I have just shown you that there is a span of absolute judgment that can distinguish about seven categories and that there is a span of attention that will encompass about six objects at a glance. What is more natural than to think that all three of these spans are different aspects of a single underlying process? And that is a fundamental mistake, as I shall be at some pains to demonstrate. This mistake is one of the malicious persecutions that the magical number seven has subjected me to.

My mistake went something like this. We have seen that the invariant feature in the span of absolute judgment is the amount of information that the observer can transmit. There is a real operational similarity between the absolute judgment experiment and the immediate memory experiment. If immediate memory is like absolute judgment, then it should follow that the invariant feature in the span of immediate memory is also the amount of information that an observer can retain. If the amount of information in the span of immediate memory is a constant, then the span should be short when the individual items contain a lot of information and the span should be long when the items contain little information. For example, decimal digits are worth 3.3 bits apiece. We can recall about seven of them, for a total of 23 bits of information. Isolated English words are worth about 10 bits apiece. If the total amount of information is to remain constant at 23 bits, then we should be able to remember only two or three words chosen at random. In this way I generated a theory about how the span of immediate memory should vary as a function of the amount of information per item in the test materials.

The measurements of memory span in the literature are suggestive on this question, but not definitive. And so it was necessary to do the experiment to see. Hayes (10) tried it out with five different kinds of test materials: binary digits, decimal digits, letters of the alphabet, letters plus decimal digits, and with 1000 monosyllabic words. The lists were read aloud at the rate of one item per second and the subjects had as much time as they needed to give their responses. A procedure described by Woodworth (20) was used to score the responses.

The results are shown by the filled circles in Fig. 7. Here the dotted line indicates what the span should have been if the amount of information in the span were constant. The solid curves represent the data. Hayes repeated the experiment using test vocabularies of different sizes but all containing only English monosyllables (open circles in Fig. 7). This more homogeneous test material did not change the picture significantly. With binary items the span is about nine and, although it drops to about five with monosyllabic English words, the difference is far less than the hypothesis of constant information would require.

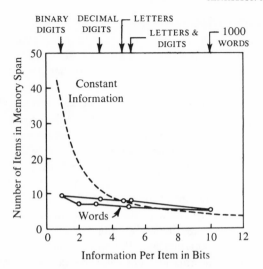

FIGURE 7   *Data from Hayes (10) on the span of immediate memory plotted as a function of the amount of information per item in the test materials.*

There is nothing wrong with Hayes's experiment, because Pollack (16) repeated it much more elaborately and got essentially the same result. Pollack took pains to measure the amount of information transmitted and did not rely on the traditional procedure for scoring the responses. His results are plotted in Fig. 8. Here it is clear that the amount of information transmitted is not a constant, but increases almost linearly as the amount of information per item in the input is increased.

And so the outcome is perfectly clear. In spite of the coincidence that the magical number seven appears in both places, the span of absolute judgment and the span of immediate memory are quite different kinds of limitations that are imposed on our ability to process information. Absolute judgment is limited by the amount of information. Immediate memory is limited by the number of items. In order to capture this distinction in somewhat picturesque terms, I have fallen into the custom of distinguishing between *bits* of information and *chunks* of information. Then I can say that the number of bits of information is constant for absolute judgment and the number of chunks of information is constant for immediate memory. The span of immediate memory seems to be almost independent of the number of bits per chunk, at least over the range that has been examined to date.

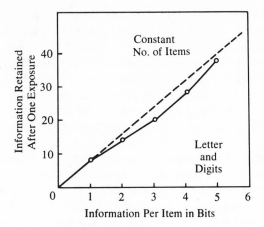

FIGURE 8   *Data from Pollack (16) on the amount of information retained after one presentation plotted as a function of the amount of information per item in the test materials.*

The contrast of the terms *bit* and *chunk* also serves to highlight the fact that we are not very definite about what constitutes a chunk of information. For example, the memory span of five words that Hayes obtained when each word was drawn at random from a set of 1000 English monosyllables might just as appropriately have been called a memory span of 15 phonemes, since each word had about three phonemes in it. Intuitively, it is clear that the subjects were recalling five words, not 15 phonemes, but the logical distinction is not immediately apparent. We are dealing here with a process of organizing or grouping the input into familiar units or chunks, and a great deal of learning has gone into the formation of these familiar units.

RECODING

In order to speak more precisely, therefore, we must recognize the importance of grouping or organizing the input sequence into units or chunks. Since the memory span is a fixed number of chunks, we can increase the number of bits of information that it contains simply by building larger and larger chunks, each chunk containing more information than before.

A man just beginning to learn radio-telegraphic code hears each *dit* and *dah* as a separate chunk. Soon he is able to organize these sounds into letters and then he can deal with the letters as chunks. Then the letters organize themselves as words, which are still larger chunks, and

he begins to hear whole phrases. I do not mean that each step is a
discrete process, or that plateaus must appear in his learning curve, for
surely the levels of organization are achieved at different rates and
overlap each other during the learning process. I am simply pointing to
the obvious fact that the dits and dahs are organized by learning into
patterns and that as these larger chunks emerge the amount of mes-
sage that the operator can remember increases correspondingly. In
the terms I am proposing to use, the operator learns to increase the bits
per chunk.

In the jargon of communication theory, this process would be called
recoding. The input is given in a code that contains many chunks with
few bits per chunk. The operator recodes the input into another code
that contains fewer chunks with more bits per chunk. There are many
ways to do this recoding, but probably the simplest is to group the
input events, apply a new name to the group, and then remember the
new name rather than the original input events.

Since I am convinced that this process is a very general and important one for psychology, I want to tell you about a demonstration
experiment that should make perfectly explicit what I am talking about.
This experiment was conducted by Sidney Smith and was reported by
him before the Eastern Psychological Association in 1954.

Begin with the observed fact that people can repeat back eight
decimal digits, but only nine binary digits. Since there is a large discrepancy in the amount of information recalled in these two cases, we
suspect at once that a recoding procedure could be used to increase
the span of immediate memory for binary digits. In Table 1 a method
for grouping and renaming is illustrated. Along the top is a sequence

TABLE 1

WAYS OF RECODING SEQUENCES OF BINARY DIGITS

Binary digits (bits)		1	0	1	0	0	0	1	0	0	1	1	1	0	0	1	1	1	0
2:1	Chunks	10		10		00		10		01		11		00		11		10	
	Recoding	2		2		0		2		1		3		0		3		2	
3:1	Chunks	101			000			100			111			001			110		
	Recoding	5			0			4			7			1			6		
4:1	Chunks	1010				0010				0111				0011				0010		
	Recoding	10				2				7				3				2		
5:1	Chunks	10100					01001					11001					00110			
	Recoding	20					9					25					6			

of 18 binary digits, far more than any subject was able to recall after a single presentation. In the next line these same binary digits are grouped by pairs. Four possible pairs can occur: 00 is renamed 0, 01 is renamed 1, 10 is renamed 2, and 11 is renamed 3. That is to say, we recode from a base-two arithmetic to a base-four arithmetic. In the recoded sequence there are now just nine digits to remember, and this is almost within the span of immediate memory. In the next line the same sequence of binary digits is regrouped into chunks of three. There are eight possible sequences of three, so we give each sequence a new name between 0 and 7. Now we have recoded from a sequence of 18 binary digits into a sequence of 6 octal digits, and this is well within the span of immediate memory. In the last two lines the binary digits are grouped by fours and by fives and are given decimal-digit names from 0 to 15 and from 0 to 31.

It is reasonably obvious that this kind of recoding increases the bits per chunk, and packages the binary sequence into a form that can be retained within the span of immediate memory. So Smith assembled 20 subjects and measured their spans for binary and octal digits. The spans were 9 for binaries and 7 for octals. Then he gave each recoding scheme to five of the subjects. They studied the recoding until they said they understood it — for about 5 or 10 minutes. Then he tested their span for binary digits again while they tried to use the recoding schemes they had studied.

The recoding schemes increased their span for binary digits in every case. But the increase was not as large as we had expected on the basis of their span for octal digits. Since the discrepancy increased as the recoding ratio increased, we reasoned that the few minutes the subjects had spent learning the recoding schemes had not been sufficient. Apparently the translation from one code to the other must be almost automatic or the subject will lose part of the next group while he is trying to remember the translation of the last group.

Since the 4:1 and 5:1 ratios require considerable study, Smith decided to imitate Ebbinghaus and do the experiment on himself. With Germanic patience he drilled himself on each recoding successively, and obtained the results shown in Fig. 9. Here the data follow along rather nicely with the results you would predict on the basis of his span for octal digits. He could remember 12 octal digits. With the 2:1 recoding, these 12 chunks were worth 24 binary digits. With the 3:1 recoding they were worth 36 binary digits. With the 4:1 and 5:1 recodings, they were worth about 40 binary digits.

It is a little dramatic to watch a person get 40 binary digits in a row

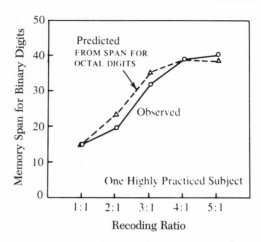

FIGURE 9   *The span of immediate memory for binary digits is plotted as a*
function of the recording procedure used. The predicted function is obtained by
multiplying the span for octals by 2, 3, and 3.3 for recoding into base 4, base 8,
and base 10, respectively.

and then repeat them back without error. However, if you think of
this merely as a mnemonic trick for extending the memory span, you
will miss the more important point that is implicit in nearly all such
mnemonic devices. The point is that recoding is an extremely powerful
weapon for increasing the amount of information that we can deal
with. In one form or another we use recoding constantly in our daily
behavior.

In my opinion the most customary kind of recoding that we do all
the time is to translate into a verbal code. When there is a story or an
argument or an idea that we want to remember, we usually try to re-
phrase it "in our own words." When we witness some event we want
to remember, we make a verbal description of the event and then remember our verbalization. Upon recall we recreate by secondary
elaboration the details that seem consistent with the particular verbal
recoding we happen to have made. The well-known experiment by
Carmichael, Hogan, and Walter (3) on the influence that names have
on the recall of visual figures is one demonstration of the process.

The inaccuracy of the testimony of eyewitnesses is well known in legal
psychology, but the distortions of testimony are not random — they
follow naturally from the particular recoding that the witness used, and
the particular recoding he used depends upon his whole life history.

Our language is tremendously useful for repackaging material into a few chunks rich in information. I suspect that imagery is a form of recoding, too, but images seem much harder to get at operationally and to study experimentally than the more symbolic kinds of recoding.

It seems probable that even memorization can be studied in these terms. The process of memorizing may be simply the formation of chunks, or groups of items that go together, until there are few enough chunks so that we can recall all the items. The work by Bousfield and Cohen (2) on the occurrence of clustering in the recall of words is especially interesting in this respect.

SUMMARY

I have come to the end of the data that I wanted to present, so I would like now to make some summarizing remarks.

First, the span of absolute judgment and the span of immediate memory impose severe limitations on the amount of information that we are able to receive, process, and remember. By organizing the stimulus input simultaneously into several dimensions and successively into a sequence of chunks, we manage to break (or at least stretch) this informational bottleneck.

Second, the process of recoding is a very important one in human psychology and deserves much more explicit attention than it has received. In particular, the kind of linguistic recoding that people do seems to me to be the very lifeblood of the thought processes. Recoding procedures are a constant concern to clinicians, social psychologists, linguists, and anthropologists and yet, probably because recoding is less accessible to experimental manipulation than nonsense syllables or T mazes, the traditional experimental psychologist has contributed little or nothing to their analysis. Nevertheless, experimental techniques can be used, methods of recoding can be specified, behavioral indicants can be found. And I anticipate that we will find a very orderly set of relations describing what now seems an uncharted wilderness of individual differences.

Third, the concepts and measures provided by the theory of information provide a quantitative way of getting at some of these questions. The theory provides us with a yardstick for calibrating our stimulus materials and for measuring the performance of our subjects. In the interests of communication I have suppressed the technical details of information measurement and have tried to express the ideas in more familiar terms; I hope this paraphrase will not lead you to think they are not useful in research. Informational concepts have already proved valuable in the study of discrimination and of language; they promise a great deal in the study of learning and memory; and it has even been proposed that they can be useful in the study of concept formation. A lot of questions that seemed fruitless twenty or thirty years ago may now be worth another look. In fact, I feel that my story here must stop just as it begins to get really interesting.

And finally, what about the magical number seven? What about the seven wonders of the world, the seven seas, the seven deadly sins, the seven daughters of Atlas in the Pleiades, the seven ages of man, the seven levels of hell, the seven primary colors, the seven notes of the musical scale, and the seven days of the week? What about the seven-point rating scale, the seven categories for absolute judgment, the seven objects in the span of attention, and the seven digits in the span of immediate memory? For the present I propose to withhold judgment. Perhaps there is something deep and profound behind all these sevens, something just calling out for us to discover it. But I suspect that it is only a pernicious, Pythagorean coincidence.

REFERENCES

1. Beebe-Center, J. G., Rogers, M. S., and O'Connell, D. N. "Transmission of information about sucrose and saline solutions through the sense of taste." *J. Psychol.*, 1955, 39, 157–160.
2. Bousfield, W. A. and Cohen, B. H. "The occurrence of clustering in the recall of randomly arranged words of different frequencies-of-usage." *J. Gen. Psychol.*, 1955, 52, 83–95.
3. Carmichael, L., Hogan, H. P., and Walter, A. A. "An experimental study of the effect of language on the reproduction of visually perceived form." *J. Exp. Psychol.*, 1932, 15, 73–86.
4. Chapman, D. W. "Relative effects of determinate and indeterminate *Aufgaben*." *Amer. J. Psychol.*, 1932, 44, 163–174.
5. Eriksen, C. W. "Multidimensional stimulus differences and accuracy of discrimination." *USAF, WADC Tech. Rep.*, 1954, No. 54–165.
6. Eriksen, C. W. and Hake, H. W. "Absolute judgments as a function of the stimulus range and the number of stimulus response categories." *J. Exp. Psychol.*, 1955, 49, 323–332.
7. Garner, W. R. "An informational analysis of absolute judgments of loudness." *J. Exp. Psychol.*, 1953, 46, 373–380.
8. Hake, H. W. and Garner, W. R. "The effect of presenting various numbers of discrete steps on scale reading accuracy." *J. Exp. Psychol.*, 1951, 42, 358–366.
9. Halsey, R. M. and Chapanis, A. "Chromaticity-confusion contours in a complex viewing situation." *J. Opt. Soc. Amer.*, 1954, 44, 442–454.

10. Hayes, J. R. M. "Memory span for several vocabularies as a function of vocabulary size." In *Quarterly Progress Report*, Cambridge, Mass.: Acoustics Laboratory, Massachusetts Institute of Technology, Jan.–June, 1952.

11. Jakobson, R., Fant, C. G. M., and Halle, M. *Preliminaries to Speech Analysis*. Cambridge, Mass.: Acoustics Laboratory, Massachusetts Institute of Technology, 1952. (Tech. Rep. No. 13.)

12. Kaufman, E. L., Lord, M. W., Reese, T. W., and Volkmann, J. "The discrimination of visual number." *Amer. J. Psychol.*, 1949, 62, 498–525.

13. Klemmer, E. T. and Frick, F. C. "Assimilation of information from dot and matrix patterns." *J. Exp. Psychol.*, 1953, 45, 15–19.

14. Külpe, O. "Versuche über Abstraktion." *Ber. ü. d. I Kongr. f. exper. Psychol.*, 1904, 56–68.

15. Miller, G. A. and Nicely, P. E. "An analysis of perceptual confusions among some English consonants." *J. Acoust. Soc. Amer.*, 1955, 27, 338–352.

16. Pollack, I. "The assimilation of sequentially encoded information." *Amer. J. Psychol.*, 1953, 66, 421–435.

17. Pollack, I. "The information of elementary auditory displays." *J. Acoust. Soc. Amer.*, 1952, 24, 745–749.

18. Pollack, I. "The information of elementary auditory displays. II." *J. Acoust. Soc. Amer.*, 1953, 25, 765–769.

19. Pollack, I. and Ficks, L. "Information of elementary multi-dimensional auditory displays." *J. Acoust. Soc. Amer.*, 1954, 26, 155–158.

20. Woodworth, R. S. *Experimental Psychology*. New York: Holt, 1938.

3. DISCRIMINATION

A. Sensory Discrimination
in Human Beings

As E. G. Boring stated, Gustav Fechner "created psycho-physics." [1] *As we would expect, therefore, research in psychophysics has been guided in large measure by Fechner's conception of how the human senses should be studied. One of Fechner's primary goals was to develop a law of psychophysics that would relate the magnitude of sensation to the physical magnitude of the stimulus. He believed that sensory magnitude could not be measured directly, but could be arrived at indirectly through the prior measurement of sensory discrimination. In brief, Fechner maintained that the way in which sensory magnitude varied as a function of stimulus magnitude was determined by how keenly observers could discern small changes in stimulation. The selections in the present section deal with the first problem encountered by Fechner, viz., the measurement of sensory discrimination. This problem is central to all psychophysical inquiry since the ability to discriminate is our most basic sensory function. The excerpts from William James'* Psychology: Briefer Course *give a glimpse of how Fechner used sensory discrimination to derive a measure of sensation but a more thorough treatment of the issues raised by Fechner's psychophysical law will be taken up in Section 4.*

In the realm of sensory psychophysics, the measurement of

---

[1] E. G. Boring, *Sensation and Perception in the History of Experimental Psychology*, 1942, p. 34.

discrimination translates into the measurement of (1) the smallest stimulus energy that an observer can detect and (2) the smallest change in stimulation that an observer can resolve. The detection problem is a special case of the resolution problem. That is, the detection task requires the observer to resolve the difference between a very weak sensation and no sensation.

In order to provide adequate ways for measuring detection and resolution Fechner worked out the details of the psychophysical methods that are now called "classical" (the method of adjustment or of average error, the method of limits or of just noticeable differences, and the method of constant stimuli or of right and wrong cases). These methods were applied most often to the measurement of two properties of sensory systems that, Fechner felt, placed ultimate limits on the keenness of discrimination: the absolute threshold and the difference threshold. Fechner conceived of thresholds as relatively stable barriers that had to be surmounted in order for detection and resolution to be accomplished. "It can be shown that every stimulus as well as every stimulus difference must already have reached a certain finite magnitude before it can be noticed at all — that is, before our consciousness is aroused by a sensation, or before a difference between sensations becomes apparent."[2] The thresholds he measured by careful experimentation served as the building blocks of Fechner's psychophysics.

The notion that discrimination is limited by a stable barrier such as a threshold is a theoretical one. In an actual experiment, an investigator sees continuous fluctuations in the performance of the psychophysical observer. That is, at one moment it may be necessary to produce a relatively large change in stimulus energy for the observer to perceive a change in stimulation, and at the next moment a smaller change may suffice. There appears therefore to be a momentary threshold that fluctuates about some average value in an apparently random fashion. Fechner was well aware of this variation. He

[2] G. Fechner, *Elemente der Psychophysik*, I, 1860. (See G. Fechner, *Elements of Psychophysics*, I, translated by H. E. Adler, and edited by D. H. Howes and E. G. Boring, 1966, p. 199.)

taught that the psychophysical or neural energy released by a stimulus caused a change in sensation whenever the activity in the system surpassed a critical or threshold level. From one moment to the next there were fluctuations in the organism (due to practice, fatigue, adaptation, etc.) and these determined how easy or difficult it was for a stimulus to release the requisite amount of psychophysical activity. A careful investigator could, Fechner felt, minimize these variations and obtain an average threshold value that approximated the true value.

Variation in the performance of the observer is the aspect of sensory discrimination that students of psychophysics have been most compelled to investigate. Fechner's interpretation of this variation and his views on the constancy of an underlying threshold were largely speculation. The important questions needed to be raised again and again. Why is there continuous fluctuation in performance? Does it originate primarily in the observer? In the stimulus? Can it be reduced? Does it depend on the psychophysical method used? And, ultimately, does the nature of this variability support Fechner's conception of the absolute threshold? And, of the difference threshold? Most of the selections in this section represent the attempts of researchers to come to grips with the sources and the nature of variation in discrimination. In some cases, these selections also represent important contributions to the understanding of a particular sense modality, such as vision or hearing.

An important contribution to the science of vision is "Energy, Quanta, and Vision" by Hecht, Shlaer, and Pirenne. They attempted to specify the number of quanta of radiant energy necessary to evoke a just detectable visual sensation. Much of the radiant energy that impinges on the outer surface of the eye is lost before it reaches the visual receptors. But the loss of energy is of little practical consequence because of the exquisite sensitivity of the visual receptors. Of general importance to the study of discrimination are the views of Hecht, Shlaer, and Pirenne on the stimulus as a source of variability and, in particular, their conclusion that variation in the stimulus may be more important than biological variation for fluctuation in the measurement of absolute sensitivity.

In most sense modalities, other than vision and hearing, little attention has been paid to how much of the overall vari-ation in discrimination results from fluctuations in the stimu-lus. Most often it is tacitly assumed that changes in fatigue, attention, memory, and the physiological state of the observer are primarily responsible for variation in performance. On the other hand, few would deny that physical and biological vari-ation combine to produce variation in the absolute detecta-bility of a stimulus. And, as James McKeen Cattell pointed out in "On Errors of Observation," both sources of variation also produce fluctuation in sensations well above threshold and in the apparent difference between suprathreshold stim-uli. Cattell argued, as did Fechner, that these fluctuations alone could cause two slightly different suprathreshold stimuli to appear discriminably different at one time and identical at another. In other words, biological and physical factors that varied presumably in a continuous manner were themselves sufficient to account for the observation that two nominally different stimuli may not always be perceived as different. But Cattell disagreed with the Fechnerian notion that differential discrimination was also limited by an underlying difference threshold. He felt it was superfluous to invoke such a concept when biological and physical variability sufficed to explain the data of differential discrimination. He asked what evi-dence there was that the perception of small differences ever had been shown to occur in discrete steps. Indeed, the psycho-metric (poikilitic) function obtained in experiments was almost always smooth and continuous with no evidence of sharp changes in the region of the so-called difference threshold. Cattell and his colleague G. S. Fullerton criticized those who adopted ". . . the curious supposition that stimuli seem exactly alike so long as the difference is less than a certain amount, whereas, when the difference is made greater than this amount, it becomes suddenly apparent. This is by no means the case. The clearness with which a difference is distin-guished varies gradually from complete doubt to complete certainty. The variation is continuous, and no point can be taken and called the 'just noticeable difference,' and kept constant for different observers, or even for the same observer at different times." [3] *In short, Fullerton and Cattell regarded the difference limen, as calculated from the normal probability integral, as an arbitrary measure of variability and not as a measure of an underlying barrier placed in the path of discrimination.*

In 1930, Georg von Békésy [4] *found that if he took precautions to minimize temporal fluctuations in the sensitivity, fatigue, and attention of his observers the psychometric function for differential loudness discrimination revealed itself as rectilinear (a straight line between 0 to 100 per cent detection) rather than ogival. He interpreted the nature of his psychometric functions as evidence that discrimination does in fact occur in discrete "quantal" steps, as Fechner maintained. In the paper "Theory of the Neural Quantum in the Discrimination of Loudness and Pitch," Stevens, Morgan, and Volkman extended Békésy's theoretical and empirical observations on the quantal nature of discrimination. The theory that they proposed is much closer to Fechner's view than to Cattell's. Moreover, it is a refinement of classical threshold theory in the sense that it predicts both the form and the rate of growth of the psychometric function, whereas classical theory predicted only the form.*

When an observer is asked to discriminate between two stimuli that are physically quite similar, he often has very little confidence in the accuracy of his judgment. Similarly, when asked if he can detect a weak stimulus he may find it difficult to decide whether he truly detected the stimulus or whether he only "imagined" its presence. The problem of how certain the observer should be before he says "yes" is ever present in the measurement of discrimination.

In the measurement of absolute sensitivity by the classical psychophysical methods, the experimenter might occasionally introduce a "blank" to test whether the observer might claim to perceive a stimulus when none had been presented. If the

[3] G. S. Fullerton and J. McK. Cattell, "On the perception of small differences," *Philosophical Series, University of Pennsylvania*, 1892, 2, pp. 10–11.

[4] G. von Békésy, "Über das Fechnersche Gesetz und seine Bedeutung für die Theorie des Hörens," *Annalen der Physik*, 1930, 7, 329–359. (See also G. von Békésy, *Experiments in Hearing*, translated and edited by E. G. Wever, 1960.)

observer responded "yes" to some of the blanks he might be told that his performance was unsatisfactory and that he should improve it. On subsequent trials, he would probably be quite reluctant to respond "yes" when he was less than absolutely certain that he had perceived the stimulus. But, in his effort to avoid "false positives," would he not also more often respond "no" to a stimulus that he had almost certainly perceived? Thus, would not the index of sensitivity be dependent partially on how conservative he chose to be? In the measurement of differential sensitivity the problem is the same. Fullerton and Cattell discussed the observer's criterion when they remarked that "If complete certainty be taken as the standard, a difference in the stimuli will be required much greater than that which can ordinarily be distinguished, and the standard will be found to differ greatly with different observers, measuring, if anything, rather their character than their fineness of sensation." [5]

The most successful effort to eliminate the confounding effects of the observer's criterion on the measure of his sensitivity has been the application of statistical decision theory to sensory discrimination. This application, called the theory of signal detection, is outlined by Swets, Tanner, and Birdsall in "Decision Processes in Perception." In the few years after this paper was published signal detection theory already had strongly affected sensory psychophysics. As the selection by Swets et al. makes clear, the theory provides a measure of sensitivity that is independent of the observer's criterion, offers testable assumptions about the distribution of sensory excitation, and makes possible comparison of the results of a real observer with the results of an "ideal" observer. These important advantages account for its wide application.

A topic that runs continuously through the history of psychophysics is the relativity of discrimination on the intensity continuum. A quantitative statement of this relativity was made by Ernst Weber, who concluded that the increment in stimulus magnitude necessary to produce a just noticeable increment in sensation is proportional to the magnitude of the background or comparison stimulus, i.e., $\Delta I = kI$. It has long

---

[5]Fullerton and Cattell, *op. cit.*, p. 11.

been known that Weber's law fails at the extremes of the intensity continuum, especially at the low extreme, but that it holds rather well in the middle. The Weber fraction ($\Delta I/I$) obtained in the middle of the continuum is therefore still used as an index of the keenness of discrimination of the various sense modalities and serves as a way of comparing the senses to each other.

Suggestions have been offered that Weber's law be modified in order to increase its validity or that it be replaced altogether. Some of these will be found in the present section, particularly in the papers of Cattell ("On Errors of Observation"), Woodworth ("Professor Cattell's Psychophysical Contributions"), and Miller ("Sensitivity to Changes in the Intensity of White Noise and Its Relation to Masking and Loudness"). It is noteworthy that a law of the relativity of discrimination, such as Weber's law, need not be based on the acceptance of the difference limen as an underlying functional entity. The essence of the law is that discriminability is proportional to the absolute magnitude of stimulation and virtually any reliable measure of discrimination, e.g., the neural quantum, can be used to test its validity. One's interpretation of why discriminability changes as a function of the magnitude of stimulation is, however, very much determined by one's view of whether the underlying nature of discrimination is continuous or steplike.

Selig Hecht, for example, attempted to explain the relativity of brightness discrimination as the result of photochemical events in the eye. He said "Starting with a given intensity, there is always a definite increase or decrease in this intensity which must be made before it can be recognized with certainty as different. In terms of our physicochemical explanation, each of these just-perceptible steps represents a constant increase in the quantity of photosensitive material decomposed in the visual cells."[6] Clearly, Hecht's view of the discontinuity of discrimination and its photochemical correlate was too static to satisfy disciples of Cattell who believed that the difference limen measured merely variation of performance and did not imply steplike changes in sensation. Hecht, therefore, did not

---

[6] S. Hecht, "Vision: II. The nature of the photoreceptor process," in C. Murchison, editor, *Handbook of General Experimental Psychology*, 1934, p. 771.

go unchallenged. Crozier and Holway in "On the Law for Minimal Discrimination of Intensities. I." argued that the size of the just noticeable difference is "determined by probability considerations which are completely independent of specific structural or other properties of the receptor field." They too saw the difference limen as a measure of variability.

THE INTENSITY OF SENSATIONS, WEBER'S LAW, FECHNER'S LAW

William James

THE INTENSITY OF SENSATIONS

A light may be so weak as not sensibly to dispel the darkness, a sound so low as not to be heard, a contact so faint that we fail to notice it. In other words, a certain finite amount of the outward stimulus is required to produce any sensation of its presence at all. This is called by Fechner the law of the *threshold* — something must be stepped over before the object can gain entrance to the mind. An impression just above the threshold is called the *minimum visible, audible,* etc. From this point onwards, as the impressing force increases, the sensation increases also, though at a slower rate, until at last an *acme* of the sensation is reached which no increase in the stimulus can make sensibly more great. Usually, before the acme, *pain* begins to mix with the specific character of the sensation. This is definitely observable in the cases of great pressure, intense heat, cold, light, and sound; and in those of smell and taste less definitely so only from the fact that we can less easily increase the force of the stimuli here. On the other hand, all sensations, however unpleasant when more intense, are rather agreeable than otherwise in their very lowest degrees. A faintly bitter taste, or putrid smell, may at least be *interesting*.

Reprinted with permission of Holt, Rinehart, and Winston, Inc. from *Psychology: Briefer Course*, 1892, pages 16–23.

WEBER'S LAW

I said that the intensity of the sensation increases by slower steps than those by which its exciting cause increases. If there were no threshold, and if every equal increment in the outer stimulus produced an equal increment in the sensation's intensity, a simple straight line would represent graphically the "curve" of the relation between the two things. Let the horizontal line stand for the scale of intensities of the objective stimulus, so that at 0 it has no intensity, at 1 intensity 1, and so forth. Let the verticals dropped from the slanting line stand for the sensations aroused. At 0 there will be no sensation; at 1 there will be a sensation represented by the length of the vertical $S^1 — 1$, at 2 the sensation will be represented by $S^2 — 2$, and so on. The line of S's will rise evenly because by the hypothesis the verticals (or sensations) increase at the same rate as the horizontals (or stimuli) to which they severally correspond. But in Nature, as aforesaid, they increase at a slower rate. If each step forward in the horizontal direction be equal to the last, then each step upward in the vertical direction will have to be somewhat shorter than the last; the line of sensations will be convex on top instead of straight.

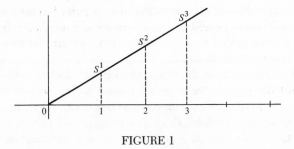

FIGURE 1

Figure 2 represents this actual state of things, 0 being the zero-point of the stimulus, and conscious sensation, represented by the curved line, not beginning until the "threshold" is reached, at which the stimulus has the value 3. From here onwards the sensation increases, but it increases less at each step, until at last, the "acme" being reached, the sensation-line grows flat. The exact law of retardation is called *Weber's law*, from the fact that he first observed it in the case of weights. I will quote Wundt's account of the law and of the facts on which it is based.

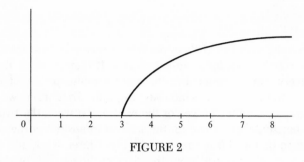

FIGURE 2

Every one knows that in the stilly night we hear things un-
noticed in the noise of day. The gentle ticking of the clock,
the air circulating through the chimney, the cracking of the
chairs in the room, and a thousand other slight noises, impress
themselves upon our ear. It is equally well known that in the
confused hubbub of the streets, or the clamor of a railway, we
may lose not only what our neighbor says to us, but even not
hear the sound of our own voice. The stars which are brightest
at night are invisible by day; and although we see the moon
then, she is far paler than at night. Every one who has had to
deal with weights knows that if to a pound in the hand a second pound be added, the difference is immediately felt; whilst
if it be added to a hundredweight, we are not aware of the
difference at all. . . .

The sound of the clock, the light of the stars, the pressure
of the pound, these are all *stimuli* to our senses, and stimuli
whose outward amount remains the same. What then do these
experiences teach? Evidently nothing but this, that one and
the same stimulus, according to the circumstances under
which it operates, will be felt either more or less intensely, or
not felt at all. Of what sort now is the alteration in the circumstances upon which this alteration in the feeling may depend?
On considering the matter closely we see that it is everywhere
of one and the same kind. The tick of the clock is a feeble stimulus for our auditory nerve, which we hear plainly when it is
alone, but not when it is added to the strong stimulus of the
carriage-wheels and other noises of the day. The light of the
stars is a stimulus to the eye. But if the stimulation which this
light exerts be added to the strong stimulus of daylight, we

feel nothing of it, although we feel it distinctly when it unites itself with the feebler stimulation of twilight. The poundweight is a stimulus to our skin, which we feel when it joins itself to a preceeding stimulus of equal strength, but which vanishes when it is combined with a stimulus a thousand times greater in amount.

We may therefore lay it down as a general rule that a stimulus, in order to be felt, may be so much the smaller if the already preexisting stimulation of the organ is small, but must be so much the larger, the greater the preëxisting stimulation is. . . . The simplest relation would obviously be that the sensation should increase in identically the same ratio as the stimulus. . . . But if this simplest of all relations prevailed . . . the light of the stars, e.g., ought to make as great an addition to the daylight as it does to the darkness of the nocturnal sky, and this we know to be not the case. . . . So it is clear that the strength of the sensations does not increase in proportion to the amount of the stimuli, but more slowly. And now comes the question, in what proportion does the increase of the sensation grow less as the increase of the stimulus grows greater? To answer this question, every-day experiences do not suffice. We need exact measurements, both of the amounts of the various stimuli, and of the intensity of the sensations themselves.

How to execute these measurements, however, is something which daily experience suggests. To measure the strength of sensations is, as we saw, impossible; we can only measure the difference of sensations. Experience showed us what very unequal differences of sensation might come from equal differences of outward stimulus. But all these experiences expressed themselves in one kind of fact, that the same difference of stimulus could in one case be felt, and in another case not felt at all — a pound felt if added to another pound, but not if added to a hundredweight. . . . We can quickest reach a result with our observations if we start with an arbitrary strength of stimulus, notice what sensation it gives us, and then *see how much we can increase the stimulus without making the sensation seem to change.* If we carry out such observations with stimuli of varying absolute amounts, we shall be forced to choose in an equally varying way the amounts of addition to the stimulus which are capable of giving us a just barely per-

ceptible feeling of *more*. A light to be just perceptible in the
twilight need not be near as bright as the starlight; it must be
far brighter to be just perceived during the day. If now we institute such observations for all possible strengths of the various stimuli, and note for each strength the amount of addition
of the latter required to produce a barely perceptible alteration of sensation, we shall have a series of figures in which is
immediately expressed the law according to which the sensation alters when the stimulation is increased. . . .

Observations according to this method are particularly easy to make
in the spheres of light, sound, and pressure. Beginning with the latter
case,

> We find a surprisingly simple result. *The barely sensible
> addition to the original weight must stand exactly in the same
> proportion to it,* be the *same fraction* of it, no matter what the
> absolute value may be of the weights on which the experiment
> is made. . . . As the average of a number of experiments, this
> fraction is found to be about ⅛; that is, no matter what pres-
> sure there may already be made upon the skin, an increase or
> a diminution of the pressure will be *felt,* as soon as the added
> or subtracted weight amounts to one third of the weight origi-
> nally there.

Wundt then describes how differences may be observed in the mus-
cular feelings, in the feelings of heat, in those of light, and in those of
sound; and he concludes thus:

> So we have found that all the senses whose stimuli we are
> enabled to measure accurately, obey a uniform law. However
> various may be their several delicacies of discrimination, *this*
> holds true of all, that *the increase of the stimulus necessary to
> produce an increase of the sensation bears a constant ratio to
> the total stimulus.* The figures which express this ratio in the
> several senses may be shown thus in tabular form:

Sensation of light	$\frac{1}{100}$
Muscular sensation	$\frac{1}{17}$
Feeling of pressure, ⎫	
" " warmth, ⎬	$\frac{1}{3}$
" " sound, ⎭	

These figures are far from giving as accurate a measure as might be desired. But at least they are fit to convey a general notion of the relative discriminative susceptibility of the different senses. . . . The important law which gives in so simple a form the relation of the sensation to the stimulus that calls it forth was first discovered by the physiologist Ernst Heinrich Weber to obtain in special cases. [1]

FECHNER'S LAW

Another way of expressing Weber's law is to say that to get equal positive additions to the sensation, one must make equal *relative* additions to the stimulus. Professor Fechner of Leipzig founded upon Weber's law a theory of the numerical measurement of sensations, over which much metaphysical discussion has raged. Each just perceptible addition to the sensation, as we gradually let the stimulus increase, was supposed by him to be a *unit* of sensation, and all these units were treated by him as equal, in spite of the fact that *equally perceptible* increments need by no means appear *equally big* when they once are perceived. The many pounds which form the just perceptible addition to a hundredweight feel bigger when added than the few ounces which form the just perceptible addition to a pound. Fechner ignored this fact. He considered that if n distinct perceptible steps of increase might be passed through in gradually increasing a stimulus from the threshold-value till the intensity s was felt, then the sensation of s was composed of n units, which were of the same value all along the line.[2] Sensations once represented by numbers, psychology may become, according to Fechner, an "exact" science, susceptible of mathematical treatment. His general formula for getting at the number of units in any sensation is $S = C \log R$, where S stands for the sensation, R for the stimulus numerically estimated, and C for a constant that must be separately determined by experiment in each particular order of sensibility. The sensation is proportional to the logarithm of the stimulus; and the absolute values, in units, of any series of sensations might be

---

[1] "Vorlesungen über Menschen u. Thierseele," Lecture VII.

[2] In other words, S standing for the sensation in general, and d for its noticeable increment, we have the equation $dS = $ const. The increment of stimulus which produces dS (call it dR) meanwhile varies. Fechner calls it the "differential threshold"; and as its *relative* value to R is always the same, we have the equation

$$\frac{dR}{R} = \text{const.}$$

got from the ordinates of the curve in Figure 2, if it were a correctly drawn logarithmic curve, with the thresholds rightly plotted out from experiments.

Fechner's psycho-physic formula, as he called it, has been attacked on every hand; and as absolutely nothing practical has come of it, it need receive no farther notice here. The main outcome of his book has been to stir up experimental investigation into the validity of Weber's law (which concerns itself merely with the just perceptible increase, and says nothing about the measurement of the sensation as a whole) and to promote discussion of statistical methods. Weber's law, as will appear when we take the senses, *seriatim,* is only approximately verified. The discussion of statistical methods is necessitated by the extraordinary fluctuations of our sensibility from one moment to the next. It is found, namely, when the difference of two sensations approaches the limit of discernibility, that at one moment we discern it and at the next we do not. Our incessant accidental inner alterations make it impossible to tell just what the least discernible increment of the sensation is without taking the average of a large number of appreciations. These *accidental errors* are as likely to increase as to diminish our sensibility, and are eliminated in such an average, for those above and those below the line then neutralize each other in the sum, and the normal sensibility, if there be one (that is, the sensibility due to constant causes as distinguished from these accidental ones), stands revealed. The methods of getting the average all have their difficulties and their snares, and controversy over them has become very subtle indeed. As an instance of how laborious some of the statistical methods are, and how patient German investigators can be, I may say that Fechner himself, in testing Weber's law for weights by the so-called "method of true and false cases," tabulated and computed no less than 24,576 separate judgments.

ENERGY, QUANTA, AND VISION

Selig Hecht, Simon Shlaer,
and Maurice Henri Pirenne

THRESHOLD ENERGIES FOR VISION

The minimum energy required to produce a visual effect achieves its significance by virtue of the quantum nature of light. Like all radiation, light is emitted and absorbed in discrete units or quanta, whose energy content is equal to its frequency v multiplied by Planck's constant h. At the threshold of vision these quanta are used for the photodecomposition of visual purple, and in conformity with Einstein's equivalence law each absorbed quantum transforms one molecule of visual purple (Dartnall, Goodeve, and Lythgoe, 1938). Since even the earliest measurements show that only a small number of quanta is required for a threshold stimulus, it follows that only a small number of primary molecular transformations is enough to supply the initial impetus for a visual act. The precise number of these molecular changes becomes of obvious importance in understanding the visual receptor process, and it is this which has led us to the present investigation.

The first measurements of the energy at the visual threshold were made by Langley (1889) with the bolometer he invented for such purposes (Langley, 1881). He found the energy to be 3×10^{-9} ergs for light of 550 mμ. Langley worked before the physiology of vision was understood, so that he used the wrong light and took none of the precautions now known to be necessary; even so, his results are too high only by a factor of 10.

In the fifty years since Langley there have been eleven efforts to redetermine the minimum energy for vision. We have carefully studied all these accounts and have done our best to evaluate the measurements. Unfortunately, many of them contain serious errors which invalidate them. Most of them involved no direct energy determinations; instead, the investigators relied on previously measured energy

From *Journal of General Physiology*, 1942, 25, 819–840. Pages 819–822 and 826–840 reprinted with permission of the Rockefeller University Press.

A preliminary report of these measurements was published in *Science* (Hecht, Shlaer, and Pirenne, 1941), and presented to the Optical Society in October, 1941 (Hecht, 1942). Maurice Henri Pirenne is fellow of the Belgian American Educational Foundation.

distributions in standard sources and made elaborate computations from them. Only a few can be considered as reliable.

After Langley, the earliest paper is by Grijns and Noyons (1905). Their data differ widely from all other measurements and cannot be accepted even though it is hard to discover their precise errors because the description is too obscure. Zwaardemaker (1905), in whose laboratory their measurements were made, reports some of his own rough determinations, which turn out to be near Langley's. Neither Grijns and Noyons nor Zwaardemaker actually measured the energies involved, but relied on Ångström's (1903) determinations of the energy distribution in the Hefner lamp.

The best of the early efforts is by von Kries and Eyster (1907); and though the results involve many calculations, they come very close to the most careful of modern measurements. Von Kries and Eyster made no direct energy determinations; they measured brightnesses, durations, and areas. The conversion of these factors into final energies requires skill and care in the evaluation of absorptions, reflections, lens factors, and the like, and it is gratifying to see the admirable way in which von Kries accomplished this task.

Computations from star magnitudes were made by Ives (1916) and by Russell (1917). However, neither they nor Reeves (1917) and Buisson (1917), who both reproduced star observations in the laboratory, employed the best physiological conditions for the measurements. Moreover, none of them took consideration of the different luminosity curves for rod vision and cone vision, and used the latter as standard in the computations.

Direct energy measurements were made by du Noüy (1921), but his work involves serious physical errors, and his results are too low by a factor of more than 100 — so low indeed as to seem impossible.

The most recent determinations are by Chariton and Lea (1929), by Wentworth (1930), and by Barnes and Czerny (1932), all of whom agree in the order of magnitude of their results. Wentworth's exposures were too long to yield minimal values; otherwise her work is excellent. She measured the energies involved, which Barnes and Czerny also did, but not as directly.

From these twelve researches, we have chosen the three sets of measurements which are free from what can now be recognized as obvious error. These are given in Table 1. Even though they differ by a factor of about 3, these data can be considered as roughly confirming

TABLE 1

Minimum Energy for Vision

Wavelength (mµ)	Energy (ergs)	No. of quanta	Source
505	0.66–1.17 $\times$ 10^{-10}	17–30[a]	Chariton and Lea (1929)
507	1.3–2.6 $\times$ 10^{-10}	34–68	von Kries and Eyster (1907)
530	1.5–3.3 $\times$ 10^{-10}	40–90	Barnes and Czerny (1932)

[a] For inexperienced observers.

one another. However, since for our purposes a factor of 3 cannot be ignored, we undertook to make the measurements again, but under the best physical and physiological conditions.

VISUAL CONDITIONS

The circumstances which will yield the maximum retinal sensibility have been adequately known for years. They involve dark adaptation, peripheral vision, small test fields, short exposures, and selected portions of the spectrum.

Complete dark adaptation means a stay of at least 30 minutes in the dark before measurements can be begun (Piper, 1903; Hecht, Haig, and Chase, 1937). After thorough dark adaptation the periphery of the retina is much more sensitive than its center. The greatest density of rod elements begins at about 18° out (Østerberg, 1935), and exploration shows that between 20 and 30° from the center there is a region of maximum sensibility to light (Wentworth, 1930). The variation within this region is not large, and for convenience we chose a retinal area situated 20° temporally on the horizontal axis.

In visual threshold measurements it has been established that the larger the test area, the smaller need the intensity be for its recognition (cf. summary by Wald, 1938 *a*). This reciprocal relation is exact only for small areas. Our preliminary experiments, as well as the work of other investigators, show a minimum for the product of area and intensity for fields of the order of 10 minutes diameter. We therefore chose a circular retinal area of 10 minutes diameter for the test field.

The energy required to pass over the visual threshold involves an approximately reciprocal relationship between intensity and time of exposure. For exposures shorter than 0.01 second, the reciprocal relation holds perfectly (Graham and Margaria, 1935). To be sure of falling within this most efficient range, our exposures were 0.001 second long.

Finally, from the measurements of the scotopic luminosity curve (Hecht and Williams, 1922), it is known that for dim vision the eye is most sensitive to a wavelength of 510 mμ, and this is the light which we used for making the measurements.

APPARATUS AND CALIBRATIONS

The physical arrangements may be seen in Fig. 1. The light source L is a ribbon filament lamp run on constant current obtained from storage cells and measured potentiometrically. By means of a lens, it is focused on the slit of a double monochromator M_1M_2 and finally on the artificial pupil P. The subject, who sits in a dark cabinet in the dark room, has his head in a fixed position by keeping his teeth in a "bite" or hard impression of his upper jaw. He has his left eye next to the pupil P, and on looking at the red fixation point FP he sees the field lens FL. The light intensity of this uniformly illuminated field is varied in large steps by the neutral filters F, and in a gradual way by the neutral wedge and balancer W. The size of the field is controlled by the diaphragms D. Its exposure is fixed by the shutter S, and is initiated by the subject. . . .

VISUAL MEASUREMENTS

From the subject's point of view, an experiment involves the report of whether or not he has seen a flash of light after he has opened the shut-

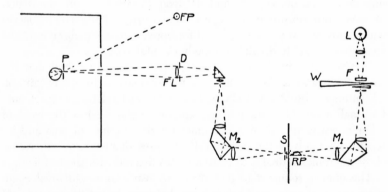

FIGURE 1   *Optical system for measuring minimum energies necessary for vision. The eye at the pupil* P *fixates the red point* FP *and observes the test field formed by the lens* FL *and the diaphragm* D. *The light for this field comes from the lamp* L *through the neutral filter* F *and wedge* W, *through the double monochromator* M₁M₂ *and is controlled by the shutter* S.

ter for an exposure. Fixation of the red point need not be continuous, a circumstance which avoids undue fatigue. The observer is told by the operator that conditions are set and that he should try a flash when he is ready. He fixates the red point, and at the moment which he considers propitious, he exposes the light to his eye. The operator changes the position of the wedge, or removes or introduces a filter until he is satisfied with the precision of the measurements.

In the early measurements we considered that the threshold had been reached when the observer saw a flash of light at a given intensity six times out of ten presentations. Later the measurements were made somewhat more elaborately. Each of a series of intensities was presented many times and the frequency of seeing the flash was determined for each. From the resulting plot of frequency against intensity we chose the threshold as that amount of light which could be seen with a frequency of 60 per cent.

During 1940 and 1941 we measured the threshold for seven subjects. With four we made several determinations each, extending over a year and a half; one subject we measured on two occasions 3 months apart; and two we measured only once. For all these observers the minimum energy necessary for vision ranges between 2.1 and 5.7 $\times$ 10^{-10} ergs at the cornea. These small energies represent between 54 and 148 quanta of blue-green light. The results for the individual subjects are in Table 2, and are given as energy and as the number of quanta required.

It is to be noticed that these values are of the same order of magnitude as those of von Kries and Eyster, and of Barnes and Czerny, but almost twice as large. Because of the fairly wide ranges, these previous measurements and our own overlap to some extent, and it is conceivable, though not probable, that their observers may actually have needed somewhat smaller energies than ours. Chariton and Lea's results, however, are much too small. Actually their value of 17 $h\nu$ is an extrapolation to zero frequency of seeing; if we take as threshold a 60 per cent frequency, their data come more nearly to 25 $h\nu$. This is still too small a value, and is probably in error, as will be apparent in later sections of our paper.

REFLECTIONS AND ABSORPTIONS

The values in Table 2, as well as those of previous investigators, are the energies incident at the cornea. Nevertheless the tacit supposition has generally been made that they represent the actual energies necessary

TABLE 2
MINIMUM ENERGY FOR VISION

Each datum is the result of many measurements during a single experimental period, and is the energy which can be seen with 60 per cent frequency. $\lambda = 510$ mμ; $h\nu = 3.84 \times 10^{-12}$ ergs.

Observer	Energy (ergs $\times 10^{-10}$)	No. of quanta	Observer	Energy (ergs $\times 10^{-10}$)	No. of quanta
S.H.	4.83	126	C.D.H.	2.50	65
	5.18	135		2.92	76
	4.11	107		2.23	58
	3.34	87		2.23	58
	3.03	79			
	4.72	123	M.S.	3.31	81
	5.68	148		4.30	112
S.S.	3.03	79	S.R.F.	4.61	120
	2.07	54			
	2.15	56	A.F.B.	3.19	83
	2.38	62			
	3.69	96	M.H.P.	3.03	79
	3.80	99		3.19	83
	3.99	104		5.30	138

to initiate a visual act. It is important to recognize that this assumption is incorrect. Before one can know how many quanta are required to start the visual process, one must apply at least three corrections to the measurements.

The first is reflection from the cornea. This is about 4 per cent and is obviously of not much importance. The second involves loss by the ocular media between the outer surface of the cornea and the retina. It has been common opinion that this loss is small. However, the measurements of Roggenbau and Wetthauer (1927) on cattle eyes, as well as the recent measurements of Ludvigh and McCarthy (1938) on human eyes, have shown that this loss is large. From the values of Ludvigh and McCarthy it appears that at 510 mμ the ocular media transmit almost exactly 50 per cent of the light entering the cornea of a young person, and less of an older one.

The next correction is much more difficult to evaluate with precision and involves the percentage of the energy absorbed by the retinal elements themselves. Since visual purple is the photosensitive substance concerned in this particular act, light which is not absorbed by it is visually useless. One cannot assume that visual purple absorbs all the light incident on the retinal cells. The fraction which it does absorb must be found by experiment.

Koenig (1894) determined the absorption of the total amount of visual purple which can be extracted from the human eye. If this amount of visual purple is spread evenly over the whole retina, his data show that it will absorb only 4 per cent of light of 510 mμ. This is a small value. Nevertheless, it is about the same as the 4 per cent and the 13 per cent recently found by Wald (1938 *b*) with a similar method for the absorption of the visual purple of the rabbit and rat retinas respectively.

These figures are probably too low, first because it is unlikely that all of the visual purple in the eye has been extracted, and second, because visual purple is not evenly distributed over the retina. It is lacking in the fovea; and even in the periphery the density of the rods is known to vary in a definite way. However, these absorptions may be considered as lower limiting values.

VISUAL PURPLE ABSORPTION

We have estimated the absorption of visual purple in the retina in a completely independent manner by comparing the percentage absorption spectrum of different concentrations of visual purple with the scotopic (rod) luminosity curve of the eye measured at the retina. The comparison rests on the fact that the shape and width of the percentage absorption spectrum of a substance varies with its concentration, and that the luminosity curve must represent the percentage absorption curve of a particular concentration of visual purple in the retina.

Figure 2 shows the absorption spectrum of frog's visual purple as determined by Chase and Haig (1938) in our laboratory, by Lythgoe (1937) in London, and by Wald (1938 *b*) at Harvard. The agreement of the data is obvious, and shows that the absorption spectrum of visual purple may be considered as well established. Table 3 gives the average of these three series of measurements computed so that the maximum density at 500 mμ has a value of 1.

From these data in Table 3 we may prepare a series of percentage absorption spectra for different concentrations of visual purple. Since we are not interested in the absolute concentration of visual purple, but rather in its absorption capacities, we can deal with the series of percentage absorption spectra entirely in terms of maximum absorption. It will be recalled that the photometric density d is related to the

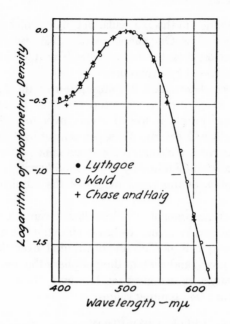

FIGURE 2   *Absorption spectrum of frog's visual purple. The data from the three sources have been made equal at 500mμ.*

transmission I_t by the equation $d = \log(1/I_t)$ and since the absorption $I_a = 1 - I_t$, it is a simple computation to find the percentage absorption corresponding to any density value, or the reverse.

We have made such computations for a variety of visual purple

TABLE 3

ABSORPTION SPECTRUM OF VISUAL PURPLE

Average of data from Chase and Haig (1938), Wald (1938 *b*), and Lythgoe (1937).

$\lambda - m\mu$	Density	$\lambda - m\mu$	Density	$\lambda - m\mu$	Density
400	0.306	480	0.900	560	0.321
410	0.317	490	0.967	570	0.207
420	0.353	500	1.000	580	0.131
430	0.408	510	0.973	590	0.0805
440	0.485	520	0.900	600	0.0473
450	0.581	530	0.780	610	0.0269
460	0.691	540	0.628	620	0.0150
470	0.811	550	0.465		

densities, and Fig. 3 shows the resulting percentage absorption curves for the different maximal absorptions of visual purple. For comparisons among the curves in Fig. 3 the maxima have all been made equal to 1, but their actual values are indicated in the figure. It is clear that the width of the curves increases as the concentration of visual purple increases.

The scotopic luminosity curve, as measured experimentally, records the reciprocal of the relative energy in different parts of the spectrum required for the production of a constant and very low brightness in the eye (Hecht and Williams, 1922). If this is to be compared with the absorption spectrum of visual purple, it must be converted into a quantum luminosity curve instead of an energy luminosity curve, because it is the number of quanta which determines the photochemical effectiveness of light and not just its energy content (Dartnall and Goodeve, 1937). Moreover, since our interest lies in retinal comparisons, the luminosity curve must be corrected for ocular media absorption in terms of the data of Ludvigh and McCarthy.

The scotopic luminosity data have been corrected in these two ways; the computed values are given in Table 4 and shown as circles in Fig. 4. Included in the same figure are two percentage absorption spectra of visual purple; the upper curve represents 20 per cent maximal absorption, while the lower curve is 5 per cent maximal absorption.

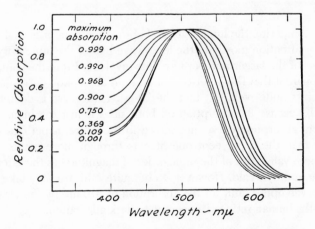

FIGURE 3   *Percentage absorption spectra of various concentrations of visual purple. For convenience in comparing the shapes of the curves, their maxima have all been equated to 1 and superimposed. The actual fraction absorbed at the maximum is shown for each curve. It is apparent that with increasing concentration the absorption curve steadily increases in width.*

TABLE 4

ROD LUMINOSITY DISTRIBUTION IN SPECTRUM

The original energy luminosity data of Hecht and Williams (1922) in column 2, when divided by the corresponding wavelengths in column 1, yield the quantum luminosity values in column 3 after being multiplied by a factor so that the maximum at 511 mμ equals 1. When these values in column 3 are divided by the ocular media transmission data in column 4 from Ludvigh and McCarthy (1938), they yield the spectral luminosity distribution at the retina given in column 5 after multiplication by a factor so that the maximum at 502 mμ is 1.

$\lambda - m\mu$	Energy luminosity at cornea	Quantum luminosity at cornea	Ocular transmission	Quantum luminosity at retina
412	0.0632	0.0779	0.116	0.336
455	0.399	0.447	0.410	0.545
486	0.834	0.874	0.472	0.926
496	0.939	0.964	0.490	0.984
507	0.993	0.998	0.506	0.986
518	0.973	0.957	0.519	0.921
529	0.911	0.877	0.540	0.812
540	0.788	0.743	0.559	0.665
550	0.556	0.515	0.566	0.455
582	0.178	0.155	0.596	0.131
613	0.0272	0.0226	0.625	0.0181
666	0.00181	0.00139	0.672	0.00104

For comparing the luminosity and absorption data, it is well to confine our attention mostly to the long wave half of the luminosity curve because of the larger number of points involved. From the comparison it is apparent that the 5 per cent maximum absorption curve describes the points quite well, but that the 20 per cent curve is definitely excluded, because its absorption on both sides is just too high. The 10 per cent absorption curve, not shown in the figure, is perhaps slightly better than the 5 per cent one; it cuts through more points. In any case, both values are of the same order of magnitude as those found by Koenig and by Wald. However, to be quite safe, we may take 20 per cent as the upper limit for the absorption of 510 mμ by the visual purple in the human retina after complete dark adaptation.

ENERGY ABSORBED BY THE RODS

It is clear now why the 54 to 148 quanta required at the cornea cannot represent the energy actually employed in vision. About 4 per cent of this incident light is reflected by the cornea; almost precisely 50 per

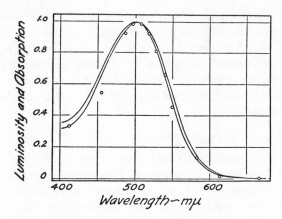

FIGURE 4 *Comparison of scotopic luminosity at the retina with visual purple absorption. The points are the data of Hecht and Williams corrected for quantum effectiveness and ocular media transmission. The curves are the percentage absorption spectra of visual purple; the upper curve represents 20 per cent maximal absorption, and the lower one 5 per cent maximal absorption. All curves have been made equal to 1 at the maximum, 500 mμ, for ease in comparison.*

cent is absorbed by the lens and other ocular media; and of the rest, at least 80 per cent passes through the retina without being absorbed. If corrections are made for these factors, the range of 54 to 148 quanta at the cornea becomes as an upper limit 5 to 14 quanta absorbed by the visual purple of the retina.

Visual purple is in the terminal segments of the rods, and the 10 minute circular visual field contains about 500 rods (Østerberg, 1935). Since the number of absorbed quanta is so small, it is very unlikely that any one rod will take up more than one quantum. In fact, the simplest statistical considerations show that if 7 quanta are absorbed by 500 rods, there is only a 4 per cent probability that 2 quanta will be taken up by a single rod. We may therefore conclude that in order for us to see, it is necessary for only 1 quantum of light to be absorbed by each of 5 to 14 retinal rods.[1]

[1] These data disprove the supposition made by Granit, Holmberg, and Zewi (1938) that most of the visual purple in the retina is inert as sensory substance, and that sensory impulses from the rods are "initiated by the bleaching of a thin surface film, which had to contain only an immeasurably small fraction of the total quantity present" (Granit, Munsterhjelm, and Zewi, 1939). Since the maximum visual purple concentration which the retina can achieve is able to absorb only 5 to 14 quanta at the threshold of vision, a very small fraction of the total visual purple would absorb much less than one quantum and would be ineffective for visual purposes.

It is very likely that the photodecomposition of visual purple in solution has a quantum efficiency of 1 (Dartnall, Goodeve, and Lythgoe, 1938). Our data then mean that 1 molecule of visual purple needs to be changed simultaneously in each of 5 to 14 rods, in order to produce a visual effect. This is indeed a small number of chemical events, but by virtue of its very smallness, its reality may be tested in an entirely independent manner.

POISSON DISTRIBUTIONS

The energy calibration of the light gives merely the average number of quanta per flash. This is in the nature of the measurement, because the thermopile records only the energy density, which is the number of quanta per second from a continuously incident light. Each flash, however, will not always deliver this average number. Sometimes the flash will yield fewer, sometimes more, quanta.

Since absorption of this group of quanta by the retina represents discrete and independent events which occur individually and collectively at random, the actual number of such retinal events which any given flash provides will vary according to a Poisson probability distribution (Fry, 1928). Let n be the number of quanta which it is necessary for the retina to absorb in order for us to see a flash of light. Let a be the average number of quanta which any flash yields to the retina. Then the Poisson distribution states that

$$P_n = a^n/e^a n!$$

in which P_n is the probability that the flash will yield the necessary n quanta, and e is the base of natural logarithms. A special virtue of the Poisson distribution is that it has only one parameter, and is thus determined when the average number a is set. The values of P_n for various values of a and n are available in printed tables (e.g., Fry, 1928).

Since for us to see a flash of light the retina must absorb n quanta, we shall also see when the retina absorbs more than n quanta. From the published Poisson distributions, one can then compute the probability that n or more quanta will be delivered to the retina in a given flash when the average number of quanta delivered by that flash is known. The values computed in this way for different values of a and n are shown in Fig. 5.

There are two significant features of Fig. 5. One is that the shape of the distributions is fixed and different for every value of n. The curve becomes steeper as n increases. It follows from this that if the prob-

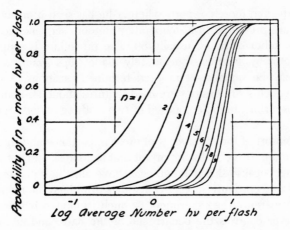

FIGURE 5   *Poisson probability distributions. For any average number of quanta* (hν) *per flash, the ordinates give the probabilities that the flash will deliver to the retina* n *or more quanta, depending on the value assumed for* n.

ability distribution could be determined by experiment, its shape would automatically reveal the value of n corresponding to it.

Another and equally important feature of Fig. 5 is that the relationship is expressed in terms of the logarithm of the average number of quanta per flash. Therefore, for comparison with the distributions in Fig. 5, the experiments need not employ the absolute values of the average number of quanta delivered per flash, but merely their relative values.

The experiments may then be made quite simply. On many repetitions of a flash of given average energy content, the frequency with which the flash is seen will depend on the probability with which it yields n or more quanta to the retina. When this frequency is measured for each of several intensities, a distribution is secured whose shape, when plotted against the logarithm of the average energy content, should correspond to one of the probability distributions in Fig. 5, and should thus show what the value of n has been.

FREQUENCY OF SEEING

We have made determinations of this kind. The experimenter varies the intensity of the light by placing the wedge in specific positions unknown to the observer. The observer then elicits the flash whenever he is ready, and merely reports whether he has seen it or not. The intensities are presented in a deliberately random sequence, each for a specific number of times, usually 50. The procedure is simplified for the operator by a series of accurately made stops against which the wedge may be rapidly set in predetermined positions. A complete series in which six intensities are used requires about 1½ hours of continuous experimentation composed of two or three periods of intensive work.

The comfort of the observer is of great importance and this must be at a maximum. It is equally important that fixation should not be rigidly continuous because this is fatiguing. Above all, the observer must be on guard to record any subjective feelings of fatigue the moment they become apparent. The experiment is much facilitated by the fact that the observer controls the occurrence of the flash, and can set it off only when he is thoroughly fixated and ready for an observation.

The data for the three observers who engaged in this experiment are given in Table 5. One experiment for each observer is plotted in Fig. 6. The points in the figure record the percentage frequency with which a flash of light is seen for flashes of average quantum content shown in the abscissas. Comparison with the curves in Fig. 5 shows that the measurements are best fitted by Poisson distributions in which n is 5, 6, and 7 quanta per flash. For the two other experiments in

TABLE 5

ENERGY AND FREQUENCY OF SEEING

Relation between the average number of quanta per flash at the cornea and the frequency with which the flash is seen. Each frequency represents 50 flashes, except for S. H., for whom there were 35 and 40 for the first and second series respectively.

S. H.		S. H.		S. S.		S. S.		M. H. P.	
No. of quanta	Fre-quency %	No. of quanta	Fre-quency %	No. of quanta	Fre-quency %	No. of quanta	Fre-quency %	No. of quanta	Fre-quency %
46.9	0.0	37.1	0.0	24.1	0.0	23.5	0.0	37.6	6.0
73.1	9.4	58.5	7.5	37.6	4.0	37.1	0.0	58.6	6.0
113.8	33.3	92.9	40.0	58.6	18.0	58.5	12.0	91.0	24.0
177.4	73.5	148.6	80.0	91.0	54.0	92.9	44.0	141.9	66.0
276.1	100.0	239.3	97.5	141.9	94.0	148.6	94.0	221.3	88.0
421.7	100.0	386.4	100.0	221.3	100.0	239.3	100.0	342.8	100.0

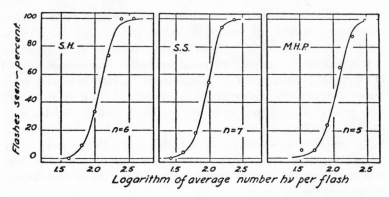

FIGURE 6 *Relation between the average energy content of a flash of light (in number of* hν*) and the frequency with which it is seen by three observers. Each point represents 50 flashes, except for S. H., where the number is 35. The curves are the Poisson distributions of Figure 6 for* n *values of 5, 6, and 7.*

Table 4, *n* is 7 and 8. No special statistical methods are necessary to determine which curve fits the data, since smaller and larger values of *n* are easily excluded by the simplest visual comparison.

From these measurements it is apparent that the number of critical events in the retina required to produce a visual effect lies between 5 and 8. These values are in such good agreement with the results determined by the straight-forward physical measurements already described that we must consider them as the actual number of quanta absorbed by the retina.

PHYSICAL FLUCTUATION AND
BIOLOGICAL VARIATION

It is unimportant that the number of quanta delivered to the cornea is very much higher than the number finally involved in vision according to these measurements. This is because most of the light incident on the cornea is wasted and does not contribute to the initiation of a visual act. The amount falling on the cornea could be greatly increased by any arrangement in the eye which would act as a filter. Thus, the cornea and the lens might be pigmented, and this probably contributes to the fact that the oldest investigator (S. H.) actually requires the highest number of quanta incident on the cornea. Indeed, one might even put a filter immediately in front of the eye since the precise position of the filter in the optical system is immaterial. Nevertheless, the probability distributions would still remain the same, and by their shape would yield the magnitude of the number of events involved in the visual act.

It is necessary to amplify this point somewhat. Fluctuations are part of all physical systems, but they become significantly large only when the number of individual events, in the modern physical sense, is small. The general phenomenon is known as the shot-effect and has been studied extensively in electron emission, though it has wide application in the problem of measurements (Schottky, 1922; Barnes and Czerny, 1932). As a rough approximation, one may say that the range of variation is proportional to the square root of the number of individual events involved in the process.

In the optical system of our apparatus, the light from the ribbon filament lamp varies in intensity from moment to moment, but because the number of quanta emitted is enormous, the variation is almost too small to be measured. However, when the light intensity has been reduced first by the filters and wedge, then by the monochromators, then by the shutter, then by the ocular media, and finally by the retina itself, it has become so low that it represents only a few quanta per flash, and is therefore subject to great variation.

Barnes and Czerny (1932), and following them Brumberg and Vavilov (1933) realized that fluctuations must occur in the energy necessary for vision, and both groups of investigators looked for them. But they both missed the point of where the source of the fluctuations is and supposed it to be the energy deposited at the cornea. Brumberg and Vavilov even expected differences in the fluctuations for different wavelengths because of the greater energy required for seeing red light, for example, than blue-green light in conformity with the scotopic visibility curve of Fig. 4. However, the comparisons in Fig. 4 show that the differences in number of quanta required for vision in different parts of the spectrum record merely their relative absorption by visual purple. The number of absorbed quanta for an ultimate effect is the same regardless of wavelength and it is this number which sets the magnitude of the physical fluctuation encountered.

In deriving the curves of Fig. 5 for the quantitative statement of this physical fluctuation in terms of the Poisson probability distribution, we have made the single assumption that a constant number of quanta n must be absorbed by the retina in order for us to see a flash of light. Since it is conceivable, in view of the variability of an organism from moment to moment, that this value n is not constant, we have considered the consequences of assuming that the number n varies from time to time. The results show that biological variation is a factor of no great importance.

The situation may be best made clear by an example. Suppose that instead of n being constant, it varies between 4 and 8 quanta per visual act, and that the frequency with which 4, 5, 6, 7, and 8 quanta are necessary is distributed in terms of an ordinary probability distribution. The curves in Fig. 6 representing the frequency distributions for various values of n may then be weighted in this way and averaged. The average curve which is then secured is practically the same as the original Poisson distributions in Fig. 5, and may be fitted by the curves for $n = 4$ or 5.

Thus, when biological variation is imposed upon the physical variation, there is no change in the essential characteristics of the physical distribution. Instead, the value of n merely falls below the average of the biological distribution, and is never below the lowest value in the distribution. This tells us that when, as in Fig. 6, the measurements yield n values of 5, 6, or 7, these numbers represent lower limiting values for the physical number of quanta. In other words, the only effect which biological variation has on the physical variation is to decrease the slope of the curves in Fig. 6 and thus make the apparent number of quanta smaller than the real number.

These considerations serve for understanding the meaning of the fluctuations shown by an organism in its response to a stimulus. It has generally been assumed that a constant stimulus, when presented frequently, remains constant, and that the fluctuations in response are an expression of the variations undergone by the organism. Indeed, this is one of the tenets of psychological measurements, and an elaborate structure of psychometrics has grown up on it as a basis (cf. Guilford, 1936).

The present evaluation of our measurements shows, however, that at the threshold the emphasis has been in the wrong place. At the threshold, where only a few quanta of energy are involved, it is the stimulus which is variable, and the very nature of this physical variability determines the variation encountered between response and stimulus. Moreover, even when biological variation is introduced, it is the physical variation which essentially dominates the relationship.

This is at the absolute threshold. One may wonder, however, whether a differential threshold at any level of intensity may also involve a small number of events which determines the differentiation, and which may therefore be subject to a similar physical variation as at the absolute threshold itself. Only experiment can decide this.

The fact that for the absolute visual threshold the number of quanta is small makes one realize the limitation set on vision by the quantum structure of light. Obviously the amount of energy required to stimulate any eye must be large enough to supply at least one quantum to the photosensitive material. No eye need be so sensitive as this. But it is a tribute to the excellence of natural selection that our own eye comes so remarkably close to the lowest limit.

SUMMARY

1. Direct measurements of the minimum energy required for threshold vision under optimal physiological conditions yield values between 2.1 and 5.7×10^{-10} ergs at the cornea, which correspond to between 54 and 148 quanta of blue-green light.

2. These values are at the cornea. To yield physiologically significant data they must be corrected for corneal reflection, which is 4 per cent; for ocular media absorption, which is almost precisely 50 per cent; and for retinal transmission, which is at least 80 per cent. Retinal transmission is derived from previous direct measurements and from new comparisons between the percentage absorption spectrum of visual purple with the dim-vision luminosity function. With these three corrections, the range of 54 to 148 quanta at the cornea becomes as an upper limit 5 to 14 quanta actually absorbed by the retinal rods.

3. This small number of quanta, in comparison with the large number of rods (500) involved, precludes any significant two quantum absorptions per rod, and means that in order to produce a visual effect, one quantum must be absorbed by each of 5 to 14 rods in the retina.

4. Because this number of individual events is so small, it may be derived from an independent statistical study of the relation between the intensity of a light flash and the frequency with which it is seen. Such experiments give values of 5 to 8 for the number of critical events involved at the threshold of vision. Biological variation does not alter these numbers essentially, and the agreement between the values measured directly and those derived from statistical considerations is therefore significant.

5. The results clarify the nature of the fluctuations shown by an organism in response to a stimulus. The general assumption has been that the stimulus is constant and the organism variable. The present considerations show, however, that at the threshold it is the stimulus

which is variable, and that the properties of its variation determine the fluctuations found between response and stimulus.

BIBLIOGRAPHY

Ångström, K. "Energy in the visible spectrum of the Hefner standard." *Physic. Rev.*, 1903, 17, 302.

Barnes, R. B. and Czerny, M. "Lässt sich ein Schroteffekt der Photonen mit dem Auge beobachten?" Z. *Physik.*, 1932, 79, 436.

Brumberg, E. and Vavilov, S. "Visuelle Messungen der statistischen Photonenschwankungen." *Bull. Acad. Sc. U.R.S.S.*, 1933, 919.

Buisson, H. "The minimum radiation visually perceptible." *Astrophys. J.*, 1917, 46, 296.

Chariton, J. and Lea, C. A. "Some experiments concerning the counting of scintillations produced by alpha particles." Part I, *Proc. Roy. Soc. London, Series A*, 1929, 122, 304.

Chase, A. M. and Haig, C. "The absorption spectrum of visual purple." *J. Gen. Physiol.*, 1938, 21, 411.

Dartnall, H. J. A. and Goodeve, C. F. "Scotopic luminosity curve and the absorption spectrum of visual purple." *Nature*, 1937, 139, 409.

Dartnall, H. J. A., Goodeve, C. F., and Lythgoe, R. J. "The effect of temperature on the photochemical bleaching of visual purple solutions." *Proc. Roy. Soc. London, Series A*, 1938, 164, 216.

du Noüy, P. Lecomte. "Energy and vision." *J. Gen. Physiol.*, 1921, 3, 743.

Fry, T. C. *Probability and its engineering uses.* New York, Van Nostrand, 1928, 476.

Graham, C. H. and Margaria, R. "Area and the intensity-time relation in the peripheral retina." *Am. J. Physiol.*, 1935, 113, 299.

Granit, R., Holmberg, T., and Zewi, M. "On the mode of action of visual purple on the rod cell." *J. Physiol.*, 1938, 94, 430.

Granit, R., Munsterhjelm, A., and Zewi, M. "The relation between concentration of visual purple and retinal sensitivity to light during dark adaptation." *J. Physiol.*, 1939, 96, 31.

Grijns, G. and Noyons, A. K. "Ueber die absolute Empfindlichkeit des Auges für licht." *Arch. Anat. u. Physiol., Physiol. Abt.*, 1905, 25.

Guilford, J. P. *Psychometric methods.* New York, McGraw-Hill, 1936.

Hecht, S. "The quantum relations of vision." *J. Opt. Soc. America*, 1942, 32, 42.

Hecht, S., Haig, C., and Chase, A. M. "The influence of light adaptation on subsequent dark adaptation of the eye." *J. Gen. Physiol.*, 1937, 20, 831.

Hecht, S., Shlaer, S., and Pirenne, M. H. "Energy at the threshold of vision." *Science*, 1941, 93, 585.

Hecht, S. and Williams, R. E. "The visibility of monochromatic radiation and the absorption spectrum of visual purple." *J. Gen. Physiol.*, 1922, 5, 1.

Ives, H. E. "The minimum radiation visually perceptible." *Astrophys. J.*, 1916, 44, 124.

Koenig, A. "Ueber den menschlichen Sehpurpur und seine Bedeutung für das Sehen." *Sitzungsber. k. Akad. Wissensch.*, Berlin, 1894, 577.

von Kries, J. and Eyster, J. A. E. "Über die zur Erregung des Sehorgans erforderlichen Energiemengen." Z. *Sinnesphysiol.*, 1907, 41, 394.

Langley, S. P. "The bolometer and radiant energy." *Proc. Am. Acad. Sc.*, 1881, 16, 342.

Langley, S. P. "Energy and vision." *Phil. Mag.*, 1889, 27, series 5, 1.

Ludvigh, E. and McCarthy, E. F. "Absorption of visible light by the refractive media of the human eye." *Arch. Ophth.*, Chicago, 1938, 20, 37.

Lythgoe, R. J. "The absorption spectra of visual purple and of indicator yellow." *J. Physiol.*, 1937, 89, 331.

Østerberg, G. "Topography of the layer of rods and cones in the human retina." *Acta Ophth., Copenhagen*, 1935, suppl. 6, 106 pp.

Piper, H. "Über Dunkeladaptation." *Z. Psychol. u. Physiol. Sinnesorgane*, 1903, 31, 161.

Reeves, P. "The minimum radiation visually perceptible." *Astrophys. J.*, 1917, 46, 167.

Roggenbau, C. and Wetthauer, A. "Über die Durchlässigkeit der brechenden Augenmedien für langwelliges Licht nach Untersuchungen am Rindsauge." *Klin. Monatsbl. Augenheilk.*, 1927, 79, 456.

Russell, H. N. "The minimum radiation visually perceptible." *Astrophys. J.*, 1917, 45, 60.

Schottky, W. "Zur Berechnung und Beurteilung des Schroteffektes." *Ann. Physik.*, 1922, 68, 157.

Shlaer, S. "A photoelectric transmission spectrophotometer for the measurement of photosensitive solutions." *J. Opt. Soc. America*, 1938, 28, 18.

Wald, G. "Area and visual threshold." *J. Gen. Physiol.*, 1938 *a*, 21, 269.

Wald, G. "On rhodopsin in solution." *J. Gen. Physiol.*, 1938 *b*, 21, 795.

Wentworth, H. A. "A quantitative study of achromatic and chromatic sensitivity from center to periphery of the visual field." Psychological Monographs, No. 183, Princeton, New Jersey, and Albany, New York, Psychological Review Co., 1930, 40, 189 pp.

Zwaardemaker, H. "Die physiologisch wahrnehmbare Energiewanderungen." *Ergebn. Physiol.*, 1905, 4, 423.

ON ERRORS OF OBSERVATION

James McKeen Cattell

Currents of thought often arise at different sources, and flow on for a long way before they mingle. This has been the case with the investigation of errors of observation in physics and in psychology. On the one hand methods for securing the nearest approximation to the true value from discordant observations have been studied by many of the most eminent mathematicians and physicists since the revival of learning. On the other hand the accuracy with which the external world is perceived has always been a central subject in psychology, and in the development of experimental psychology no portion has received more

From *American Journal of Psychology*, 1893, 5, 285–293. Pages 285–292 reprinted with permission of the University of Illinois Press.

Read at the meeting of the American Psychological Association, Philadelphia, 1892.

attention than the perception and comparison of differences in intensity. It has, however, to a considerable extent been overlooked that physics and psychology are concerned with the same phenomena. This is not surprising, as the points of view of the two sciences are different. Physics seeks to eliminate errors of observation; psychology seeks to study their nature. But the time has now come when each science should profit from the progress of the other. Physical science can better eliminate errors of observation by learning what is known of their cause and nature. Psychology will gain greatly in clearness and accuracy by using the methods of physics and mathematics.

The errors of observation with which physics and mathematics have dealt are variable errors, such errors as would occur were each error composed of a very large number of comparatively small and independent errors, equally likely to be positive or negative. In this case the average of the observations is the most likely value, and its approximation to the true value is measured by the dispersion of the errors, and increases as the square root of the number of observations. In two important respects the mathematical theory needs to be supplemented by psychological experiment. In the first place, constant errors are entirely beyond the range of the method of least squares, and yet these are evidently more dangerous in physical observations than variable errors. Thus, for example, in the case of the personal equation of the astronomers, the variable error of an observer can be reduced to any desired extent by increasing the number of observations. But it was found on comparing the observations of different observers that they had constant errors far more serious than their variable errors. It was (and apparently is still) thought that the constant error of an observer becomes a variable error when the observations of several observers are combined. It is very unlikely that this is the case. The uniformity of the processes of perception and movement is greater than their variability. We may feel confident that the combined personal equations of all the astronomers would be subject to a constant error which cannot be eliminated by physical or mathematical science. But such constant errors depend on fixed psycho-physical conditions, and can be measured by the psychologist.

In the second place it may be urged that the theory of probability can only give a rough and ready account of the distribution even of variable errors. In measuring an inch an error of a mile will not occur, and a negative error of a mile is inconceivable. The probability assigned to such errors by theory is, indeed, extremely small, but the same probability is assigned to positive and negative errors, and they are not equally likely. It would seem that as a rule positive errors are more likely than negative errors. In measuring an actual inch, a positive error of two inches might occur, a negative error of the same size cannot occur. In ordinary errors of observation a corresponding preponderance of positive errors may be expected, and a correction for such excess must be empirically determined. The same holds for the averages which are so widely used in statistics. Thus, if the average weight of men be 150 pounds, men weighing 300 pounds occur, men weighing 0 do not occur. The average is not identical with the median, as required by the theory of probability. The assumption made by the mathematicians, that an error is composed of a very large number of comparatively small and independent errors, cannot be admitted by the psychologist. If the fiction of indefinitely small errors be accepted at all, the elemental errors cannot be regarded as independent, but are interdependent and occur in groups. The distribution of errors will not follow simple and universal formulæ, but the greater our knowledge the more complicated will the formulæ become, and they will be as numerous as there are observers and observations. The deductions of Laplace and Gauss are of the greatest importance, but it should not be forgotten that the laws of nature cannot be invented, they must be discovered. It is within the province of psychology to supply physics with the formulæ it requires for eliminating errors of observation in special cases.

Turning now to what psychology can learn from physics, we find that the variable error of the method of average error and the probable error (or h as used in Germany) of the method of right and wrong cases are the error of observation of physical science. We may ask, why should there be an error of observation? Why should not the same stimulus be accompanied by the same sensation? The natural answer is that the conditions do not remain the same. In the first place the stimulus itself cannot be kept exactly constant. Lights are always variable, and sounds and touches cannot be exactly reproduced. Temperatures and smells are especially inconstant. Weights may remain nearly the same, but the manner of lifting them is always different. We have, therefore, a variable stimulus which in part accounts for the variation in sensation. In the second place the nervous mechanism is constantly changing. The sense organ is rhythmically exhausted and restored, and is subject to various irregular alterations. The nerves and paths of conduction in the brain would transmit more or less of the energy of the stimulus according to their ever changing condition. Lastly, the brain centres immediately concerned with perception alter greatly in metabolism. These latter changes are best known to us on the side of consciousness; there is a more or less regular rhythm in attention, and very numerous irregularities due to fatigue, interest, inhibition, etc. These sources of variation will sufficiently account for the fact that the same sensation does not recur. They are, indeed, so numerous and to a certain extent so independent, that they justify roughly the assumption of the mathematician, and the results of experiments show that the errors are in a general way distributed as required by the theory of probability.

In psycho-physical experiment two magnitudes are perceived and compared. The combined error of perception would be larger than a single error of perception, being the square root of the sum of the squares of the separate errors, or nearly the error in a single case multiplied by the square root of two. We have further the errors of memory and comparison. The analysis of these factors at the present time would be very difficult, but I believe they would simply increase the variable error of observation, and introduce additional constant errors. This is not the view taken by Fechner, Müller, Wundt and others, to whom we chiefly owe the development of psycho-physical research and theory. They maintain that there is a threshold of difference, and when sensations differ by less than this amount there is no difference in consciousness, Fechner does not question the application of the probability integral to the comparison of magnitudes,[1] on the contrary it was he who first applied it to the method of right and wrong cases. He argues that a difference in the stimuli smaller than the threshold might be made apparent in consciousness by the error of observation, and would give the preponderance of right cases required by theory. But in about one-seventh of his trials he was doubtful as to which of the weights used by him was the heavier, and holds that in these cases the difference in the weights and the error of observation combined fell within the threshold, and that there was no difference in consciousness.

Prof. Fullerton and the writer [2] made experiments with lifted weights

[1] As implied by Peirce and Jastrow in their important paper (*On Small Differences in Sensation*, National Academy of Sciences, III. [1884]), which for the first time denied the supposed fact of the threshold.

[2] *On the Perception of Small Differences*, Univ. of Penn. Press, 1892. The present paper is largely based on this monograph.

similar to Fechner's. In one series of 3000 experiments in which the probable error was much the same as Fechner's, the observers were doubtful 23% of the time, but on guessing which of the weights was the heavier they were right 62½% of the time. This is the percentage of right cases required by the theory of probability, on the supposition that the differences in consciousness follow Gauss' formula, and we may conclude that the difference in consciousness always exists and affects the course of mental life, even when it is so small that it cannot be detected.

Another case in which German psychologists have run counter to the theory of probability is in the assumption of a just noticeable difference. According to the theory of probability the apparent difference in sensation and the probability of correct judgment tend to increase continuously as the difference between the stimuli is made greater, but it is entirely arbitrary to choose one difference and call it just noticeable. A difference in the stimuli can be found which will be obscured by the error of observation 1 time in 10, or 1 time in 1000, but no difference can be called just noticeable, meaning that it and larger differences will be correctly distinguished, while smaller differences will be indistinguishable. In actual experiments Prof. Fullerton and the writer found that the difference fixed on by the same observer under changed conditions as just noticeable was not at all proportional to the error of observation, and with different observers the difference which they considered just noticeable in no way measured their accuracy of discrimination. In the many researches in which the method of just noticeable difference has been used, the just noticeable difference fixed on by the observer has probably been determined partly by his general knowledge of his error of observation (the difference he would seldom mistake) and partly by association, he choosing an apparently equal difference.

The last application of the theory of probability which I wish to make concerns the relation of the error of observation to the magnitude of the stimulus. The algebraic sum of a number of variable errors tends to increase as the square root of the number. In measuring the base line of a survey the variable error of observation increases as the square root of the length of the line. It seems to me the same relation might be expected to hold in a general way when the length of a line is estimated by the eye or compared with another line. Or to take another example, if we estimate one second of time and repeat the trial four times, the algebraic sum of the four variable errors, or the combined error in estimating the four seconds, will tend to be twice as great as the error in estimating a single second. If we estimate or compare the four seconds continuously, the same elements would to a considerable extent be present, and we might expect an error twice as great as in estimating a single second — not four times as great as required by Weber's law.[3] The error in estimating each of the several seconds might and doubtless would be different, and in the case of intensive magnitudes equal objective increments would seldom or never be accompanied by equal changes in consciousness, nor be subject to equal and independent errors. The theory of probability only considers the simplest and most general case. We must use all the knowledge we have as well as our theory, and the general formula must be adjusted to each special case.

In attempting to pull a dynamometer twice with the same force we do not compare the movements as we proceed, but the final result, and if the force were near the limit of our strength, the error might be less than for a smaller magnitude. We should expect a post-office clerk to judge very light weights better than a blacksmith, a blacksmith to judge heavy weights the better. We should expect to discriminate lights best within the range of ordinary daylight, and sounds best within the range of the human voice. Such results would be contrary to Weber's law, but are simply factors additional to the summation of errors required by the theory of probability. The relation between the error of observation and the magnitude of the stimulus will differ for each stimulus and for each observer, and will not remain constant even for the same stimulus and the same observer. But the usual increase of the error of observation with the magnitude of the stimulus is accounted for in a satisfactory manner by the summation of errors, and I should substitute for Weber's law the following: *The error of observation tends to increase as the square root of the magnitude, the increase being subject to variation whose amount and cause must be determined for each special case.*[4]

It may be asked if this view be correct, why do the results of re-

[3] Constant errors increase in direct ratio to the magnitude, and would tend to follow Weber's law. But, curiously enough, constant errors have not been supposed by the psychologists to follow Weber's law. As a matter of fact "constant errors" are very inconstant and difficult to investigate.

[4] Prof. Fullerton pointed out at the meeting of the association that the conditions which made the first fractional or elemental error positive or negative might make the following error tend in the same direction. So far as such a tendency is present the error of observation would increase more rapidly than the square root of the stimulus, and more nearly in direct proportion to it (Weber's law).

searches confirm Weber's law? As a matter of fact Weber's law has not yet been confirmed exactly by any careful research, the error of observation usually becoming larger as the magnitude of the stimulus is taken larger, but almost always more slowly than in direct proportion to the magnitude. The attempt has been made by Fechner, Wundt, Helmholz and others to explain away the variations by additional hypotheses, but it is universally admitted that the validity of a law or hypothesis decreases as the number of subsidiary hypotheses increases.

I venture to think that it is an open question whether in the researches hitherto made the error of observation increases more nearly as the magnitude or as the square root of the magnitude. Researches in which the method of just noticeable difference has been used do not of necessity measure the error of observation at all. The variation in adjusting the just noticeable difference would roughly measure the error of observation, but this has been neglected. All the researches on lights with which I am acquainted [5] (excepting that by Prof. Fullerton and the writer) used the method of just noticeable (or more than noticeable) difference. Now it is natural enough (considering its elasticity) to make the just noticeable difference within the range of ordinary daylight proportional to the intensity of the light. We see the same objects more or less brightly illuminated, and should tend to regard the differences in shade and color as equal differences, whatever the intensity. It may also be remarked that the mechanism of the eye (accommodation of the pupil and sensitiveness of the retina) tends to obliterate objective differences in brightness. Further in all these researches on lights (excepting Merkel's) the lights were side by side, and the time of exposure was not limited. In such a case the error of observation becomes much obscured, and almost any result can be obtained.

I venture to maintain this conclusion even against the very careful research by König and Brodhun, which supports Weber's law for a considerable range of intensity. It is especially difficult to adjust a just noticeable difference when the areas of light are very small, and for colors not usually seen. König and Brodhun found the just noticeable difference for different colors of apparently the same intensity to be the same (ca. $\frac{1}{75}$ of the light). Previously with much the same methods Lamansky found the just noticeable difference for red $\frac{1}{70}$, for yellow

---

[5] Bouguer, Lambert, Arago, Masson, Fechner, Volkmann, Aubert, Helmholz, Plateau, Delbœuf, Kræpelin, Dobrowolsky, Lamansky, Breton, Ebbinghaus, Merkel, Lehmann, Neiglick, Schirmer, Müller-Lyer, König and Brodhun.

and green ½₂₈₆, for violet ½₀₆, whereas Dobrowolsky found for red ½₄, yellow ½₆, green ½₉, violet ½₆₈-½₇. The three researches were carried out in Helmholz' laboratory, and we may well be at a loss to draw any conclusions from such discordant results.[6] Perhaps the two best researches with lights have been carried out by Aubert and by Müller-Lyer. Both of these writers think their results do not support Weber's law.

It is not necessary in this place further to review and compare results of researches on lights and other stimuli. If it be admitted that the just noticeable difference be not proportional to the error of observation, the amount of work to be considered would be greatly reduced. Further, many researches by the method of average error and right and wrong cases have only a tolerable validity (e.g., Fechner's and Merkel's) because the observer knew the relation of the stimuli before comparing them. In other cases (e.g., with tastes, temperatures, touches and sounds), the stimuli have not been measured in a satisfactory manner. I believe the various researches are so disparate, having been made by so many observers (often young men working for a degree) and by such varying (and in many cases inadequate) methods, that the only general conclusion which can be drawn is that the error of observation tends to increase as the stimulus is made larger and usually more slowly than in direct proportion to the stimulus. . . .

PROFESSOR CATTELL'S
PSYCHOPHYSICAL CONTRIBUTIONS

R. S. Woodworth

. . . In the experiments of Fullerton and Cattell, the variable error increased nearly as demanded by Weber's law, in the case of time of movement, and nearly as demanded by the square root law, in the case of extent of movement, while it fell midway between the two formulæ

---

[6] More especially as Helmholz, in the revision of his *Physiologische Optik*, does not even mention Lamansky and Dobrowolsky. Nor does he refer to work not done in Berlin.

From *Archives of Psychology*, 1914, 30, 60–74. Pages 70–73 reprinted with permission of Columbia University Press.

in the case of force of movement. Some years ago,[1] I collated the results of other experimenters within the field of perception of movement, and found the same general range of results. In nearly every case, the error increases more slowly than demanded by Weber's law, and more rapidly than demanded by the square root. I believe this to be the fact also in other fields, so that Weber's law and the square root law appear as the boundaries of the range of empirical fact. Following the lead of some suggestions made by Fullerton and Cattell, and also incited by the interesting fact that Solomons [2] had attempted a derivation of Weber's law from the combination of variations, and therefore, curiously enough, from essentially the same considerations as those from which Cattell derived the square root law, I have come to the conclusion that the actual increase in the error with increase in the stimulus can be regarded as an index of the degree of correlation between the partial processes included in a total act of perception. I may be permitted to explain this conception a little more fully here.

If we combine two variables in such a way that the variations of the one are completely dependent upon the variations of the other, then for every variation of the one there will be an exactly corresponding variation of the other, and the total variation of the combination will be the arithmetical sum of these two corresponding variations. The variability of the combination will therefore be equal to the sum of the variabilities of the separate variables. Two variables equal to each other in average magnitude and in variability, when thus combined, will give a compound having twice the variability of either of the components; and if a magnitude is composed of several equal variables, all perfectly correlated, the variability of the compound will be proportional to the magnitude — a result corresponding exactly to Weber's law. If, on the other hand, there is no dependence between the variations of the component variables, so that they combine by chance, then the variability will increase as the square root of the magnitude. If there should be a negative correlation between the component variables, the total variability would increase even more slowly than the square root of the magnitude, and if there were a moderate degree of positive correlation, the total variability would increase more rapidly than the square root but less rapidly than the magnitude itself. The lower the correlation between the components, the more nearly would the increase of the

[1] "Le mouvement," 1903, p. 194.

[2] *Psychol. Review*, 1900, 7, 234.

total variability approximate to the square root formula, and the higher the correlation, the closer the approximation to Weber's law.

A formula now well-known, though, as I suppose, of recent introduction, expresses the general relation between the variabilities of two components and the variability of the compound. If v_1 and v_2 are the variabilities of the components and v_s that of the compound, and if r be the coefficient of correlation between the two components, then

$$v_s^2 = v_1^2 + v_2^2 + 2rv_1v_2.$$

This formula reduces to Weber's law if $r = +1$, and to the square root law if $r = 0$; and I suggest that it be regarded as the general law of combination of variabilities or of errors of observation, and that Weber's law and Cattell's law be regarded as special cases under it, and practically as the limiting cases. If the components are equal and of equal variability, then, calling the variability of each component v_a and that of the compound v_{2a}, we reduce the above formula to the following:

$$v_{2a}^2 = 2v_a^2(1+r),$$

or,

$$v_{2a}/v_a = \sqrt{2(1+r)}.$$

Doubling the magnitude, then, increases the variability in the ratio given by this equation. If we know r, we can determine the increase of variability, or if we measure experimentally the increase of variability, we can calculate r from this equation,[3] and express the result of our experiment finally as a certain value of r.

For example, if we assume for the moment that it is legitimate to apply this simple analysis to the process of reproducing movements, we may take the values for the variable error, obtained in experiments by Fullerton and Cattell,[4] and compute r, as follows.

In reproducing an arm movement of 100 millimeters, the variable

[3] If, instead of compounding two variables, we compound any number, n, equations analogous to the above can be obtained, leading finally to the following, in which v_a is the variability of each component, v_{na} that of the compound, and Av r the average of all the coefficients of correlation between the components taken two by two:

$$v_{na}/v_a = \sqrt{n + n(n-1)\text{Av } r},$$

from which, given the ratio of increase of the variability, we can compute the average correlation existing among the components.

[4] P. 48.

error was 5.3; and in reproducing 500 millimeters, the V.E. was 9.5. The increase is here even slower than called for by the square root formula, and the correlation comes out as −.09.

In some experiments on the force of movement,[5] the V.E. was 12.3 for a standard of 2 kilograms, 20.5 for a standard of 4 kilograms, and 37.1 for a standard of 8 kilograms. As between 2 and 4 kilograms, r here = +.40, as between 4 and 8, r = +.64, and as between 2 and 8, r = +.43.

In some experiments on the time of movement,[6] the V.E. was 27.9 for a standard of ¼ second, 52.0 for a standard of ½ second, and 99.8 for a standard of 1 second. Here, as between ¼ and ½ second, r = +.73; and between ½ and 1 second, r = +.84; and as between ¼ and 1 second, r = +.75.

In some of Fechner's experiments[7] on lifted weights, the error increased in the ratio of 1 to 1.66 in passing from a standard of 1,000 grams to one of 2,000 grams, giving r = +.23; and increased in the ratio of 1 to 1.74 in passing from 1,500 to 3,000 grams, giving r = +.57.

It remains to consider whether the conception of combination of errors or variations can be justly applied to the perception of magnitudes. Can the perception of a large magnitude be conceived as a sum or combination of the perceptions of smaller magnitudes? Since we are here concerned with the total physiological processes involved, and not simply with the conscious sensation, we are not entangled in the old difficulty of considering a large sensation as a sum of smaller sensations. The reaction of the organism to a stimulus is always a complex activity, composed of many elementary activities; and the reaction to a greater stimulus is undoubtedly a larger complex, composed of more numerous elementary activities, than the reaction to a smaller stimulus. Each elementary activity is variable, and these elementary variations combine in the process leading to the final reaction or percept. Hence there can be no doubt that, in a broad way, the law of combination of variations applies to the process of perception. In the case of extent, or of time, as shown by Fullerton and Cattell, the perception of a large magnitude can rather easily be thought of as a combination of perceptions of smaller magnitudes, though with a degree of fusion or continuity in the total that might easily modify the outcome. A stimulus of two inches, whether presented to the eye or to the skin, enters

[5] P. 84.
[6] P. 107.
[7] *Psychophysik*, 1889, I., 193.

the system by way of twice as many elementary end-organs as does a stimulus of one inch. Each of these end-organs is variable in its activity, and the variations must combine in the further course of the reaction. In the case of intensive magnitudes, the case is not so clear because we do not know that the more intense stimulus excites more numerous elementary end-organs than the less intense; and, in fact, we do not know in what the difference of intensity consists within the sense organs. We do know, however, that the more intense stimulus gives rise to a wider diffusion of nerve currents, and this fact gives reason to believe that the number of nerve elements engaged in the perception increases with increase in the intensity of the stimulus. If so, the law of combination of variations would be at least partially applicable to the perception of intensive magnitudes. . . .

ON THE LAW FOR MINIMAL DISCRIMINATION OF INTENSITIES. I

W. J. Crozier and A. H. Holway

I. The sensory discrimination of intensities is measured by obtaining differentiating response to two just distinguishable intensities of an excitatory agency. The quantitative data of discrimination are the materials for the theory of sensory discrimination. It has also been held, or taken for granted, that they are to be interpreted in terms of peripheral sensory mechanisms. The fact is, however, that the really significant and characteristic properties of these data are essentially nonspecific with reference to their receptor origins. A general law describing these properties has therefore important consequences for the use of the data of sensorial discrimination. We shall illustrate such a general rule by means of a variety of examples from recent experimentation. It is to be shown that the properties of the marginally discriminable interval of intensity ΔI, where $\Delta I = \tilde{I}_2 - I_1$, are determined by probability considerations [1] which are completely independent of specific struc-

From *Proceedings of the National Academy of Sciences*, 1937, 23, 23–28. Reprinted with permission of the National Academy of Sciences.
[1] Crozier, W. J. *Proc. Nat. Acad. Sci.*, 22, 412 (1936). $I_2 = $ "I_2 adjusted."

tural or other properties of the receptor field.[2] The demonstration of this fact provides basic conditions which must be satisfied by any proposed construction from such data of the laws of sensory effect as a function of intensity. The existing constructions do not meet these requirements.[3]

The respects in which the demonstrable properties of ΔI can be shown to possess a statistical basis depend for their recognition upon the use of homogeneous data.[4,1] That these may be obscured in data which are in one way or another non-homogeneous is easily verified experimentally. It follows that attempted analysis of non-homogeneous measurements is likely to be highly unprofitable and even misleading.

II. A direct proportionality has been shown to exist, in homogeneous series of measurements, between ΔI_m for visually aroused responses of various lower animals and the variability of $\breve{I}_2$.[4] Precisely the same rule holds for human visual determinations of ΔI_m as a function of I. Regardless of the transition from rod- to cone-excitation, ΔI and σ_{I_2} $(= \sigma_{\Delta I})$ are in simple proportion.[5] It does not affect the form of this relationship (1) if the method of comparison be that of simultaneous or of successive exposure, (2) if ΔI_m for given I_1 is altered by changing the area of the test-patch, (3) whether a "surround" or an artificial pupil is used, (4) if the experiment be made by the "method of limits" or by that of "average error" or (5) if the ΔI_m is obtained by increasing or decreasing I_2.[6] There are quantitative differences between the results in these vasious cases, which are interesting and important, but the law of the result is in each case that ΔI_m and σ_{I_2} are directly proportional. Figure 1 contains illustrations. The relationship to the identical law for flicker has been discussed elsewhere.[7]

The rule applies equally in auditory intensity-discrimination.[8] It continues to hold when, at fixed I_1, exposure-time also enters as a variable and ΔI systematically changes.[9] It is not disturbed by the use of binaural or of monaural stimulation [10] (Fig. 2).

[2] Upton, M. and Crozier, W. J. *Proc. Nat. Acad. Sci.*, 22, 417 (1936).

[3] Crozier, W. J. and Pincus, G. *Jour. Gen. Physiol.*, 11, 789 (1927–28).

[4] Crozier, W. J. *Jour. Gen. Physiol.*, 19, 503 (1936).

[5] Holway, A. H., *J. O. S. A.*, 27, 120 (1937).

[6] Holway, A. H. and Hurvich, L. M. *Amer. Jour. Psychol.*, 51, 687 (1938).

[7] Crozier, W. J., Wolf, E. and Zerrahn-Wolf, G. *Jour. Gen. Physiol.*, 20, 211 (1936–37).

[8] Upton, M. and Crozier, W. J. *Proc. Nat. Acad. Sci.*, 22, 417 (1936).

[9] Upton, M. and Holway, A. H. *Proc. Nat. Acad. Sci.*, 23, 29 (1937).

[10] Upton, M. and Holway, A. H. *Proc. Nat. Acad. Sci.*, 23, 32 (1937). This has an important bearing upon the problem of comparing results for differential sensitivity and those for the bisection of "sense-distances."

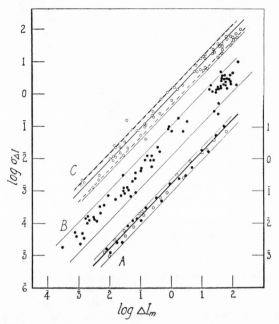

FIGURE 1 Vision. *Mean $\Delta I(\Delta I_m$, millilamberts) is directly proportional to the root-mean-square departure $(\sigma_{\Delta I})$. Graph A is from homogeneous data by Holway[5] using the method of limits (simultaneous comparison) for one observer: the open circles denote $\sigma_{\Delta I}$ for increasing I_2; the solid circles, $\sigma_{\Delta I}$ for decreasing I_2. The central line has a slope $= 1$, and it bisects arithmetically the vertical distance between the enclosing limits. Plots B and C are from data of Holway and Hurvich,[6] using the method of limits (successive comparison), for two observers. Scale for A is at right; ordinates for C have been multiplied by 10. All lines have slope $= 1$.*

Curve C illustrates the procedure (see text) in which a mean line, and mean $\pm\sigma_{\sigma_{\Delta I}}$ are fitted.

The interdependence of ΔI_m and $\sigma_{\Delta I}$ is apparent in various other sensory fields. We take an illustration from an extensive investigation of the properties of ΔW in the judgment of differences in weights [11] (Fig. 3). The form of the relationship is independent of the mode of lifting, of W_1, and of the frequency of arm movements, even though

[11] Holway, A. H., Harvard University Thesis, Harvard College Library, 65 pp. (1936); cf. also, Holway, A. H. and Hurvich, L. M., *Jour. Psychol.*, 4, 309 (1937); and Holway, A. H. and Crozier, W. J., *Proc. Nat. Acad. Sci.*, 23, 509 (1937).

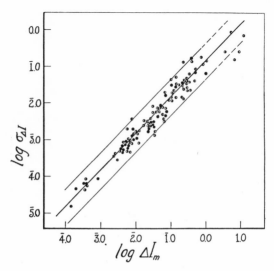

FIGURE 2   Audition. *Showing that $\sigma_{\Delta I}$ is proportional to ΔI_m (bars) for homogeneous data obtained by Upton and Holway[9],[10] using the method of limits. (The precise positions of the five points at the right, taken at very high intensities (I_1), are of lesser reliability, owing to the uncertainty as regards the shape of the calibration curves for the ear phones in this region.) Three levels of intensity were employed and exposure-time was varied. The half-shaded circles are for monaural presentation: those shaded on the left are for the left ear; those on the right, for the right ear. The solid circles stand for values secured under the conditions of binaural stimulation.*

when frequency is increased ΔW for fixed W_1 goes through a minimum.[12] The relationship is quite apparent in data from studies of other modes of sensitivity for which it is not possible to work so accurately and over so wide a range of I [13] (Fig. 4); neater examples are given by data for deep pressure from Wundt's laboratory.[14]

III. In a homogeneous body of determinations of ΔI_m as a function of I_1 each value of ΔI_m is associated with a $\sigma_{\Delta I}$; and each $\sigma_{\Delta I}$ carries with it a σ_σ, $= k\sigma_{\Delta I}$. The width of the band shown upon a log-log plot of ΔI_m vs. $\sigma_{\Delta I}$ is therefore constant, with equivalent intrinsic precision in the determinations of $\sigma_{\Delta I}$ at all points, and is proportional to $k\sigma_{\Delta I}$;

[12] Holway, A. H., Smith, J. and Zigler, M. J. *Jour. Exp. Psychol.*, 21, 423 (1938).

[13] Gatti, A. and Dodge, R. *Arch. ges. Psychol.*, 69, 405 (1929).

[14] Stratton, G. M. *Philos. Stud.*, 12, 525 (1896).

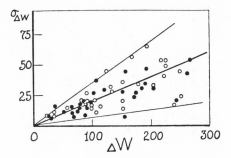

FIGURE 3   Kinesthesis *(lifted weights). Showing that* $\sigma_{\Delta w}$ *is proportional to* ΔW *(grams). Homogeneous data from Holway and Hurvich[11] using the method of limits (simultaneous comparison; continuous change; direction of increase) for one observer. The open circles denote values for active procedure (weights rhythmically elevated and lowered at a rate of "30 per minute"); the closed circles are for passive procedure. The central line vertically bisects the enclosing limits, and has an equal number of points on either side of it.*

it therefore measures σ_σ. This width supplies a means of estimating, by its reciprocal, the comparative precision of different procedures for determining ΔI_m with the same observer. It also gives a basis for the comparison of the intrinsic precision of judgment for different observers, using the same methods. These estimates of precision are independent of I_1. When an arithmetic plot is used (Figs. 3, 4), the points are necessarily distributed in a fan. The principles of curve fitting which apply here are similar to those involved in the reduction of data upon temperature characteristics.[15]

IV. Plots such as those in Figures 1, 2, 3 show that the proportionality between ΔI_m and $\sigma_{\Delta I}$ is simple and direct. If $\sigma_{\Delta I}$ could be obtained for a large number of successive sets of determinations of ΔI_m having exactly the same magnitude, $\sigma_{\Delta I}$ would be normally distributed. We can test this by reducing the data in, for example, Figure 1C to a condition in which the ordinary considerations of statistical theory apply. These considerations do not apply directly when σ is proportional to the mean — a fact which must not be overlooked. The reduction is obtained by projecting each point to an ordinate, on a path with slope $= 1$. The line of slope $= 1$ which passes through the arithmetic mean $(\bar{\sigma}_{\Delta I})$ of the projected $\sigma_{\Delta I}$'s should then divide the as-

[15] Crozier, W. J. *Déterminisme et variabilité*, Paris, Hermann, 56 pp. (1935).

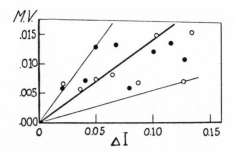

FIGURE 4   Cutaneous pressure. *Showing that M. V.$_{\Delta I}$ is proportional to ΔI (gm./mm.). Homogeneous data from Gatti and Dodge,*[13] *obtained for the tip of the little finger under conditions of rapid loading with microscopic stimuli and using the method of limits for one observer. The open circles denote increasing I$_2$; the solid circles, decreasing I$_2$. The central line vertically bisects the enclosing limits, and has an equal number of points on either side of it.*

semblage of plotted points into two equally numerous groups; the line through mean ΔI for levels of $\sigma_{\Delta I}$ does not. In non-homogeneous data this will not be true, in general, since in that case the ordinate projection of the line of $\bar{\sigma}_{\Delta I}$ as well as $\sigma_{\sigma_{\Delta I}}$ will itself be distributed in some fashion, and the various sets of homogeneous points will be more or less haphazardly intermingled. For a homogeneous set, use can be made of the theorem of Tchebycheff to establish the marginal enclosing lines, since mean $\bar{\sigma}_{\Delta I} \pm \sigma_{\bar{\sigma}_{\Delta I}}$ must enclose more than 75 per cent of the observations. In Figure 1C, the dashed lines through $\bar{\sigma}_{\Delta I} \pm \sigma_{\bar{\sigma}_{\Delta I}}$ enclose 80 per cent of the points. Reciprocally, if the data are sufficiently numerous, marginal lines may without violence be drawn by inspection, and the central line dividing the region between into arithmetically equal parts should divide the observations equally.

From this relationship it follows that a given level of $\sigma_{\Delta I}$ is not associated with a certain mean value of ΔI, but that a certain level of ΔI_m is governed by a given mean $\sigma_{\Delta I}$ (i.e., by a given $\sigma_{\Delta I} \pm \sigma_{\sigma_{\Delta I}}$). The mean value of ΔI obtained for a given I_1 is determined by the test-organism's capacity for variation of performance. The direct experimental proof of this is obtained by tests into which we need not now go. The propriety of the calculation of the quantitative properties of ΔI on this basis has been demonstrated. The significance is that the law for intensity-discrimination is primarily to be a law for the "capacity to vary performance"; this capacity for variation of performance is responsible for the fluctuation of intensity (I_2) required to produce the index-response.

V. The properties of ΔI_m indicate that $\breve{I}_2$ is discriminated from I_1 in terms of the (variable) effect of I_1 and the effect produced by an exposure to an I_2. The variability of I_2 is due to the fact that the organism's capacity to be excited fluctuates. A mean value of I_2 gives $\breve{I}_2 - I_1 = \Delta I_m$. The recognition of I_2 as different from I_1 requires that the effect to be produced by recognizably different I_2 shall be statistically far enough removed from the central tendency of the effects produced by I_1, otherwise the probability of the occurrence of the index-response will not be great enough to give a detectable result. The magnitude of ΔI_m is therefore determined by the variability. This is particularly striking when illuminated area of retina is increased: the total sensory effect is then greater, but $\sigma_{\Delta I}$ and ΔI_m decrease;[6] similarly, in audition, when I_1 is delivered to the two ears, the subjective effect is reported as having "twice the loudness" resulting when I_1 is delivered to one ear alone, but $\sigma_{\Delta I}$ and ΔI_m decrease; whereas with constant area of sensory field $\sigma_{\Delta I}$ (and ΔI_m) increases with I_1.[12]

VI. *Summary.* Sensory discrimination of two just recognizably different intensities I_1 and $\breve{I}_2$ is governed by the fact that the just discriminable ΔI is directly proportional to, and determined by, σ_{I_2}. The properties of the data of sensory discrimination arise from the essentially statistical (i.e., probability) character of the basis for comparison between the effects due to I_1 and the variable capacity of the organism to give a statistically distinguishable effect under the action of a compared I_2. The governance of ΔI by σ_{I_2} is independent of any specific properties of a particular peripheral or central sensory mechanism.

THEORY OF THE NEURAL QUANTUM
IN THE DISCRIMINATION OF LOUDNESS
AND PITCH

S. S. Stevens, C. T. Morgan,
and J. Volkmann

The advantage of a *quantal theory* of sensory discrimination lies not solely in the fact that it makes explicit the role of neural processes that are all-or-none, but also in the fact that it enables us to predict the form and the slope of certain psychometric functions. The *classical theory* left these matters to the operation of a multitude of unknown factors combining in random formations to help or hinder discrimination as chance might have it. This older theory is indeed quite adequate to the data of most conventional experiments in psychophysics, but results of the sort to be presented later seem definitely to elude the classical assumptions. Instead of psychometric functions resembling the probability integral, we find rectilinear functions. Instead of curves of unpredictable slope, we find lines whose slopes are proportional to the differential sensitivity of the O. Instead of failure of even the smallest stimulus-increments to produce zero perceptions of increase, we find a critical value below which no increment is ever perceived. Faced with such data, the classical theory helps our understanding not at all, but the quantal theory appears quite capable of taking these results in stride and of accounting, as well, for the traditional psychometric functions in those experiments where rectilinear functions are not obtained. The form of an empirical function depends, of course, upon methods and procedures, but before discussing this vital aspect of the problem let us first review the salient features of the classical and the quantal theories.

From *American Journal of Psychology*, 1941, 54, 315–335. Reprinted with permission of the authors and the University of Illinois Press.

This paper reports the results of two experiments. The first, dealing with the problem of intensity discrimination, was carried out by Stevens and Volkmann. A brief report of this work has already appeared: S. S. Stevens and J. Volkmann, The quantum of sensory discrimination, *Science*, 92, 1940, 583–585. The later work on the quantum of frequency discrimination was carried through by Stevens and Morgan.

THE CLASSICAL THEORY

What we have taken the liberty of calling the "classical theory" refers to the assumptions commonly invoked to explain the behavior of an O whose task it is to report whenever a detectable increment is added to a stimulus. The human organism can detect a change in the loudness of a tonal stimulus when its intensity is increased by a sufficient increment. But always we find a range of increments which, upon repeated presentation, are sometimes perceived and sometimes not. If we plot the percentage of presentations the O hears against the size of the increment presented, the result is a psychometric function. Now, in the usual experiment, where a standard stimulus, I, is followed after a short interval of time by a comparison stimulus, $I + \Delta I$, the psychometric function tends to resemble the S-shaped normal probability integral (the phi-function of gamma). The result is similar to the curve we obtain when we shake repeatedly a handful of coins and plot the frequency of the throws on which the percentage of heads exceeds different proportions of the number of coins.[1] This resemblance of the psychometric function to a cumulative "chance" distribution leads to the argument "that the stimulated organs, including the brain with its momentary states of equilibrium, are variously disposed toward a given impression. These dispositions are dependent upon a great many different factors ("coins"), each one of which can be favorable or unfavorable for a judgment. . . . These dispositions, being independent, are favorable or unfavorable in chance combinations. For a weaker, or smaller, stimulus [increment] more of them must be favorable than for a stronger, or larger, stimulus [increment]."[2]

The convention then is to define as the difference limen that increment which is noticed 50% of the time. It is sometimes argued that when the difference limen is small the slope of the psychometric function must be steep — its h must be high; but precisely what slope we are to expect, the theory is unable to disclose. As to whether we should expect ever to perceive *no* increments, or *all* of them, the classical theory, in assuming the phi-function of gamma, says *never*.

---

[1] E. G. Boring, "A Chart of the Psychometric Function," this journal, 28, 1917, 281–285.

[2] J. P. Guilford, *Psychometric Methods,* 1936, 173.

THE QUANTAL THEORY

The quantal theory derives from the assumption that the basic neural processes mediating a discrimination are of an all-or-none character. That our knowledge of the nervous system calls for the existence of "sensory quanta" was evident to Boring[3] in 1926, and he hoped as evidence for them to be able to find discontinuities, or steps, in such psychological continua as pitch and loudness. The discontinuities he sought have not appeared, but our researches now show that, if we look for proof in experiments of the proper design, we find sensory quanta revealing themselves precisely as scheduled by theory. The theoretical argument is as follows.

We assume that the neural structures initially involved in the perception of a sensory continuum are divided into functionally distinct units. Békésy[4] thought of these units as single afferent fibers, but, as we shall see later, the evidence indicates that the functional units are "larger" than fibers and that they are probably centrally located. A stimulus of a given magnitude excites, at a particular instant, a certain number of these quantal units, and, in order for an increment to be noticeable, it must excite at least one additional quantum. That is the basic picture; but here enter some additional considerations. The stimulus which excites a certain number of quanta will ordinarily do so with a little to spare — it will excite these quanta and leave a small "surplus" insufficient to excite some additional quantum. This surplus stimulation will contribute, along with the increment, ΔI, to bring into activity the added quantum needed for discrimination. Consequently, at any instant, the size of the increment necessary to add another quantum to the total number excited must depend upon the amount of "left-over" stimulation.

The next problem is: how much of this left-over stimulation or surplus excitation are we to expect? Here we must raise the question of the overall fluctuation in the sensitivity of the organism. From the behavior

[3] E. G. Boring, "Auditory Theory with Special Reference to Intensity, Volume and Localization," this journal, 37, 1926, 157–188. In discussing the all-or-none principle, Troland also speaks of "neural quanta:" L. T. Troland, *Psychophysiology*, II, 1930, 17. Further on, in describing the nerve process (p. 37) he introduces us to the adjective *quantal*.

[4] G. von Békésy, "Über das Fechner'sche Gesetz und seine Bedeutung für die Theorie der akustischen Beobachtungsfehler und die Theorie des Hörens," *Ann. d. Phys.*, 7, 1930, 329–359. See also S. S. Stevens and H. Davis, *Hearing: Its Psychology and Physiology*, 1938, 145–147.

of the absolute threshold of hearing,[5] for example, we know that this over-all sensitivity fluctuates in "random" fashion — due perhaps to breathing, heart beat, etc. If such fluctuation is large compared to the size of an individual quantum, it is evident that over the course of time all values of the surplus stimulation occur equally often. In other words, in the presence of a "steady" stimulus one amount of surplus stimulation contributing toward the excitation of an additional quantum is, at each instant, as likely as any other.

Now, the frequency with which a given stimulus-increment will excite an additional quantum depends upon the frequency with which the surplus stimulation exceeds a certain crucial amount, and this occurs a proportion of the time which is dependent directly upon the amount to be exceeded. From these considerations it follows that, if the increment is added instantaneously to the stimulus, it will be perceived a certain fraction of the time, and this fraction is directly proportional to the size of the increment itself.

This argument can be rendered more precise with the aid of a little mathematics. As already stated, we assume that at a given moment a steady stimulus excites completely a certain number of quanta and leaves a small surplus, p, which goes part way toward exciting the quantum next in line; and that the stimulus increment, ΔI, which is required to complete the excitation of this quantum is smaller when the surplus, p, is larger. Now, let us measure the size of a quantum in terms of the increment, Q, which will just succeed *always* in exciting it. Then, the ΔI just sufficient to complement the surplus, p, and thereby excite an additional quantum is given by

$$\Delta I = Q - p \tag{1}$$

A given ΔI will excite an additional quantum whenever $\Delta I \geqq Q - p$. Since p fluctuates at random (due to the large over-all fluctuation in sensitivity) between $O \leqq p \leqq Q$, this condition will obtain a proportion of the time given by

$$r_1 = \Delta I/Q \tag{2}$$

where r_1 is the relative frequency of the instants during which ΔI excites one additional quantum. The value of r_1 varies between zero and one.

[5] S. Lifschitz, "Fluctuation of the hearing threshold," *J. Acoust. Soc. Amer.*, 11, 1939, 118–121.

Equation (2) tells us that under certain conditions the psychometric function should be a straight line and that zero increment in the stimulus should produce no responses. Békésy was able to produce data satisfying this equation to a fair approximation, but before we consider the necessary experimental conditions, let us examine another case.

Suppose we provide conditions under which the O is able to report a change whenever *two* additional quanta are excited, but is unable to detect a single quantum. Then equation (2) becomes

$$r_2 = (\Delta I - Q)/Q = \Delta I/Q - 1 \tag{3}$$

and again r_2 varies only between zero and one.

Or, in terms of the percentage, R, of the increments which an O should be able to detect

$$R = (\Delta I/Q - 1) \times 100 \tag{4}$$

and R varies between zero and 100.

This equation, derived from the assumption that the addition of *two* quanta is required for a discrimination, also calls for a rectilinear psychometric function, and it is this equation which best describes the data reported below. Its graph is shown by the rectilinear function in Fig. 1. There we have plotted equation (4), using the value of Q as the unit for measuring the stimulus-increment. In these units the slope of the straight psychometric function is exactly determined. Furthermore, when a discrimination requires the addition of two quanta, we note

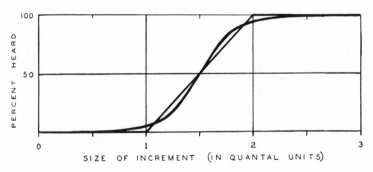

FIGURE 1   *The Quantal and Phi-Gamma functions. The straight line shows the results expected on the basis of the quantal theory. It is the graph of equation (4) of the text. The S-shaped curve was constructed by fitting the phi-function of gamma to the rectilinear quantal function.*

that stimulus-increments of less than one quantum are never detected, whereas those greater than two quanta are always detected.

EXPERIMENTAL CONDITIONS

It is, of course, one thing to derive an equation but quite another to satisfy the experimental conditions it presupposes. If we are to devise an adequate experimental technique, we must bear in mind particularly the two major assumptions we have made: (1) the existence of fixed neural units or quanta; and (2) the fact of a relatively large over-all fluctuation in the sensitivity of the organism. Since this fluctuation is always in process, it is evident that if we are to determine the effect of a given ΔI, as of a particular instant in time, we must add ΔI instantaneously, and remove it before the organism is able to change in sensitivity by more than a negligible amount. No time-interval between the standard stimulus and the augmented stimulus, and a very brief duration for the latter! Although other precautions are also necessary, it is in these particulars that we must depart most completely from the traditional methodology if we are to obtain rectilinear psychometric functions. A time-interval between stimuli would allow the random fluctuations in over-all sensitivity to manifest themselves in the form of a non-rectilinear psychometric function.

In order to test the quantal theory, Békésy presented a tone lasting 0.3 sec. followed immediately by a second tone of the same duration but of variable intensity. He recorded the percentage of times O heard the second tone as different in loudness from the first one. After what he describes as a month's practice, he was able to obtain results satisfying equation (2), except for a constant difference resembling a time error; but mostly he got data fitting equation (4) again with a constant error. Some of these data, corrected for the error, are shown in Fig. 4. Békésy's O usually required the addition of two quanta in order to perform a discrimination.

The design of our experiment was such that the addition of two quanta was always required to invoke a discrimination. The O listened to a continuous 1000-⌐ tone, one of whose parameters, either intensity or frequency, was momentarily increased at intervals of 3 sec. and his task was simply to press a key whenever he heard an increase and to refrain from pressing when no change was detectable. (This procedure eliminates the constant error that troubled Békésy.) Under these conditions a discrimination *always* requires two quanta, because the excitation due to the continuous tone, against which the O must make his judgment, fluctuates up and down at random by single quantal jumps. From this "steady"-tone condition only double quantal jumps can be discriminated. Hence, equation (4) always applies, and it is this equation which, in practice, offers the best means of measuring the size of the sensory quantum.

APPARATUS

Only certain crucial aspects of the apparatus need be described in detail. As already indicated, the technical problem was to generate a steady pure tone whose intensity (or frequency) could be increased for a brief period at regular intervals. The apparatus for working with variable increments of intensity is shown in Fig. 2. An oscillator fed a 1000-∼ current into two amplifiers in parallel. The output of each amplifier was led through filters and attenuators to the primary of a transformer. The secondaries of the transformers were connected in series with each other and with an earphone in such a way as to keep the currents in phase. Thus the currents from the two amplifiers summated in the secondary circuit, a fact carefully checked with the aid of a cathode-ray oscillograph and with an electrical wave-analyzer. (The resistors in the earphone circuit were for impedance matching.) The current from the second amplifier was controlled by a rotary switch and was allowed to pass for a period of 0.15 sec. at 3 sec. intervals. Thus a known increment was added every 3 sec. to the steady tone from the first amplifier.

The 1000-∽ filter in the circuit of the second amplifier calls for special mention. It is a well known fact that the intensity (or frequency) of a tone can not be changed abruptly without the scattering of energy into other regions of the frequency spectrum. The ear hears this scat-

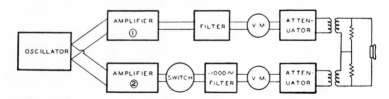

FIGURE 2   *Schema of the apparatus. The increment in intensity was supplied to the earphone through the circuit following amplifier 2. Increments of frequency were obtained with a modification of this arrangement in which the switch was used to introduce a tuning capacitance into the oscillator circuit.*

tering as a "click," and in an experiment of the sort we are conducting the elimination of this click is imperative. It can be suppressed only by a gradual rather than an abrupt transition from the steady tone to the augmented tone. But, if the transition is too slow, we should no longer be able to measure the quantum, and so we must seek a compromise. From preliminary experimentation we found that, if the transition occupies 0.01 sec., all perceptible click is abolished, and the transition-time is still negligible relative to the rate of fluctuation in the over-all sensitivity of the organism.

The transition-time of 0.01 sec. was obtained by passing the increment from the second amplifier through two sharply tuned 1000-∼ filters (General Radio, type 830-R) connected in cascade. These filters make an abrupt transition impossible by eliminating all frequencies except those close to 1000 ∼. Thus, if a train of waves that start and stop instantaneously are sent into these filters, the output at the other end is a train which begins and terminates gradually. Figure 3 shows this effect. On a cathode-ray oscillograph the increment sent to the earphone is seen to begin and end as shown in Fig. 3. The time-constant for the growth and decay of this wave is 0.005 sec., and the effective time of transition from *on* to *off*, or *off* to *on*, is approximately 0.01 sec.

Fortunately, the same general considerations apply both to a change in frequency and to a change in intensity. Hence, the same filtering arrangement was used for the experiment on frequency. This was possible because the largest increments in frequency used were less than 10 ∼, and 10 ∼ is slightly less than the "width" of the band-pass filters. Because of these filters an abrupt change in frequency was converted into a gradual change, and all perceptible clicks were eliminated. (This method of presenting tones and changes in tones recommends

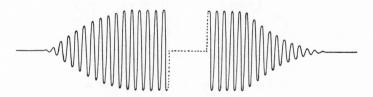

FIGURE 3 *Build-up and decay of the filtered increment. A pulse of a 1000-∼ tone which reaches full amplitude instantaneously and later stops abruptly looks like this after it is passed through a sharply tuned 1000-∼ filter. The dotted portion means that a number of waves have been omitted.*

itself on many counts, but its disadvantage is that separate filters are required for different frequencies — and filters are expensive to construct.)

The rest of the apparatus for working with variable increments in frequency has not been diagrammed. It was like the arrangement shown in Fig. 2 except that amplifier (1) was turned off and the rotary switch was removed from behind amplifier (2) and used to insert periodically a variable condenser into the circuit of the oscillator. This condenser was carefully calibrated to produce known changes in frequency. The rotary switch was adjusted to produce every 3 sec. an increment lasting 0.3 sec.

PROCEDURE

We adopted what is perhaps the unorthodox philosophy that the O should be given every possible aid and convenience in carrying out his task. He was comfortably seated in a sound-proofed room and asked to press a key with his right hand whenever the steady tone in an earphone changed in loudness or in pitch, as the case might be. The key operated a counter. The apparatus was adjusted to produce a certain increment every 3 sec. and the rotary switch set running. Through a communication system the O was then told to begin reporting whenever he was ready. When he was ready—when he was through swallowing, scratching and shifting about—in other words, when by his own criteria he was all set to attend, he rested his left hand on another key which started a recorder to count the number of increments presented. After 25 presentations, lasting 1¼ min., he was told to rest and a new value of the increment was set up on the apparatus. Ordinarily about 200 judgments were obtained at each of several experimental sittings.

Some Os found it easier to keep oriented to the increments when a small light was flashed midway between successive increments. Others considered the light somewhat distracting, and for them it was turned off. Thus each O was given his choice as to light or no light. Actually, half of them used it and half did not, apparently without producing any systematic difference in the results.

As already stated, each value of the increment was presented 25 times in succession. The first increment presented in any experimental session was one the O could report 100% of the time. Thereafter other values of the increment were presented in "random" order. What we have described is the procedure as it finally evolved — after much testing and exploring. It departs from the more conventional methods in several particulars. *O* reports only when he hears an increment, and he is not required to report both *greater* and *less*. The judgments are made at the rate of about 500 per hr., including rest periods. Furthermore, it was found to be quite unnecessary to vary the size of successive increments in irregular or random order — as many as 25 increments of constant size are presented in succession. The possible *a priori* objections to this seem not to be of much consequence in practice.

THE QUANTUM OF INTENSITY DISCRIMINATION

Our data for intensity discrimination are less extensive than those obtained with frequency as a variable. We wanted principally to test a method and to verify, if possible, the results reported by Békésy.[6] We worked, therefore, with one ear (left) of a single well-practiced *O* (*J.V.*) and obtained the results shown in Fig. 4. The solid lines in this figure are drawn in such a way as to satisfy equation (4) above, provided we interpret Q as the value on the abscissa where the functions first depart from 0%. This value measures, in terms of the stimulus, the size of the differential quantum for intensity discrimination.

As equation (4) predicts, the functions between 0 and 100% are very nearly rectilinear. They obviously do not conform well to the phi-function of gamma. Furthermore, the points on the abscissa where the functions depart from 0% are exactly one half of the value at which they reach 100%.

It is of interest to compare the size of the quantum, as measured by the data of plots A, C, D and E of Fig. 4, with the ratio ∆E/E as measured by the method of beats (Riesz).[7] Since we have measured intensity in terms of acoustic pressure, our data must first be converted into energy ratios to make them comparable with those of Riesz. When this is done we find that the quantum is roughly half as large as the average differential sensitivity of Riesz's 12 *O*s. Whether this discrepancy is due to method or to individual differences in sensitivity can not now be stated. Riesz's method did not allow him to obtain psychometric functions.

Our data do, however, confirm Riesz's finding that relative sensitivity improves when the intensity of the stimulus is increased. This fact is evident from inspection of Fig. 4.

[6] Von Békésy, *op. cit.*
[7] For a table of Riesz's results see Stevens and Davis, *op. cit.*, 140.

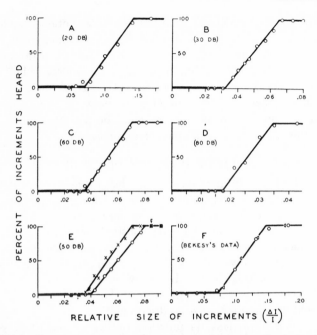

FIGURE 4 *Functions measuring the quantum of intensity discrimination. The solid lines are the theoretical functions and the points show the obtained frequencies with which various increments in the intensity (sound pressure) of a 1000-~ tone are heard as increases in loudness. The size of the quantum, measured in terms of the stimulus-ratio, $\Delta I/I$, is given by the point on the abscissa where the function first departs from zero. The initial intensity, I, of the 1000-~ tone (in db. above O's threshold) is indicated on each plot. Each point is the average of from 50 to 100 observations (J. V.). Békésy obtained the circles in plot F for an increase and the half circles for a decrease in intensity (ΔI positive and negative).*

It should be pointed out that, strictly speaking, data yielding rectilinear psychometric functions when plotted against sound pressures do not show absolute rectilinearity when expressed in terms of sound energy, but calculation shows that the departure from rectilinearity is negligible. The reason is simply that we are dealing with small differences. Even in the case where the differences are largest (Fig. 4, plot A), transformation of the function into units of sound energy does not alter the shape of the graph by more than the width of the line itself — a thoroughly negligible amount.

Plot B of Fig. 4 represents an artificially small quantum. This is due to the fact that these data were obtained with the apparatus adjusted to produce a more nearly instantaneous transition from the steady tone to the augmented tone. The energy, thereby scattered into other frequency regions, produced a faint click which presumably offered additional cues for discrimination. At higher intensities than 30 db. above threshold, this click was very noticeable and rectilinear psychometric functions could not be obtained. It would seem, therefore, that the effect of transition time on the measured size of the quantum varies with intensity. The precise nature of this effect remains to be determined.

Plot E of Fig. 4 shows that the size of the quantum as measured by the stimulus does not remain invariant under all conditions. The same is also true of the quantum of frequency discrimination. What factors influence the size of the quantum we do not know, but the fact that it can change should caution us against trying to test the quantal theory by averaging data taken at different sessions. If the quantum changes during the collecting of the data, the psychometric function tends to assume a sigmoid form, as is apparent if we average the data of the two functions in plot E.

(Actually, in our later work on frequency discrimination we became impressed more by the stability of the quantum than by its ability to change. Most of our measurements showed high repeat reliability.)

THE QUANTUM OF FREQUENCY DISCRIMINATION

The results for frequency discrimination show what to us is remarkable similarity to those obtained for intensity. Psychometric functions for six different *O*s are shown in Fig. 5. Each *O* had made approximately 800 judgments before these data were recorded. The functions themselves are based upon 800 to 1000 judgments each. (Work with two other *O*s was discontinued after 2 hr. practice because they failed to settle down to the point of giving reasonably consistent results.)

The data of Fig. 5 were obtained for a 1000-$\sim$ tone at 54 db. above threshold. Here, as in Fig. 4, the two criteria of a "good" psychometric quantal function are fulfilled: (a) there is rectilinearity to a high degree; and (b) a two-to-one ratio obtains between the value at which the function reaches 100% and the value at which it first departs from 0%. These two criteria are met despite wide variation in the sensitivity of different *O*s. Among these *O*s we find quanta ranging in size from 1.1 to 2.8$\sim$.

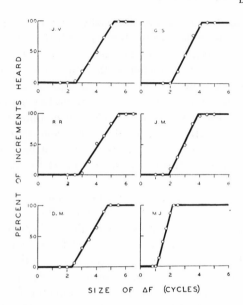

FIGURE 5   *Functions measuring the quantum of frequency discrimination for six different Os. In each case the stimulus was a 1000-∼ tone 54 db. above threshold. The solid lines were drawn so as to fit the points and at the same time satisfy equation (4) of the text. Each point is the average of 100 judgments.*

Not only is there variability among individuals but for a given O the measured size of the quantum varies with the intensity of the 1000-∼ tone. Psychometric functions obtained at different sensation-levels (db. above threshold) are shown for one O (S.S.S.) in Fig. 6 and for another O (C.T.M.) in Fig. 7. In each case the quantum is larger at low intensities and smaller at high. This dependence of the size of the quantum upon intensity can be seen in Fig. 8. There we see that the sensitivity of each O is related in a similar fashion to the sensation-level of the stimulus. Furthermore, the difference in sensitivity between these Os remains rather constant at all intensities.

In Fig. 8 are also plotted the data of Shower and Biddulph (triangles) on differential sensitivity to frequency. These investigators exposed 10 ears to a tone whose frequency was modulated twice per sec. and determined the least perceptible amplitude of modulation by what appears to be the method of limits. The average values for 1,000∼ at various sensation levels are seen, in Fig. 8, to be definitely larger than the respective quanta of the two *O*s (*S.S.S.* and *C.T.M.*). This difference is most likely due in part to method and in part to the fact that the size of the quantum, as we have measured it, is systematically smaller than the conventional measure of the difference limen — the 50% point on the psychometric function. As demonstrated in Fig. 1, the quantum is exactly two-thirds the size of the difference limen measured by this 50% point. When we take this fact into account, we find reasonable agreement between our data and those of Shower and Biddulph. Better still is the agreement between our data and the few data reported by these authors from an experiment in which they employed an abrupt transition between the standard and the comparison tones.

An interesting phenomenon appeared when we tried to experiment with very faint tones of the order of 10 db. above threshold. At these intensities the *O*s found that the fluctuations in the loudness of the steady tone were sometimes large enough to leave them in doubt as to whether the tone was still present. Under these conditions rectilinear quantal functions were not obtained.

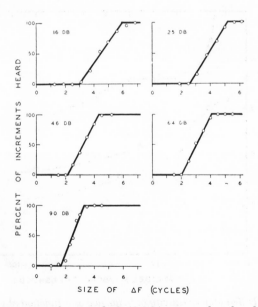

FIGURE 6 *Functions for a single O (S.S.S.) measured at five different sensation-levels. Each point is the average of 100 judgments.*

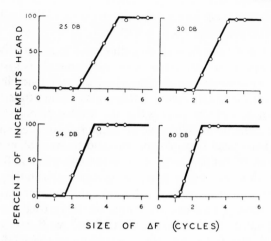

FIGURE 7   *Functions for a single O (C.T.M.) measured at four different sensa-tion-levels. Each point is the average of 100 judgments.*

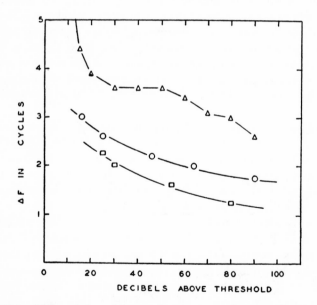

FIGURE 8   *Differential sensitivity to frequency as a function of intensity. The rectangles (C.T.M.) and circles (S.S.S.) show the size of the quantum of fre-quency discrimination at various sensation-levels. The triangles represent the DLs for frequency as measured by Shower and Biddulph at 1000 ∼.*

STATISTICAL TESTS

The 15 rectilinear psychometric functions in Figs. 5, 6, and 7 were fitted by inspection in such a way as to represent the data and at the same time to satisfy equation (4). These functions meet the two criteria derived from the quantal theory: rectilinearity and a two-to-one ratio between the values of the functions at the 100% and 0% points. Now the question arises as to how well, by mathematical test, the data fit equation (4). We shall attempt an answer by showing first that rectilinear functions fit the data better than do phi-functions of gamma, and second that these rectilinear functions tend to exhibit the required slopes.

By the method of least squares rectilinear functions were fitted to the data of Figs. 5, 6 and 7, and by the method proposed by Boring,[8] which utilizes Urban's weightings, the phi-function of gamma was fitted to these same 15 sets of data. In each case ΔF was taken as the independent variable. In keeping with conventional procedure, extreme values of the dependent variable (percentage of increments heard) were not used. Points falling below 3% and above 97% were neglected for the purpose of curve-fitting because of the undue influence they would have on the constants of the fitted functions. After fits had been obtained, the chi-square test of goodness of fit was applied and the P-values determined.[9] In fitting both types of functions we took as the number of degrees of freedom two less than the number of points to be fitted.

Table I presents these P-values, together with the measures of slope, $(\Delta F)_{100}/(\Delta F)_0$, of the fitted rectilinear functions. In 14 of the 15 sets of data the P-values for the rectilinear functions are higher than those for the phi-functions of gamma. In general, the P-values for the function predicted by the quantal theory are above 0.5, whereas those for the phi-functions of gamma are less than 0.5.

A more decisive difference between the goodness of the fits can be demonstrated if we take a composite of the individual P-values. We add the chi-squares from which each P was derived, count up the total degrees of freedom, and enter the chi-square tables in the usual manner. The results of these operations are recorded in Table I. We note

---

[8] E. G. Boring, "Urban's tables and method of constant stimuli," this journal, 28, 1917, 280–293.

[9] For the method used, see Guilford, *op. cit.*, 1936, 176 ff.

TABLE I

GOODNESS OF FIT OF THE PHI-GAMMA HYPOTHESIS AND
OF THE QUANTAL HYPOTHESIS STATED IN TERMS
OF P-VALUES AND OF $(\Delta F)_{100}/(\Delta F)_0$

(The composite P-values of the right-hand column were obtained by adding the chi-squares,
together with the number of degrees of freedom, of the P-values from the row in which the
composite P-values appear.)

VARIOUS Os AT A SENSATION LEVEL OF 54 db.

	Observer						Composite values
	J.V.	G.S.	R.R.	J.M.	D.M.	M.J.	
P for $\phi(\gamma)$ function	.19	.26	.03	.31	.16	.38	.03
P for rectilinear f.	.56	.66	.48	.56	.83	.94	.92
$(\Delta F)_{100}/(\Delta F)_0$	2.09	1.91	1.97	2.18	2.07	1.89	2.02

DIFFERENT SENSATION LEVELS FOR S.S.S.

	Sensation level (db.)					Composite values
	16	25	46	64	90	
P for $\phi(\gamma)$ function	.36	.44	.12	.44	.07	.08
P for rectilinear f.	.29	.80	.50	.57	.13	.37
$(\Delta F)_{100}/(\Delta F)_0$	2.12	1.93	1.89	2.13	1.96	2.01

DIFFERENT SENSATION LEVELS FOR C.T.M.

	Sensation level (db.)				Composite values
	25	30	54	80	
P for $\phi(\gamma)$ function	.53	.34	.06	.48	.19
P for rectilinear f.	.72	.95	.63	.88	.95
$(\Delta F)_{100}/(\Delta F)_0$	2.34	1.95	2.20	2.19	2.17

that the composite P-values for all 15 sets of data taken together are
0.931 when the rectilinear functions are fitted, and only 0.008 when
the phi-functions of gamma are tested. This comparison not only favors
the function derived from the quantal theory, but, by conventional
standards, it makes the classical hypothesis quite unacceptable as a
description of the data.

This clear difference between the rectilinear function and the phi-
function of gamma emerges in the face of a fact well illustrated in

Fig. 1. There we see that when the phi-function of gamma is fitted directly to a rectilinear function by the method of least squares, the absolute differences between the two functions are nowhere very great. The two functions cross at three points, and at these points it is impossible experimentally to differentiate between the two theories. Even where the functions are maximally separated the discrepancies are not large. We should therefore expect random deviations in the observed proportions often to affect the fit of one function as much as the fit of the other, and in general we find that low P-values for the rectilinear functions tend to be associated with low values for the phi-function of gamma. The rank-difference correlation is 0.52. Fluctuations in the observed proportions have therefore *tended* to affect the fits of the two theoretical functions in the same way. This fact makes it easy to understand why, as far as the individual P-values are concerned, there is only a general tendency for the quantal hypothesis to be superior to the phi-gamma hypothesis, and why it is necessary to combine a large number of observations in order to obtain so clear a distinction between the applicability of the hypotheses that the phi-function of gamma can be rejected.

The second criterion derived from the quantal theory is that the ratio between the value of ΔF, where the rectilinear function reaches 100%, and the value where it departs from 0% should be equal to 2. We have computed these ratios, $(\Delta F)_{100}/(\Delta F)_0$, from the rectilinear functions fitted by the method of least squares, and they are recorded in Table I.

In all 15 sets of data for frequency discrimination, these ratios do not exceed 2.34, nor are they ever smaller than 1.89. The average ratio for the 6 Os tested at a sensation level of 54 db. was 2.02; for one O (S.S.S.) tested at different sensation levels, it was 2.01; and the average ratio of the other O (C.T.M.) for comparable tests was 2.17.

It appears reasonable, therefore, to conclude that our experimental findings have fulfilled the predictions of the quantal theory not only in respect of goodness of fit, but also with respect to what we believe is the more crucial criterion of slope.

THE QUANTUM AS A MEASURE OF
DIFFERENTIAL SENSITIVITY

Altogether we have recorded more than 30 rectilinear psychometric functions showing good agreement with equation (4). That it is possible to design experimental conditions capable of testing the quantal theory appears, therefore, to be reasonably assured. Since we have not explored by systematic variation all the parameters of our experimental conditions, we can not say with finality, however, just what factors are important and which are irrelevant from the point of view of method. Nevertheless our experience suggests that some of the conditions necessary in order to obtain unobscured rectilinear quantal functions are these.

1. The experiment must be "easy" from the point of view of the O. He needs optimal conditions for stabilizing his attention and his criteria of judgment. He usually needs a period of practice.

2. Data need to be taken with sufficient rapidity to obviate the necessity of averaging results from widely separated experimental sessions. Our rate of 20 judgments per min. may not be optimal, but it is apparently an adequate rate.

3. For some Os it seems advantageous to supply a "warning" signal, such as a light, to indicate when they should attend. This enables them to adjust their breathing to the rhythm of the stimuli and relieves them of the necessity of sustained attention.

4. It is of crucial importance that the interval of time between the presentation of the standard stimulus and the augmenter stimulus be negligible. Data satisfying equation (4) are not obtained when the overall sensitivity of the organism is allowed to change during the interval between the two stimuli. On the other hand, it appears that the quantal functions are obscured or distorted when the transition between stimuli is so abrupt that unwanted transients are introduced.

Given an experimental method adequate to reveal the size of the individual quantum of sensory discrimination, we have open to us a new approach to the problems of differential sensitivity. The quantum is plainly simpler, more elemental, more basic than the classical limen which is a statistical average of a set of indeterminately varying values. Perhaps, then, we ought to measure the difference limen not by the size of the increment heard as greater half of the time, but in terms of the quantum itself. The quantal theory proposes that certain aspects of the rectilinear psychometric function reflect the magnitude of a "unit process" somewhere in the nervous system. It seems reasonable to suppose that the psychophysiologist will find a measure of this unit process to be a more significant datum than the somewhat arbitrary measure of sensitivity conventionally employed.

Applied to the data of the present experiments, the conventional measure of sensitivity — in terms of the 50% point — gives values 1.5 times as large as the respective quanta. How general is this relation? In those psychophysical researches where experimental method precludes rectilinear functions is it possible to measure the quantum of discrimination merely by taking two-thirds of that increment which yields as many positive as negative reports? That this simple operation should be always valid seems hardly likely, but that it sometimes works we have been able to demonstrate in preliminary experimentation with 3 Os.

Instead of no interval of time between the standard and the augmented stimulus, a separation of 0.5 sec. was introduced. In one series of observations the standard stimulus was presented first, and O pressed a key when the second tone appeared higher in pitch than the standard; in another series the standard was presented second and O pressed only when he heard an apparent reduction in pitch. When the results from both series were averaged, non-rectilinear psychometric functions were obtained. These functions were typical of those usually obtained under such conditions, and at the 50% point these functions coincided with the rectilinear functions obtained from the respective Os.

The effect of a time-interval between the standard and comparison stimuli reveals itself as a decrease in the slope of the psychometric function and a departure from rectilinearity. As a matter of fact, the precise form of the function for separated tones can be predicted from the assumptions of the quantal theory. Although the general equation for this function (involving the sum of three integrals) has been derived, an adequate experimental test of its predictive power has not been completed, and here we state merely that the equation predicts non-rectilinear psychometric functions for the condition of stimuli separated in time. For separated tones the predicted functions are not normal probability integrals, although their departure from probability integrals is never more than about 10% at any value.

THE NATURE AND LOCUS OF THE QUANTUM

What one cares to surmise about the mechanism responsible for what we have called "quantal functions" must be mainly speculative. Our own opinion is that the "neural unit" is functional rather than anatomical. The organism behaves as though a definite increment of excitation, or potential, or chemical concentration is needed at some central locus in order to enlist a "final common path" and thereby produce a "key-pressing." Conceivably the organism behaves in this respect much like a relaxation oscillator [10] — a potential builds up to a critical value and the system discharges. The critical value is analogous to the quantal increment.

Three reasons prompt us to reject Békésy's suggestion that the neural unit is a nerve fiber and to propose the notion that the quantum is a central rather than a peripheral phenomenon.

1. The critical increment in "excitation" (the quantum) is of no fixed value. Although throughout many experimental sessions the quantum remains sufficiently constant to produce rectilinear psychometric functions, changes in its magnitude are occasionally observed.

2. There are more nerve fibers in the auditory nerve than there are quanta in a given sensory attribute. Complete data for determining the precise number of quanta of pitch and of loudness remain to be obtained, but the size of the quanta thus far measured would indicate that several fibers might conceivably be involved in the production of a quantal discrimination.

3. For binaural listening the size of the quantum is generally smaller than for measurements made on a single ear. Fig. 9 shows typical results for frequency discrimination. When the stimulus and its increment enter both ears, the quantum is reduced to about two-thirds of its monaural value. The results in Fig. 9 are typical of 3 Os, but with one O (S.S.S.) no reliable difference between binaural and monaural listening was detectable in two different experiments.

If the quantum were dependent upon the addition of a single afferent nerve fiber (in the case of loudness) or upon the substitution of one fiber for another (in the case of pitch), we should expect that binaural listening would alter the psychometric function, but not in the manner illustrated in Fig. 9. Listening with two ears would presumably increase the probability of activating another nerve fiber. Or, considering inverse probabilities, we can say that a stimulus having 0.5 probability of failing to activate an additional fiber in one ear would have only 0.25 probability of failing in two ears. Extending this reasoning to other values we find that the peripheral theory of the quantum leads us to expect, for binaural listening, a curvilinear psychometric function coinciding with the rectilinear monaural function at 0 and 100%. Instead,

---

[10] For a discussion of this analogy see Balth. van der Pol, "Beyond radio," *Proc. World Radio Convention*, Institution of Radio Engineers, Australia, 1938.

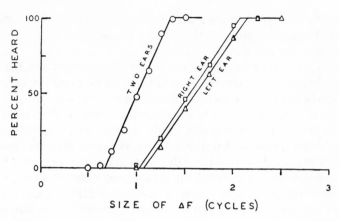

FIGURE 9 *Functions obtained from the same* O *(M.J.) for monaural and binaural listening.*

the typical finding is a rectilinear function satisfying the two criteria of a quantal function. Apparently, then, the two ears coöperate in some Os to produce "excitation" at the functional center where the quantum is located.

One additional fact ought to be mentioned. For a given increment the O either hears a change or he does not. In this respect, the discrimination is an all-or-none phenomenon. Of those increments he hears, all are not, however, of the same subjective magnitude. That is to say, most Os report that some of the increments they perceive are larger and plainer than others. Increments heard 80% of the time tend to be subjectively larger than increments heard only 20% of the time. It would appear, therefore, that the judgment of magnitude is to some degree independent of the all-or-none judgment of presence or absence. Of course, if the increment is not perceived as present, its subjective magnitude cannot be reported, but it seems that different perceptions of magnitude can follow the excitation of a single discriminatory quantum. Conceivably, the perception of magnitude could in turn be a quantal phenomenon involving quanta of smaller size than those mediating the discrimination of presence or absence; but on these problems only speculation is at present possible.

SUMMARY

We have presented experimental evidence that the neural processes determining differential sensory sensitivity are better understood in terms of a concept of neural quanta than in terms of a random variation of sensitivity as subsumed under the phi-gamma hypothesis.

Because the assumptions underlying the quantal and the classical theories lead to different mathematical predictions regarding the form of psychometric functions, it is possible to devise experimental conditions to be employed as a crucial test of the two theories. The principal condition required is a nearly instantaneous transition from the standard to the comparison stimulus. Under these circumstances, the classical theory predicts that the relation between the proportion of increments heard and the size of the increment will be described by the phi-function of gamma, but the quantal theory shows that this relation will be rectilinear and, moreover, when two additional quanta are required for discrimination, that the smallest increment which is always heard will be two times the largest increment which is never heard.

Data obtained when the intensity of the 1000-$\sim$ tone is given brief periodic increases are adequately described by rectilinear functions fulfilling the two-to-one relation as predicted by the quantal theory. More extensive experimentation with judgments of differences in frequency by 8 Os yielded similar results. Moreover it was shown that naïve Os give results in accordance with the quantal theory just as consistently as do trained Os, and that satisfactory quantal functions can be obtained with tones of widely different intensities.

These conclusions are supported by a statistical analysis in which the phi-function of gamma and the rectilinear function were fitted by the method of least squares to 15 sets of psychometric data. That the P-values derived from the chi-square test of goodness of fit favor the quantal hypothesis is evidenced by a composite coefficient of 0.008 for the phi-function of gamma and 0.931 for the rectilinear function. In addition, the slopes of the best-fitting rectilinear functions are uniformly those predicted by the quantal theory.

Not only do our results support the quantal theory and lead us to reject the phi-function of gamma, but they supply us with a precise measure of the size of the differential quantum. We have suggested therefore that differential sensitivity be expressed in terms of the quantum. In certain instances the DL, as classically defined, may be converted into a quantal measure by multiplying it by the factor 2/3.

The size of the quantum is determined by several parameters. It is quite different, of course, for different Os tested under similar conditions. The size of the quantum also varies with tonal intensity and we have presented curves of this relationship in the present paper. For

3 Os, the quantum for frequency discrimination under binaural stimulation is about two-thirds the size of *the* monaural quantum; but with one *O* we found no difference between monaural and binaural listening.

The fact that the two predicted consequences of the quantal theory are met as well in binaural as in monaural stimulation, even though the size of the quantum may vary, leads us to believe that the quantum is centrally, not peripherally, located. That it is a structural unit such as the neuron seems unlikely, but somewhat more reasonable is the view that it is some *functional* unit of the nervous system involving a number of fibers.

SENSITIVITY TO CHANGES IN THE INTENSITY OF WHITE NOISE AND ITS RELATION TO MASKING AND LOUDNESS

George A. Miller

Differential sensitivity to intensity is one of the oldest and most important problems in the psychophysics of audition. But previous experiments have concerned themselves mainly with sensitivity to changes in the intensity of sinusoidal tones, and if we want to know the differential sensitivity for a complex sound, it is necessary either to extrapolate from existing information, or actually to conduct the experiment for the sound in question. This gap in our knowledge is due to expediency, not oversight. The realm of complex sounds includes an infinitude of acoustic compounds, and experimental parameters extend in many directions. Just which of these sounds we select

From *Journal of the Acoustical Society of America*, 1947, 19, 609–619. Pages 609–617 reprinted with permission of the author and the American Institute of Physics.

This research was conducted under contract with the U.S. Navy, Office of Naval Research (Contract N5ori-76, Report PNR-28).

The author wishes to express his gratitude to Miss Shirley Mitchell, who assisted in obtaining the experimental data, and to Professor S. S. Stevens, who contributed valuable criticism and advice during the preparation of this manuscript.

for investigation is an arbitrary matter. Of the various possibilities, however, one of the most appropriate is random noise, a sound of persistent importance and one which marks a sort of ultimate on a scale of complexity.

Although the instantaneous amplitude varies randomly, white noise is perceived as a steady "hishing" sound, and it is quite possible to determine a listener's sensitivity to changes in its intensity.[1] The present paper reports the results of such determinations for a range of noise intensities.

APPARATUS AND PROCEDURE

A white-noise voltage, produced by random ionization in a gas tube, was varied in intensity by shunting the line with known resistances provided by a General Radio Decade Resistance Box. A schematic diagram of the equipment is shown in Fig. 1. The attenuators were used to keep constant the values of source and load impedance, R_0 and R_L, surrounding the shunt resistances, R_1 and R_2, since these values must enter into the computation of the increment which is produced by the insertion of the variable resistance, R_2. The whole system can

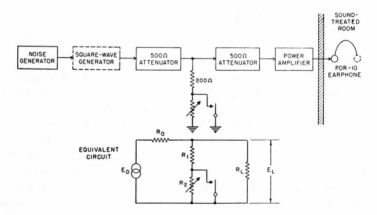

FIGURE 1   *Schematic diagram of equipment with the equivalent circuit used in the computation of the size of the increment in intensity.*

[1] J. E. Karlin, *Auditory tests for the ability to discriminate the pitch and the loudness of noises*, OSRD Report No. 5294 (Psycho-Acoustic Laboratory, Harvard University, August 1, 1945) (available through the Office of Technical Services, U.S. Department of Commerce, Washington, D.C.).

be represented by the equivalent circuit, also shown in Fig. 1. For this circuit, the size of an increment in voltage ΔE_L is given by

$$\frac{\Delta E_L}{E_L} = \frac{R_0 R_2 R_L}{R_1[R_0(R_1 + R_2 + R_3) + R_L(R_1 + R_2)]} \ .$$

If the system does not introduce amplitude distortion after the increments are produced, the increment in sound pressure, expressed in decibels, can be taken as $20 \log_{10}(1 + \Delta E_L/E_L)$.

Throughout the following discussion the intensity of the noise will be stated in terms of its sensation level — the number of decibels above the listener's absolute threshold for the noise. If the sound-pressure level of the noise is taken to be the level generated by a moving-coil earphone (Permoflux PDR-10) when the voltage across the earphone (measured by a thermocouple) is the same as the voltage required for a sinusoidal wave (1000 cycles) to generate the given sound pressure in a volume of 6 cc, then the absolute threshold for the noise corresponds to a sound pressure of approximately 10 db re 0.0002 dyne/cm^2. Thus the sensation level can be converted into sound-pressure level by the simple procedure of adding 10 db to the value given for the sensation level. The spectrum of the noise was relatively uniform (± 5 db) between 150 and 7000 c.p.s. The measurement and spectrum of the noise transduced by the earphone PDR-10 has been discussed in detail by Hawkins.[2]

Once the sound-pressure level and the relative size of the increment in decibels are known, the absolute value of the increment can be computed. Those interested in converting the decibels into dynes/cm^2 will find the nomogram of Fig. 2 a considerable convenience. A straight line which passes through a value of ΔI in decibels on the left-hand scale, and through a value of the sound pressure on the middle scale, will intersect the right-hand scale at the appropriate value of ΔP in dyne/cm^2. When the stimulus is a plane progressive sound wave, its acoustic intensity in watts/cm^2 is proportional to the square of the pressure: $I = kp^2$.

The peak amplitudes in the wave of a white noise are not constant. It is reasonable to expect, therefore, that the size of the just noticeable

[2] J. E. Hawkins, "The masking of pure tones and of speech by white noise," in a report entitled *The Masking of Signals by Noise,* OSRD Report No. 5387 (Psycho-Acoustic Laboratory, Harvard University, October 1, 1945) (available through the Office of Technical Services, U.S. Department of Commerce, Washington, D.C.).

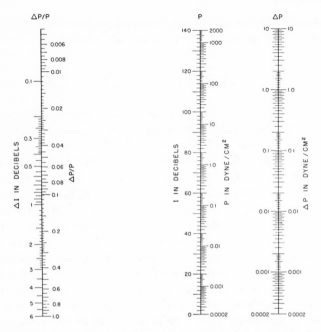

FIGURE 2   *Nomogram to convert values of* $\Delta P/P$ *to* ΔP *when P is known.*

difference might vary as a function of the distribution of peak amplitudes in the wave. In order to evaluate this aspect of the stimulus, a second experiment was conducted. The noise voltage was passed through a square-wave generator (Hewlett-Packard, Model 210-A) before the increments were introduced. The spectrum and subjective quality of the noise are not altered by the square-wave generator, but the peak amplitudes are "squared off" at a uniform level. The resulting wave form might be described as a square-wave modulated randomly in frequency.

The experimental procedure for determining differential sensitivity was the same as that employed by Stevens, Morgan, and Volkmann.[3] The only difference was the omission of a signal light which they sometimes used to indicate the impending presentation of an increment. The observer, seated alone in a sound-treated room, listened to the

[3] S. S. Stevens, C. T. Morgan, and J. Volkmann, "Theory of the neural quantum in the discrimination of loudness and pitch," *Am. J. Psychol.* 54, 315–335 (1941).

noise monaurally through a high quality, dynamic earphone (PDR-10). The listener heard a continuous noise, to which an increment was added periodically. A series of 25 identical increments (1.5 sec. duration at intervals of 4.5 sec.) was presented, and the percentage heard was tabulated. Four such series were used to determine each of 5 to 8 points on a psychometric function, and from this function the differential threshold was obtained by linear interpolation. Thus 500 to 800 judgments by each of two experienced listeners were used to determine each differential threshold at the 16 different intensities.

RESULTS

The increments in decibels which the two listeners could hear 50 per cent of the time are presented in Table 1 as a function of the sensation level of the noise. It will be noted that the differential sensitivity for "square-wave noise" is not significantly greater than that for random noise. Apparently the fluctuations in the peak amplitude of the wave do not influence the size of the just noticeable increment. The response of the ear is probably too sluggish to follow these brief fluctuations.

TABLE 1

Differential sensitivity for intensity of noise. Increments in decibels which two listeners could hear 50 per cent of the time, as a function of sensation level.

Sensation level (db)	Random noise		Square-wave noise	
	GM	SM	GM	SM
3	3.20	3.20		
5	3.00	2.10		
10	1.17	1.17		
12			0.97	0.89
15	0.85	0.66		
20	0.49	0.55		
25	0.46	0.54		
32			0.40	0.39
35	0.40	0.50		
45	0.42	0.44		
52			0.40	0.46
55	0.39	0.50		
70	0.39	0.47		
82			0.32	0.47
85	0.33	0.48		
100	0.28	0.40		

And since the difference between the two wave forms is essentially a matter of the phase relations among the components, we may conclude that these phase relations have no important effect on differential sensitivity.

The data indicate that, for intensities 30 db or more above the absolute threshold, the relative differential threshold is approximately constant. At the highest intensities the value is about 0.41 db, which corresponds to a Weber-fraction of 0.099 for sound energy, or 0.048 for sound pressure. The range over which the increment is proportional to the level of stimulation is indicated by the horizontal portion of the solid curve in Fig. 3. The values over this range of intensities agree quite well with the values obtained by Karlin[1] with a group of 50 listeners.

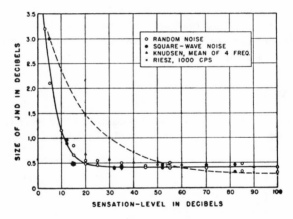

FIGURE 3   *Increments in intensity heard 50 percent of the time are plotted as a function of the intensity of the noise in decibels above the threshold of hearing. Data for tones are presented for purposes of comparison. The solid line represents Eq. (2).*

For purposes of comparison, Fig. 3 includes data obtained by Riesz[4] and by Knudsen[5] for tones. Knudsen's results do not differ markedly from those obtained for noise, but Riesz's data are quite different, especially at low intensities. Possibly Knudsen's data represent sensi-

[4] R. R. Riesz, "Differential intensity sensitivity of the ear for pure tones," *Phys. Rev.* 31, 867–875 (1928).

[5] V. O. Knudsen, "The sensibility of the ear to small differences in intensity and frequency," *Phys. Rev.* 21, 84–103 (1923).

tivity to the "noise" introduced by the abrupt onset of his tones, or possibly Riesz's data at low intensities are suspect because of his use of beats to produce increments in intensity. Data obtained by Stevens and Volkmann [6] for a single listener at four intensities of a 1000 cycle tone seem to agree more closely with the present results than with Riesz's, but their data are not complete enough to determine a function. Churcher, King, and Davies[7] have reported data with a tone of 800 c.p.s. which compare favorably with the function of Riesz. Taken together, all these studies indicate that the difference limen for intensity is of the same order of magnitude for noise as it is for tones, at least at the higher levels of intensity.[8] At the lower intensities the discrimination for a noise stimulus may be somewhat more acute than for tones.

IMPLICATIONS FOR A QUANTAL THEORY OF DISCRIMINATION

The notion that the difference limen depends upon the activation of discrete neural units is not new. It is suggested by the discreteness of the sensory cells themselves. Only recently, however, has evidence been obtained to support the assumption that the basic neural processes mediating a discrimination are of an all-or-none character.

The principal evidence derives from the shape of the psychometric function. Stevens, Morgan, and Volkmann [9] present the argument in the following way:

> We assume that the neural structures initially involved in the perception of a sensory continuum are divided into functionally distinct units. . . . The stimulus which excites a certain number of quanta will ordinarily do so with a little to spare — it will excite these quanta and leave a small surplus insufficient to excite some additional quantum. This surplus stimulation will contribute, along with the increment, ΔI, to bring into activity the added quantum needed for discrimination . . . How much of this left-over stimulation or surplus ex-

[6] S. S. Stevens and J. Volkmann, "The quantum of sensory discrimination," *Science* 92, 583–585 (1940).

[7] B. G. Churcher, A. J. King, and H. Davies, "The minimum perceptible change of intensity of a pure tone," *Phil. Mag.* 18, 927–939 (1934).

[8] Of the modern investigations, only Dimmick's disagrees strikingly with the values reported here for the higher intensities. F. L. Dimmick and R. M. Olson, "The intensive difference limen in audition," *J. Acous. Soc. Am.* 12, 517–525 (1941).

[9] See reference 3.

citation are we to expect? If [the over-all fluctuation in sensitivity] is large compared to the size of an individual quantum, it is evident that over the course of time all values of the surplus stimulation occur equally often. . . . From these considerations it follows that, if the increment is added instantaneously to the stimulus, it will be perceived a certain fraction of the time, and this fraction is directly proportional to the size of the increment itself.

When the increments are added to a continuous stimulus, however, the listener finds it difficult to distinguish one-quantum changes in the stimulus from the changes which are constantly occurring because of fluctuations in his sensitivity. In order to make reliable judgments, the listener is forced to ignore all one-quantum changes. Consequently, a stimulus increment under these conditions must activate at least two additional neural units in order that a difference will be perceived and reported. Thus, in effect, a constant error of one quantum is added to the psychometric function.

The psychometric function predicted by this line of reasoning can be described in the following way. When the stimulus increments to a steady sound are less than some value ΔI_Q, they are never reported, and over the range of increments from 0 to ΔI_Q the psychometric function remains at 0 per cent. Between ΔI_Q and $2\Delta I_Q$ the proportion of the increments reported varies directly with the size of the increment, and reaches 100 per cent at $2\Delta I_Q$. Such a function is illustrated by the solid line of Fig. 4.

It will be noted that the difference which is reported 50 per cent of the time is equivalent to 1.5 times the quantal increment. If we take this value as defining a unit increment in the stimulus, all the psychometric functions obtained for the two listeners can be combined into a single function. In other words, we can adjust the individual intensity scales against which the functions are plotted in order to make all the functions coincide at the 50 per cent point. In Fig. 4 the size of the relative increment in sound pressure, $\Delta P/P$, has been adjusted so that the increment which was heard 50 per cent of the time is plotted as 1.5 times the quantal increment.

Figure 4 shows that the characteristic quantal function was not obtained in this experiment. The data are better described by the phi-function of gamma (the normal probability integral) indicated by the dashed line.

The classical argument for the application of the cumulative prob-

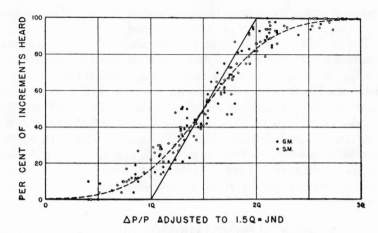

FIGURE 4 *The 32 psychometric functions combined in a single graph. Values of ΔP/P heard 50 percent of the time are designated as 1.5 Q, and the datum points on each function are plotted relative to this value. Each point represents 100 judgments.*

ability function to the difference limen assumes a number of small, indeterminate variables which are independent, and which combine according to chance. When these variables are controlled or eliminated, the step-wise, "quantal" relation is revealed.[10] If this reasoning is correct, then the deviations of the points in Fig. 4 from the quantal hypothesis should be attributable to the introduction of random variability into the listening situation.

Is there any obvious source of randomness in the experiment? Certainly there is, for white noise is a paradigm of randomness. The statistical nature of the noise means that the calculated value of the increment is merely the most probable value, and that a certain portion of the time the increment will depart from this probable value by an amount sufficient to affect the discrimination. And in view of the fluctuating level of the stimulus, it would be surprising indeed if the rigorous experimental requirements of the quantal hypothesis were fulfilled. This situation demonstrates the practical difficulty in obtaining the rectilinear functions predicted by the quantal hypothesis. Any

[10] G. A. Miller and W. R. Garner, "Effect of random presentation on the psychometric function: Implications for a quantal theory of discrimination," *Am. J. Psychol.* 57, 451–467 (1944).

source of variability tends to obscure the step-wise results and to produce the S-shaped normal probability integral.

It should be noted, however, that the shape of the psychometric function is only one of the implications of the quantal argument. According to the hypothesis, the slope of the psychometric function is determined by the size of the difference limen for all values of stimulus-intensity. The present data accord with this second prediction. The standard deviations of the probability integrals which describe the data are approximately one-third the means (or $0.5\Delta I_Q$) for all the thresholds measured for both subjects. This invariance in the slope of the function is necessary but not sufficient evidence for a neural quantum, and it makes possible the representation of the results in the form shown in Fig. 4.

SYMBOLIC REPRESENTATION OF THE DATA

In order to represent the experimental results in symbolic form, the following symbols will be used:

b numerical constant $= 1.333$,

c numerical constant $= 0.066 = \Delta I_Q/I$ when $I \gg I_0$,

DL difference limen (just noticeable difference, expressed in decibels),

f frequency in cycles per second,

I sound intensity (energy flow),

$I\frown$ sound intensity per cycle,

I_0 sound intensity which is just audible in quiet,

I_m sound intensity which is just masked in noise,

ΔI_Q quantal increment in sound intensity $= 0.667\Delta I_{50}$,

ΔI_{50} increment in sound intensity heard 50 per cent of the time,

L loudness in sones,

M masking in decibels,

N_Q number of quantal increments above threshold,

R signal-to-noise ratio per cycle at any frequency,

Z effective level of noise at any frequency.

An adequate description of the data in Table I can be developed from the empirical equation

$$\Delta I_Q = cI + bI_0, \quad I \geq I_0, \tag{1}$$

where the quantal increment in the stimulus-energy is assumed to have a fixed and a variable component. Since ΔI_{50} — the increment which can be heard 50 per cent of the time — equals $1.5\Delta I_Q$, we can write

$$DL = 10 \log_{10}(I + \Delta I_{50}/I) = 10 \log_{10}[1 + 1.5c + 1.5b(I_0/I)]. \tag{2}$$

From (2) it is possible to compute the just noticeable increment in decibels as a function of sensation level, although we know only the ratio between I and I_0 and not their absolute values. When the computations are carried through, the values indicated by the solid curve in Fig. 3 are obtained. The fit of this curve to the data is good enough to justify the use of Eq. (2) to obtain smoothed values of the function.

It is interesting to note that at high intensities Eq. (1) is equivalent to the well-known "Weber's Law," which states that the size of a just noticeable difference is proportional to the intensity to which it is added. Differential sensitivity characteristically departs from Weber's law at low intensities, and Fechner long ago suggested a modification of the law to the form expressed in Eq. (1).[11] The essential feature of this equation is the rectilinear relation between ΔI and I; the obvious difficulty is the explanation of the intercept value bI_0 which appears in Eq. (1) as an additive factor. Fechner supposed that this added term is attributable to intrinsic, interfering stimulation which cannot be eliminated in the measurement of the difference limen. Body noises, the spontaneous activity of the auditory nervous system, or the thermal noise of the air molecules have been suggested as possible sources of this background stimulation, but proof of these possibilities is still lacking. For the present, therefore, we must regard Eq. (1) as a purely empirical equation.

RELATION TO MASKING

There is an operational similarity between experiments designed to study differential sensitivity for intensity and experiments devised to measure auditory masking. This similarity is usually obscured by a

[11] H. Helmholtz, *Treatise on physiological optics*, translated by P. C. Southall from 3rd German edition, "The Sensations of Vision," Vol. II (1911) (Optical Society of America, 1924), pp. 172–181.

practical inclination to ignore the special case where one sound is masked by another sound identical with the first.

Suppose we want to know how much a white noise masks a white noise. What experimental procedures would we adopt? Obviously, the judgment we would ask the listener to make is the same judgment made in the present experiment. In the one case, however, we present the data to show the smallest detectable increment, while in the other we use the same data to determine the shift in threshold of the masked sound. When the masked and masking sounds are identical, the difference between masking and sensitivity to changes in intensity lies only in the way the story is told.

A striking example of this similarity is to be found in the work of Riesz. In order to produce gradual changes in intensity, Riesz used tones differing in frequency by 3 cycles and instructed his listeners to report the presence or absence of beats. Although his results are generally accepted as definitive measures of sensitivity to changes in the intensity of pure tones, it is equally correct to interpret them as measures of the masking of one tone by another tone differing in frequency by 3 cycles.

Let us, therefore, reconsider the data of Table I. In this table we have presented in decibels both the sensation level of the noise and the size of the increment which can be heard 50 per cent of the time. How can these data be transformed to correspond with the definition of masking?

First, consider that we are mixing two noises in order to produce the total magnitude $I + \Delta I$. Since I is analogous to the intensity of the masking sound, $I + \Delta I$ must equal the intensity of the masking sound plus the intensity of the masked sound, $I + I_m$. Thus $I_m = \Delta I$, and from the definition of masking M we can write

$$M = 10 \log_{10}(I_m/I_0) = 10 \log_{10}(\Delta I/I_0). \tag{3}$$

Because there appears to be some basic significance to the quantal unit, whereas the criterion of hearing 50 per cent of the increments is arbitrary, we will use the quantal increment ΔI_Q in Eq. (3). ΔI_Q is defined as 0.667 times the value of the increment which is heard 50 per cent of the time.

$$M = 10 \log_{10}(\Delta I_Q/I_0). \tag{3a}$$

Equation (3a) tells us, then, that the logarithm of the ratio of the quantal increment to the absolute threshold is proportional to the masking of a sound by an identical sound.

It is now possible to determine the values of ΔI_Q and I_o from the information given in Table I, and to substitute these values into Eq. (3a). The results of converting the differential thresholds into quantal increments and then into masked thresholds are given in Table II for the two listeners, and are shown in Fig. 5 where masking is plotted as a function of the sensation level of the masking noise. In addition, Table II contains values of masking which are computed when Eqs. (1) and (3a) are combined:

$$M = 10 \log_{10}[(cI/I_0) + b]. \tag{4}$$

For intensities 25 db or more above threshold, the masking noise is about 12 db more intense than the masked noise.

The obvious next step is to ask whether these results correspond to the functions obtained when noise is used to mask tones or human speech. Fortunately, we are able to answer this question. Hawkins [2] has measured the masking effects of noise on tones and speech with

TABLE II

Masking of white noise by white noise. Quantal increments in decibels and the values of masking obtained for two listeners as a function of the sensation level of the masking noise. Computed values of masking according to Eq. (4).

Sensation level (db)	Quantal increment in decibels		Masking obtained (db)		Masking computed (db)
	GM	SM	GM	SM	
3	2.37	2.37	1.61	1.61	1.65
5	2.21	1.51	3.26	1.18	1.88
10	0.81	0.81	3.14	3.14	3.00
12	0.67	0.61	4.22	3.80	3.76
15	0.58	0.45	6.58	5.39	5.33
20	0.33	0.37	9.00	9.54	8.99
25	0.31	0.37	13.73	14.45	13.44
32	0.27	0.27	20.06	19.97	20.25
35	0.27	0.34	23.06	24.10	23.22
45	0.29	0.30	33.33	33.53	33.20
52	0.27	0.31	40.06	40.73	40.20
55	0.27	0.34	42.97	44.10	43.20
70	0.27	0.32	57.97	58.81	58.20
82	0.22	0.32	68.32	70.81	70.20
85	0.22	0.33	72.22	73.91	73.20
100	0.19	0.27	86.43	88.06	88.20

experimental conditions and equipment directly comparable with those used here.

Suppose, for purposes of comparison, we choose to mask a 1000 cycle tone. We find over a wide range of intensities that this particular white noise just masks a 1000 cycle tone which is 20 db less intense. Since the corresponding value is 12 db when this noise masks itself, we conclude that, for this specific noise spectrum, 8 db less energy is needed for audibility when the energy is concentrated at 1000 c.p.s. than when the energy is spread over the entire spectrum. In order to compare the forms of the two masking functions, therefore, we can subtract 8 db from the level of the noise which masks the 1000-cycle tone.

When we make this correction of 8 db in the noise level for Hawkins' data for a 1000 cycle tone and plot the masking of this tone as a function of the corrected noise intensity, we obtain the solid line shown in Fig. 5. The correspondence between this curve, taken from Hawkins' data, and the points obtained in the present experiment is remarkably close. The function computed from Eq. (4) falls too close to Hawkins' function to warrant its separate presentation in Fig. 5.

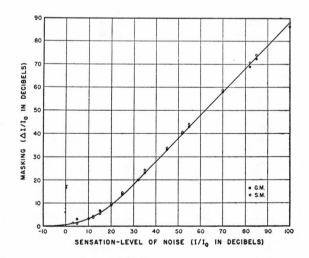

FIGURE 5 *Discriminable increments in intensity of white noise plotted in a manner analogous to masking experiments. Solid line represents function obtained by Hawkins for the masking of tones and speech by white noise.*

The choice of 1000 c.p.s. is not crucial to this correspondence. As Fletcher and Munson [12] have pointed out, a single function is adequate to describe the masking by noise of pure tones, if the intensity of the noise is corrected by a factor which is a function of the frequency of the masked tone. This factor is given at any frequency f by the ratio R of the intensity of the masked tone to the intensity per cycle of the noise at that frequency: $R = I_m/I_\sim$. R is experimentally determined for all frequencies at intensities well above threshold — on the rectilinear portion of the function shown in Fig. 5.

For noises with continuous spectra, the masking of a tone of frequency f can be attributed to the noise in the band of frequencies immediately adjacent to f.[13] Consequently, it is convenient to relate the masking of a tone of frequency f to the intensity per cycle of the noise at f, and to express this intensity in decibels *re* the threshold of hearing at any frequency. This procedure gives $10 \log_{10}(I_\sim/I_0)$, which can be regarded as the sensation level at f of a one-cycle band of noise. The effective level Z of the noise at that frequency is then defined as

$$Z = 10 \log_{10}(I_\sim/I_0) + 10 \log_{10}R. \tag{5}$$

When the masking of pure tones is plotted as a function of Z, the relation between M and Z is found to be independent of frequency. A single function expresses the relation between M and Z for all frequencies.

When we compare the function relating M to Z with the function obtained in the present experiment, we find that the sensation level of the noise is equivalent to $Z + 11.8$ db. Therefore,

$$I/I_o = 15.14R(I_\sim/I_0).$$

Substituting this expression into Eq. (4) gives

$$M = 10 \log_{10}[R(I_\sim/I_0) + b]. \tag{6}$$

This equation, along with the functions relating R and I_o to frequency, enables us to compute the masking of pure tones by any random noise of known spectrum. When $10 \log_{10}(I_\sim/I_0)$ is greater than about 15 db, b is negligible for all frequencies, and the masking can be computed more simply as $10 \log_{10}R + 10 \log_{10}(I_\sim/I_0)$.

---

[12] H. Fletcher and W. A. Munson, "Relation between loudness and masking," *J. Acous. Soc. Am.* 9, 1–10 (1937).

[13] H. Fletcher, "Auditory patterns," *Rev. Mod. Phys.* 12, 47–65 (1940).

Hawkins' results show that the function of Eq. (4) can also be adapted to describe the masking of human speech by white noise.

Thus the correspondence seems complete. When the masking and the masked sounds are identical, masking and sensitivity to changes in intensity are equivalent. The results obtained with identical masking and masked noises are directly comparable to results obtained with different masked sounds. It is reasonable to conclude, therefore, that the determination of sensitivity to changes in intensity is a special case of the more general masking experiment.

It is worth noting that this interpretation of masking is also applicable to visual sensitivity to changes in the intensity of white light. Data obtained by Graham and Bartlett[14] provide an excellent basis for comparison, because of the similarity of their procedure to that of the masking experiment, and because they used homogeneous, rod-free, foveal areas of the retina. When these data are substituted into Eq. (3) and plotted as measures of visual masking, the result can be described by the same general function that we have used to express the auditory masking by noise of tones, speech, and noise. . . .

CORRECTION[*]

In 1963 D. H. Raab, E. Osman, and E. Rich noticed an error in Eq. (3), which is written as if the masked and masking noises had been generated independently. In fact, however, the two noises were perfectly correlated (cf. Fig. 1), so their sound pressures added in phase; their combined power was the square of their summed pressures, not the sum of their squared pressures. When the amount of masking is recomputed from Table I using $M = 20 \log_{10} (\Delta P/P_0)$, then for intensities 25 db or more above threshold, the masking noise is about 25 db more

[14] C. H. Graham and N. R. Bartlett, "The relation of stimulus and intensity in the human eye: III. The influence of area on foveal intensity discrimination," *J. Exper. Psychol.* 27, 149–159 (1940).

Crozier has used similar visual data to demonstrate that the reciprocal of the just detectable increment is related to the logarithm of the light intensity by a normal probability integral. This is deduced on the assumption that sensitivity is determined by the not-already-excited portion of the total population of potentially excitable neural effects. Crozier's equations give an excellent description of the auditory data presented here. W. J. Crozier, "On the law for minimal discrimination of intensities. IV. ΔI as a function of intensity," *Proc. Nat. Acad. Sci.* 26, 382–388 (1940).

[*] Author's correction from *Readings in Mathematical Psychology*, R. Duncan Luce, Robert R. Bush, and Eugene Galanter (editors), Volume 1, p. 134. Copyright © 1963 by Wiley & Sons.

intense than the masked noise (not 12 db as stated on page 135). At sensation levels below about 25 db, therefore, there was facilitation (negative masking) instead of masking; listeners were able to hear in-phase increments which would have been inaudible if presented alone in the absence of the "masking" noise. This fact was verified directly by Raab, Osman, and Rich; a similar effect for sinusoids has been reported by S. M. Pfafflin and M. V. Mathews, Energy-detection model for monaural auditory detection, *J. Acoust. Soc. Am.*, 1962, 34, 1842–1853.

DECISION PROCESSES IN PERCEPTION

John A. Swets, Wilson P. Tanner, Jr.,
and Theodore G. Birdsall

About five years ago, the theory of statistical decision was translated into a theory of signal detection.[1] Although the translation was motivated by problems in radar, the detection theory that resulted is a general theory for, like the decision theory, it specifies an ideal process.

From *Psychological Review*, 1961, 68, 301–340. Pages 301–311 reprinted with permission of the authors and the American Psychological Association.

This paper is based upon Technical Report No. 40, issued by the Electronic Defense Group of the University of Michigan in 1955. The research was conducted in the Vision Research Laboratory of the University of Michigan with support from the United States Army Signal Corps and the Naval Bureau of Ships. Our thanks are due H. R. Blackwell and W. M. Kincaid for their assistance in the research, and D. H. Howes for suggestions concerning the presentation of this material. This paper was prepared in the Research Laboratory of Electronics, Massachusetts Institute of Technology, with support from the Signal Corps, Air Force (Operational Applications Laboratory and Office of Scientific Research), and Office of Naval Research. This is Technical Report No. ESD-TR-61-20.

[1] For a formal treatment of statistical decision theory, see Wald (1950); for a brief and highly readable survey of the essentials, see Bross (1953). Parallel accounts of the detection theory may be found in Peterson, Birdsall, and Fox (1954) and in Van Meter and Middleton (1954).

The generality of the theory suggested to us that it might also be relevant to the detection of signals by human observers. Beyond this, we were struck by several analogies between this description of ideal behavior and various aspects of the perceptual process. The detection theory seemed to provide a framework for a realistic description of the behavior of the human observer in a variety of perceptual tasks.

The particular feature of the theory that was of greatest interest to us was the promise that it held of solving an old problem in the field of psychophysics. This is the problem of controlling or specifying the criterion that the observer uses in making a perceptual judgment. The classical methods of psychophysics make effective provision for only a single free parameter, one that is associated with the sensitivity of the observer. They contain no analytical procedure for specifying independently the observer's criterion. These two aspects of performance are confounded, for example, in an experiment in which the dependent variable is the intensity of the stimulus that is required for a threshold response. The present theory provides a quantitative measure of the criterion. There is left, as a result, a relatively pure measure of sensitivity. The theory, therefore, promised to be of value to the student of personal and social processes in perception as well as to the student of sensory functions. A second feature of the theory that attracted us is that it is a normative theory. We believed that having a standard with which to compare the behavior of the human observer would aid in the description and in the interpretation of experimental results, and would be fruitful in suggesting new experiments.

This paper begins with a brief review of the theory of statistical decision and then presents a description of the elements of the theory of signal detection appropriate to human observers. Following this, the results of some experimental tests of the applicability of the theory to the detection of visual signals are described.

The theory and some illustrative results of one experimental test of it were briefly described in an earlier paper (Tanner & Swets, 1954). The present paper contains a more nearly adequate description of the theory, a more complete account of the first experiment, and the results of four other experiments. It brings together all of the data collected to date in vision experiments that bear directly on the value of the theory.[2]

---

[2] Reports of several applications of the theory in audition experiments are available in the literature; for a list of references, see Tanner and Birdsall (1958).

THE THEORY

Statistical Decision Theory

Consider the following game of chance. Three dice are thrown. Two of the dice are ordinary dice. The third die is unusual in that on each of three of its sides it has three spots, whereas on its remaining three sides it has no spots at all. You, as the player of the game, do not observe the throws of the dice. You are simply informed, after each throw, of the total number of spots showing on the three dice. You are then asked to state whether the third die, the unusual one, showed a 3 or a 0. If you are correct — that is, if you assert a 3 showed when it did in fact, or if you assert a 0 showed when it did in fact — you win a dollar. If you are incorrect — that is, if you make either of the two possible types of errors — you lose a dollar.

How do you play the game? Certainly you will want a few minutes to make some computations before you begin. You will want to know the probability of occurrence of each of the possible totals 2 through 12 in the event that the third die shows a 0, and you will want to know the probability of occurrence of each of the possible totals 5 through 15 in the event that the third die shows a 3. Let us ignore the exact values of these probabilities, and grant that the two probability distributions in question will look much like those sketched in Figure 1.

Realizing that you will play the game many times, you will want to establish a policy which defines the circumstances under which you will make each of the two decisions. We can think of this as a *criterion* or a cutoff point along the axis representing the total number of spots showing on the three dice. That is, you will want to choose a number on this axis such that whenever it is equaled or exceeded you will state that a 3 showed on the third die, and such that whenever the total number of spots showing is less than this number, you will state that a 0 showed on the third die. For the game as described, with the a priori probabilities of a 3 and a 0 equal, and with equal values and costs associated with the four possible decision outcomes, it is intuitively clear that the optimal cut-off point is that point where the two curves cross. You will maximize your winnings if you choose this point as the cutoff point and adhere to it.

Now, what if the game is changed? What, for example, if the third die has three spots on five of its sides, and a 0 on only one? Certainly you will now be more willing to state, following each throw, that the third die showed a 3. You will not, however, simply state more often

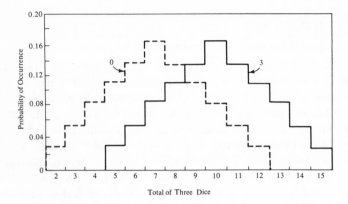

FIGURE 1   *The probability distributions for the dice game.*

that a 3 occurred without regard to the total showing on the three dice. Rather, you will lower your cutoff point: you will accept a smaller total than before as representing a throw in which the third die showed a 3. Conversely, if the third die has three spots on only one of its sides and 0's on five sides, you will do well to raise your cutoff point — to require a higher total than before for stating that a 3 occurred.

Similarly, your behavior will change if the values and costs associated with the various decision outcomes are changed. If it costs you 5 dollars every time you state that a 3 showed when in fact it did not, and if you win 5 dollars every time you state that a 0 showed when in fact it did (the other value and the other cost in the game remaining at one dollar), you will raise your cutoff to a point somewhere above the point where the two distributions cross. Or if, instead, the premium is placed on being correct when a 3 occurred, rather than when a 0 occurred as in the immediately preceding example, you will assume a cutoff somewhere below the point where the two distributions cross.

Again, your behavior will change if the amount of overlap of the two distributions is changed. You will assume a different cutoff than you did in the game as first described if the three sides of the third die showing spots now show four spots rather than three.

This game is simply an example of the type of situation for which the theory of statistical decision was developed. It is intended only to recall the frame of reference of this theory. Stastical decision theory — or the special case of it which is relevant here, the theory of testing statistical hypotheses — specifies the optimal behavior in a situation where one must choose between two alternative statistical hypotheses on the basis of an observed event. In particular, it specifies the optimal cutoff, along the continuum on which the observed events are arranged, as a function of (*a*) the a priori probabilities of the two hypotheses, (*b*) the values and costs associated with the various decision outcomes, and (*c*) the amount of overlap of the distributions that constitute the hypotheses.

According to the mathematical theory of signal detectability, the problem of detecting signals that are weak relative to the background of interference is like the one faced by the player of our dice game. In short, the detection problem is a problem in statistical decision; it requires testing statistical hypotheses. In the theory of signal detectability, this analogy is developed in terms of an idealized observer. It is our thesis that this conception of the detection process may apply to the human observer as well. The next several pages present an analysis of the detection process that will make the bases for this reasoning apparent.[3]

Fundamental Detection Problem

In the fundamental detection problem, an observation is made of events occurring in a fixed interval of time, and a decision is made, based on this observation, whether the interval contained only the background interference or a signal as well. The interference, which is random, we shall refer to as *noise* and denote as *N;* the other alternative we shall term *signal plus noise, SN.* In the fundamental problem, only these two alternatives exist — noise is always present, whereas the signal may or may not be present during a specified observation interval. Actually, the observer, who has advance knowledge of the ensemble of signals to be presented, says either "yes, a signal was present" or "no, no signal was present" following each observation. In

---

[3] It is to be expected that a theory recognized as having a potential application in psychophysics, although developed in another context, will be similar in many respects to previous conceptions in psychophysics. Although we shall not, in general, discuss explicitly these similarities, the strong relationship between many of the ideas presented in the following and Thurstone's earlier work on the scaling of judgments should be noted (see Thurstone, 1927a, 1927b). The present theory also has much in common with the recent work of Smith and Wilson (1953) and of Munson and Karlin (1956). Of course, for a new theory to arouse interest, it must also differ in some significant aspects from previous theories — these differences will become apparent as we proceed.

the experiments reported below, the signal consisted of a small spot of light flashed briefly in a known location on a uniformly illuminated background. It is important to note that the signal is always observed in a background of noise; some, as in the present case, may be introduced by the experimenter or by the external situation, but some is inherent in the sensory processes.

Representation of Sensory Information

We shall, in the following, use the term *observation* to refer to the sensory datum on which the decision is based. We assume that this observation may be represented as varying continuously along a single dimension. Although there is no need to be concrete, it may be helpful to think of the observation as some measure of neural activity, perhaps as the number of impulses arriving at a given point in the cortex within a given time. We assume further that any observation may arise, with specific probabilities, either from noise alone or from signal plus noise. We may portray these assumptions graphically, for a signal of a given amplitude, as in Figure 2. The observation is labeled x and plotted on the abscissa. The left-hand distribution, labeled $f_N(x)$, represents the probability density that x will result given the occurrence of noise alone. The right-hand distribution, $f_{SN}(x)$, is the probability density function of x given the occurrence of signal plus noise. (Probability density functions are used, rather than probability functions, since x is assumed to be continuous.) Since the observations will tend to be of greater magnitude when a signal is presented, the mean of the SN distribution will be greater than the mean of the N distribution. In general, the greater the amplitude of the signal, the greater will be the separation of these means.

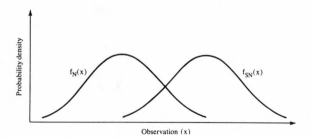

FIGURE 2   *The probability density functions of noise and signal plus noise.*

Observation as a Value of Likelihood Ratio

It will be well to question at this point our assumption that the observation may be represented along a single axis. Can we, without serious violation, regard the observation as unidimensional, in spite of the fact that the response of the visual system probably has many dimensions? The answer to this question will involve some concepts that are basic to the theory.

One reasonable answer is that when the signal and interference are alike in character, only the magnitude of the total response of the receiving system is available as an indicator of signal existence. Consequently, no matter how complex the sensory information is in fact, the observations may be represented in theory as having a single dimension. Although this answer is quite acceptable when concerned only with the visual case, we prefer to advance a different answer, one that is applicable also to audition experiments, where, for example, the signal may be a segment of a sinusoid presented in a background of white noise.

So let us assume that the response of the sensory system does have several dimensions, and proceed to represent it as a point in an m-dimensional space. Call this point y. For every such point in this space there is some probability density that it resulted from noise alone, $f_N(y)$, and, similarly, some probability density that it was due to signal plus noise, $f_{SN}(y)$. Therefore, there exists a likelihood ratio for each point in the space, $\lambda(y) = f_{SN}(y)/f_N(y)$, expressing the likelihood that the point y arose from SN relative to the likelihood that it arose from N. Since any point in the space, i.e., any sensory datum, may be thus represented as a real, nonzero number, these points may be considered to lie along a single axis. We may then, if we choose, identify the observation x with $\lambda(y)$; the decision axis becomes likelihood ratio.[4]

Having established that we may identify the observation x with $\lambda(y)$, let us note that we may equally well identify x with any monotonic transformation of $\lambda(y)$. It can be shown that we lose nothing by distorting the linear continuum as long as order is maintained. As a matter of fact we may gain if, in particular, we identify x with some trans-

[4] Thus the assumption of a unidimensional decision axis is independent of the character of the signal and noise. Rather, it depends upon the fact that just two decision alternatives are considered. More generally, it can be shown that the number of dimensions required to represent the observation is $M - 1$, where M is the number of decision alternatives considered by the observer.

formation of $\lambda(y)$ that results in Gaussian density functions on x. We have assumed the existence of such a transformation in the representation of the density functions, $f_{SN}(x)$ and $f_N(x)$, in Figure 2. We shall see shortly that the assumption of normality simplifies the problem greatly. We shall also see that this assumption is subject to experimental test. A further assumption incorporated into the picture of Figure 2, one made quite tentatively, is that the two density functions are of equal variance. This is equivalent to the assumption that the SN function is a simple translation of the N function, or that adding a signal to the noise merely adds a constant to the N function. The results of a test of this assumption are also described below.

To summarize the last few paragraphs, we have assumed that an observation may be characterized by a value of likelihood ratio, $\lambda(y)$, i.e., the likelihood that the response of the sensory system y arose from SN relative to the likelihood that it arose from N. This permits us to view the observations as lying along a single axis. We then assumed the existence of a particular transformation of $\lambda(y)$ such that on the resulting variable, x, the density functions are normal. We regard the observer as basing his decisions on the variable x.

Definition of the Criterion

If the representation depicted in Figure 2 is realistic, then the problem posed for an observer attempting to detect signals in noise is indeed similar to the one faced by the player of our dice game. On the basis of an observation, one that varies only in magnitude, he must decide between two alternative hypotheses. He must decide from which hypothesis the observation resulted; he must state that the observation is a member of the one distribution or the other. As did the player of the dice game, the observer must establish a policy which defines the circumstances under which the observation will be regarded as resulting from each of the two possible events. He establishes a criterion, a cutoff x_c on the continuum of observations, to which he can relate any given observation x_i. If he finds for the ith observation, x_i, that $x_i > x_c$, he says "yes"; if $x_i < x_c$, he says "no." Since the observer is assumed to be capable of locating a criterion at any point along the continuum of observations, it is of interest to examine the various factors that, according to the theory, will influence his choice of a particular criterion. To do so requires some additional notation.

In the language of statistical decision theory the observer chooses a subset of all of the observations, namely the Critical Region A, such that an observation in this subset leads him to accept the Hypothesis *SN*, to say that a signal was present. All other observations are in the complementary Subset *B;* these lead to rejection of the Hypothesis *SN*, or, equivalently, since the two hypotheses are mutually exclusive and exhaustive, to the acceptance of the Hypothesis *N*. The Critical Region *A*, with reference to Figure 2, consists of the values of *x* to the right of some criterion value x_c.

As in the case of the dice game, a decision will have one of four outcomes: the observer may say "yes" or "no" and may in either case be *correct* or *incorrect*. The decision outcome, in other words, may be a *hit* $(SN \cdot A$, the joint occurrence of the Hypothesis *SN* and an observation in the Region A), a *miss* $(SN \cdot B)$, a *correct rejection* $(N \cdot B)$, or a *false alarm* $(N \cdot A)$. If the a priori probability of signal occurrence and the parameters of the distributions of Figure 2 are fixed, the choice of a criterion value x_c completely determines the probability of each of these outcomes.

Clearly, the four probabilities are interdependent. For example, an increase in the probability of a hit, $p(SN \cdot A)$, can be achieved only by accepting an increase in the probability of a false alarm, $p(N \cdot A)$, and decreases in the other probabilities, $p(SN \cdot B)$ and $p(N \cdot B)$. Thus a given criterion yields a particular balance among the probabilities of the four possible outcomes; conversely, the balance desired by an observer in any instance will determine the optimal location of his criterion. Now the observer may desire the balance that maximizes the expected value of a decision in a situation where the four possible outcomes of a decision have individual values, as did the player of the dice game. In this case, the location of the best criterion is determined by the same parameters that determined it in the dice game. The observer, however, may desire a balance that maximizes some other quantity — i.e., a balance that is optimum according to some other definition of optimum — in which case a different criterion will be appropriate. He may, for example, want to maximize $p(SN \cdot A)$ while satisfying a restriction on $p(N \cdot A)$, as we typically do when as experimenters we assume an .05 or .01 level of confidence. Alternatively, he may want to maximize the number of correct decisions. Again, he may prefer a criterion that will maximize the reduction in uncertainty in the Shannon (1948) sense.

In statistical decision theory, and in the theory of signal detectability, the optimal criterion under each of these definitions of optimum is specified in terms of the likelihood ratio. That is to say, it can be shown that, if we define the observation in terms of the likelihood ratio, $\lambda(x) = f_{SN}(x)/f_N(x)$, then the optimal criterion can always be specified by some value of β of $\lambda(x)$. In other words, the Critical Region A that corresponds to the criterion contains all observations with likelihood ratio greater than or equal to β, and none of those with likelihood ratio less than β.

We shall illustrate this manner of specifying the optimal criterion for just one of the definitions of optimum proposed above, namely, the maximization of the total expected value of a decision in a situation where the four possible outcomes of a decision have individual values associated with them. This is the definition of optimum that we assumed in the dice game. For this purpose we shall need the concept of *conditional probability* as opposed to the *probability of joint occurrence* introduced above. It should be stated that conditional probabilities will have a place in our discussion beyond their use in this illustration; the ones we shall introduce are, as a matter of fact, the fundamental quantities in evaluating the observer's performance.

There are two conditional probabilities of principal interest. These are the conditional probabilities of the observer saying "yes": $p_{SN}(A)$, the probability of a Yes decision *conditional upon*, or *given*, the occurrence of a signal, and $p_N(A)$, the probability of a Yes decision given the occurrence of noise alone. These two are sufficient, for the other two are simply their complements: $p_{SN}(B) = 1 - p_{SN}(A)$ and $p_N(B) = 1 - p_N(A)$. The conditional and joint probabilities are related as follows:

$$p_{SN}(A) = \frac{p(SN \cdot A)}{p(SN)}$$

$$(1)$$

$$p_N(A) = \frac{p(N \cdot A)}{p(N)}$$

where: $p(SN)$ is the a priori probability of signal occurrence and $p(N) = 1 - p(SN)$ is the a priori probability of occurrence of noise alone.

Equation (1) makes apparent the convenience of using conditional rather than joint probabilities — conditional probabilities are independent of the a priori probability of occurrence of the signal and of noise alone. With reference to Figure 2, we may define $p_{SN}(A)$, or the conditional probability of a hit, as the integral of $f_{SN}(x)$ over the Critical Region A, and $p_N(A)$, the conditional probability of a false alarm, as the integral of $f_N(x)$ over A. That is, $p_N(A)$ and $p_{SN}(A)$ represent, respectively, the areas under the two curves of Figure 2 to the right of some criterion value of x.

To pursue our illustration of how an optimal criterion may be specified by a critical value of likelihood ratio β, let us note that the expected value of a decision (denoted EV) is defined in statistical decision theory as the sum, over the potential outcomes of a decision, of the products of probability of outcome and the desirability of outcome. Thus, using the notation P for *positive* individual values and K for costs or *negative* individual values, we have the following equation:

$$\begin{aligned} EV = \ & V_{SN \cdot A} p(SN \cdot A) \\ & + V_{N \cdot B} p(N \cdot B) \\ & - K_{SN \cdot B} p(SN \cdot B) \\ & - K_{N \cdot A} p(N \cdot A) \end{aligned} \tag{2}$$

Now if a priori and conditional probabilities are substituted for the joint probabilities in Equation (2) following Equation (1), for example, $p(SN)p_{SN}(A)$ for $p(SN \cdot A)$, then collecting terms yields the result that maximizing EV is equivalent to maximizing:

$$p_{SN}(A) - \beta p_N(A) \tag{3}$$

where

$$\beta = \frac{p(N)}{p(SN)} \cdot \frac{(V_{N \cdot B} + K_{N \cdot A})}{(V_{SN \cdot A} + K_{SN \cdot B})} \tag{4}$$

It can be shown that this value of β is equal to the value of likelihood ratio, $\lambda(x)$, that corresponds to the optimal criterion. From Equation (3) it may be seen that the value β simply weights the hits and false alarms, and from Equation (4) we see that β is determined by the a priori probabilities of occurrence of signal and of noise alone and by the values associated with the individual decision outcomes. It should be noted that Equation (3) applies to all definitions of optimum. Equation (4) shows the determinants of β in only the special case of the expected-value definition of optimum.

Return for a moment to Figure 2, keeping in mind the result that β is a critical value of $\lambda(x) = f_{SN}(x)/f_N(x)$. It should be clear that the optimal cutoff x_c along the x axis is at the point on this axis where the ratio of the ordinate value of $f_{SN}(x)$ to the ordinate value of $f_N(x)$ is a certain number, namely β. In the symmetrical case, where the two a priori probabilities are equal and the four individual values are equal, $\beta = 1$ and the optimal value of x_c is the point where $f_{SN}(x) = f_N(x)$, where the two curves cross. If the four values are equal but $p(SN) = \frac{5}{6}$ and $p(N) = \frac{1}{6}$, another case described in connection with the dice game, then $\beta = \frac{1}{5}$ and the optimal value of x_c is shifted a certain distance to the left. This shift may be seen intuitively to be in the proper direction — a higher value of $p(SN)$ should lead to a greater willingness to accept the Hypothesis SN, i.e., a more lenient cutoff. To consider one more example from the dice game, if $p(SN) = p(N) = 0.5$, if $V_{N \cdot B}$ and $K_{N \cdot A}$ are set at 5 dollars and $V_{SN \cdot A}$ and $K_{SN \cdot B}$ are equal to 1 dollar, then $\beta = 5$ and the optimal value of x_c shifts a certain distance to the right. Again intuitively, if it is more important to be correct when the Hypothesis N is true, a high, or strict, criterion should be adopted.

In any case, β specifies the optimal weighting of hits relative to false alarms: x_c should always be located at the point on the x axis corresponding to β. As we pointed out in discussing the dice game, just where this value of x_c will be with reference to the x axis depends not only upon the a priori probabilities and the values but also upon the overlap of the two density functions, in short, upon the signal strength. We shall define a measure of signal strength within the next few pages. For now, it is important to note that for any detection goal to which the observer may subscribe, and for any set of parameters that may characterize a detection situation (such as a priori probabilities and values associated with decision outcomes), the optimal criterion may be specified in terms of a single number, β, a critical value of likelihood ratio.[5]

Receiver-Operating-Characteristic

Whatever criterion the observer actually uses, even if it is not one of the optimal criteria, can also be described by a single number, by some value of likelihood ratio. Let us proceed to a consideration of how the

[5] We have reached a point in the discussion where we can justify the statement made earlier that the decision axis may be equally well regarded as likelihood ratio or as any monotonic transformation of likelihood ratio. Any distortion of the linear continuum of likelihood ratio that maintains order is equivalent to likelihood ratio in terms of determining a criterion. The decisions made are the same whether the criterion is set at likelihood ratio equal to β or at the value that corresponds to β of some new variable. To illustrate, if a criterion leads to a Yes response whenever $\lambda(y) > 2$, if $x = [\lambda(y)]^2$ the decisions will be the same if the observer says "yes" whenever $x > 4$.

observer's performance may be evaluated with respect to the location of his criterion, and at the same time we shall see how his performance may be evaluated with respect to his sensory capabilities.

As we have noted, the fundamental quantities in the evaluation of performance are $p_N(A)$ and $p_{SN}(A)$, these quantities representing, respectively, the areas under the two curves of Figure 2 to the right of some criterion value of x. If we set up a graph of $p_{SN}(A)$ versus $p_N(A)$ and trace on it the curve resulting as we move the decision criterion along the decision axis of Figure 2, we sketch one of the arcs shown in Figure 3. Ignore, for a moment, all but one of these arcs. If the decision criterion is set way at the left in Figure 2, we obtain a point in the upper right-hand corner of Figure 3: both $p_{SN}(A)$ and $p_N(A)$ are unity. If the criterion is set at the right end of the decision axis in Figure 2, the point at the other extreme of Figure 3, $p_{SN}(A) = p_N(A) = 0$, is obtained. In between these extremes lie the criterion values of more practical interest. It should be noted that the

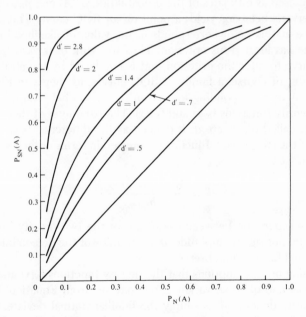

FIGURE 3 *The receiver-operating-characteristic curves. (These curves show* $p_{SN}(A)$ *vs.* $p_N(A)$ *with* d' *as the parameter. They are based on the assumptions that the probability density functions,* $f_N(x)$ *and* $f_{SN}(x)$, *are normal and of equal variance.)*

exact form of the curve shown in Figure 3 is not the only form which might result, but it is the form which will result if the observer chooses a criterion in terms of likelihood ratio, and the probability density functions are normal and of equal variance.

This curve is a form of the *operating characteristic* as it is known in statistics; in the context of the detection problem it is usually referred to as the *receiver-operating-characteristic*, or ROC, curve. The optimal "operating level" may be seen from Equation (3) to be at the point of the ROC curve where its slope is β. That is, the expression $p_{SN}(A) - \beta p_N(A)$ defines a utility line of slope β, and the point of tangency of this line to the ROC curve is the optimal operating level. Thus the theory specifies the appropriate hit probability and false alarm probability for any definition of optimum and any set of parameters characterizing the detection situation.

It is now apparent how the observer's choice of a criterion in a given experiment may be indexed. The proportions obtained in an experiment are used as estimates of the probabilities, $p_N(A)$ and $p_{SN}(A)$; thus, the observer's behavior yields a point on an ROC curve. The slope of the curve at this point corresponds to the value of likelihood ratio at which he has located his criterion. Thus we work backward from the ROC curve to infer the criterion that is employed by the observer.

There is, of course, a family of ROC curves, as shown in Figure 3, a given curve corresponding to a given separation between the means of the density functions $f_N(x)$ and $f_{SN}(x)$. The parameter of these curves has been called d', where d' is defined as the difference between the means of the two density functions expressed in terms of their standard deviation, i.e.:

$$d' = \frac{M_{f_{SN}(x)} - M_{f_N(x)}}{\sigma_{f_N(x)}} \tag{5}$$

Since the separation between the means of the two density functions is a function of signal amplitude, d' is an index of the detectability of a given signal for a given observer.

Recalling our assumptions that the density functions $f_N(x)$ and $f_{SN}(x)$ are normal and of equal variance, we may see from Equation (5) that the quantity denoted d' is simply the familiar normal deviate, or x/σ measure. From the pair of values $p_N(A)$ and $p_{SN}(A)$ that are obtained experimentally, one may proceed to a published table of areas under the normal curve to determine a value of d'. A simpler computational procedure is achieved by plotting the points $[p_N(A), p_{SN}(A)]$ on graph paper having a probability scale and a normal deviate scale on both axes.

We see now that the four-fold table of the responses that are made to a particular stimulus may be treated as having two independent parameters — the experiment yields measures of two independent aspects of the observer's performance. The variable d' is a measure of the observer's sensory capabilities, or of the effective signal strength. This may be thought of as the object of interest in classical psychophysics. The criterion β that is employed by the observer, which determines the $p_N(A)$ and $p_{SN}(A)$ for some fixed d', reflects the effect of variables which have been variously called the set, attitude, or motives of the observer. It is the ability to distinguish between these two aspects of detection performance that comprises one of the main advantages of the theory proposed here. We have noted that these two aspects of behavior are confounded in an experiment in which the dependent variable is the intensity of the signal that is required for a threshold response.

Relationship of d' to Signal Energy

We have seen that the optimal value of the criterion, β, can be computed. In certain instances, an optimal value of d', i.e., the sensitivity of the mathematically ideal device, can also be computed. If, for example, the exact wave form and starting time of the signal are determinable, as in the case of an auditory signal, then the optimal value of d' is equal to $\sqrt{2E/N_o}$, where E is the signal energy and N_o is the noise power in a one-cycle band (Peterson, Birdsall, and Fox, 1954). A specification of the optimal value of d' for visual signals has been developed very recently.[6] Although we shall not elaborate the point in this paper, it is worth noting that an empirical index of detectability may be compared with ideal detectability, just as observed and optimal indices of decision criteria may be compared. The ratio of the squares of the two detectability indices has been taken as a measure of the observer's sensory efficiency. This measure has demonstrated its usefulness in the study of several problems in audition (Tanner & Birdsall, 1958).

Use of Ideal Descriptions as Models

It might be worthwhile to describe at this point some of the reasons for the emphasis placed here on optimal measures, and, indeed, the

[6] W. P. Tanner, Jr. and R. C. Jones, personal communication, November 1959.

reasons for the general enterprise of considering a theory of ideal behavior as a model for studies of real behavior.[7] In view of the deviations from any ideal which are bound to characterize real organisms, it might appear at first glance that any deductions based on ideal premises could have no more than academic interest. We do not think this is the case. In any study, it is desirable to specify rigorously the factors pertinent to the study. Ideal conditions generally involve few variables and permit these to be described in simple terms. Having identified the performance to be expected under ideal conditions, it is possible to extend the model to include the additional variables associated with real organisms. The ideal performance, in other words, constitutes a convenient base from which to explore the complex operation of a real organism.

In certain cases, as in the problem at hand, values characteristic of ideal conditions may actually approximate very closely those characteristics of the organism under study. The problem then becomes one of changing the ideal model in some particular so that it is slightly less than ideal. This is usually accomplished by depriving the ideal device of some particular function. This method of attack has been found to generate useful hypotheses for further studies. Thus, whereas it is not expected that the human observer and the ideal detection device will behave identically, the emphasis in early studies is on similarities. If the differences are small, one may rule out entire classes of alternative models, and regard the model in question as a useful tool in further studies. Proceeding on this assumption, one may then in later studies emphasize the differences, the form and extent of the differences suggesting how the ideal model may be modified in the direction of reality. . . .

REFERENCES

Bross, I. D. J. *Design for Decision*. New York: Macmillan, 1953.

Horton, J. W. *Fundamentals of Sonar*. Annapolis: United States Naval Institute, 1957.

Munson, W. A. and Karlin, J. E. "The measurement of the human channel transmission characteristics." *J. Acoust. Soc. Amer.*, 1956, 26, 542–553.

Peterson, W. W., Birdsall, T. G., and Fox, W. C. "The theory of signal detectability." *IRE Trans.*, 1954, PGIT-4, 171–212.

Shannon, C. E. "The mathematical theory of communication." *Bell Sys. Tech. J.*, 1948, 27, 379–423.

Smith, M. and Wilson, Edna A. "A model of the auditory threshold and its application to the problem of the multiple observer." *Psychol. Monogr.*, 1953, 67(9, Whole No. 359).

[7] The discussion immediately following is in part, a paraphrase of one in Horton (1957).

Tanner, W. P., Jr. and Birdsall, T. G. "Definitions of d' and η as psychophysical measures." *J. Acoust. Soc. Amer.*, 1958, 30, 922–928.

Tanner, W. P., Jr. and Swets, J. A. "A decision-making theory of visual detection." *Psychol. Rev.*, 1954, 61, 401–409.

Thurstone, L. L. "A law of comparative judgment." *Psychol. Rev.*, 1927, 34, 273–286. (a)

Thurstone, L. L. "Psychophysical analysis." *Amer. J. Psychol.*, 1927, 38, 368–389. (b)

Van Meter, D. and Middelton, D. "Modern statistical approaches to reception in communication theory." *IRE Trans.*, 1954, PGIT-4, 119–145.

Wald, A. *Statistical Decision Functions*. New York: Wiley, 1950.

B. Sensory discrimination in animals

Both papers in this section were written by D. S. Blough, who has displayed ingenuity in his efforts to obtain reliable data on the sensory capacity of behaving animals. In each of these papers he showed how techniques of human psychophysics can be applied in the realm of animal behavior.

In "Method for Tracing Dark Adaptation in the Pigeon," Blough showed how pigeons could be trained to yield measures of their absolute thresholds for vision. The measurements were obtained by a procedure that is formally similar to the tracking method (see "Psychophysics" by J. C. Stevens). This method is especially well suited to the study of time-dependent sensory processes, such as adaptation, and it allowed Blough to map the complete course of dark adaptation in the pigeon.

In the second paper Blough relates signal detection theory to animal psychophysics. As Swets, Tanner, and Birdsall showed in their article in Section 3A, an experimenter can construct an empirical ROC curve if he has an estimate of the probability of a "hit" and the probability of a "false alarm" for at least two values of an observer's likelihood ratio criterion. In a "yes/no" (binary decision) experiment, the observer adopts one criterion at a time and, from one long series of observations to another, the experimenter manipulates the observer's criterion and thereby obtains the data necessary to construct the ROC curve. One alternative to this procedure is to allow the observer to adopt multiple criteria within any one series of observations. In particular, the observer can be instructed to use, say, a six-point scale to rate on each trial his confidence that the "signal" or "noise" was presented. A rating of "1" would represent a "yes" under a very strict criterion ("very certain that a signal was presented"), a rating of "2" would represent a "yes" under a less strict criterion ("moderately certain a signal was presented"), and so on.

These data can be treated in the same way as yes/no data, i.e., the experimenter treats each of the five boundaries between categories in turn as a different response criterion. Thus, he first treats all responses of *1* on signal-trials as "hits" and all responses of *2* through *6* on signal-trials as "misses"; similarly, he treats all responses of *1* on noise-trials as "false alarms" and all responses of *2* through *6* on noise-trials as "correct rejections." The results of this procedure yield the estimates of probability needed to plot one point of an ROC curve. To obtain the second point of the curve, the experimenter follows a similar procedure. He treats all responses of *1* and *2* on signal-trials as "hits," responses of *3* through *6* on signal-trials as "misses," responses of *1* and *2* on noise-trials as "false alarms," and responses of *3* through *6* on noise-trials as "correct rejections." He continues this procedure until he has treated each of the boundaries between categories as a different criterion and has thereby obtained five points on a curve.

In "Stimulus Generalization as Signal Detection in Pigeons," Blough treated the number of responses that a pigeon emitted on a trial as a measure of the animal's "confidence" that a signal had been presented on that trial. Blough went on to analyze the number of pecks emitted on signal-trials and noise-trials in the manner used to analyze rating responses from humans. In this way, he was able to obtain measures of sensitivity for differential discrimination of wavelength that were free of the confounding effects of the pigeon's criterion.

METHOD FOR TRACING DARK ADAPTATION IN THE PIGEON

Donald S. Blough

Animal subjects are not often used in psychophysical research, because they cannot follow complex instructions or report verbally what they see or hear. The method described in this paper represents an attempt to overcome these difficulties and to obtain with animals some of the efficiency and control that human subjects provide. The method owes much to the work of Skinner and his associates (1) and to Békésy's method of human audiometry (2). The procedure outlined here is designed for the study of dark adaptation in the pigeon (3), but with modifications, it may be applied to a variety of animal discrimination problems.

Automatic apparatus is used. It includes the following items: (i) a light-tight adaptation box, containing pigeon, response keys; food magazine, and stimulus patch; (ii) a network of relays and timers that control the stimulus luminance and the presentation of food; (iii) a light source and an optical system, with a device that continuously records the stimulus luminance.

A panel divides the adaptation box into two chambers. The bird is trained to stand in one chamber and place its head through a round hole in the panel (Fig. 1). The bird faces a small window through which it views a stimulus patch, 1 cm in diameter, 4 cm beyond the frame of the window. The only light in the adaptation box comes from this stimulus patch. There are two small response keys, A and B, just below the window. Each peck on one of these keys momentarily opens a switch that is connected with the controlling relay network. When the bird is to be rewarded, a solenoid raises a magazine containing grain to an opening in the floor below the response keys.

The stimulus patch is illuminated from behind by a beam of light. A motor-driven optical wedge in the path of the light beam regulates the luminance of the patch. A shutter may be closed to black out the

From *Science*, 13 May 1955, 121, 703–704. Copyright © 1955 by the American Association for the Advancement of Science. Reprinted with permission of the author and the publisher.

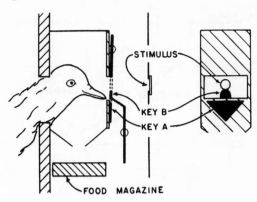

FIGURE 1 *Response chamber of the adaptation box. (Left) Side view, show-ing relative positions of pigeon, food magazine, response keys, and stimulus patch. (Right) Keys A and B and patch seen from the pigeon's position.*

stimulus patch completely. The movements of both the wedge and the shutter are controlled through the relay network.

The pigeon's basic task is to peck key *A* when the stimulus patch is visible and to peck key *B* when the patch is dark. Training on this dis-crimination proceeds in several stages. When the bird becomes pro-ficient at one stage, the next stage is introduced; 50 training hours may be needed before experimental data can be collected.

First, the hungry bird (70 to 80 per cent of free-feeding cage weight) is trained to peck the two keys at random by the "response differentia-tion" technique described by Ferster (4). Next, the stimulus patch is illuminated, and the control circuit is so adjusted that a peck on key *A* closes the shutter, blacking out the patch. After a peck on key *A* has blacked out the patch, a peck on key *B* causes the food magazine to be raised within reach for about 5 sec. Pecks on key *B* are useless when the patch is lighted, and pecks on key *A* are useless when the patch is dark. After most rewards, the shutter opens, and the lighted patch re-appears. Continued darkness follows one reward in five; in this case, a peck on key *B* brings food a second time. These double rewards train the bird to attend to the stimulus patch after eating; without them, the bird would always peck key *A* after eating, regardless of the condition of the stimulus patch.

In the next stage of training, several pecks in a row, rather than a

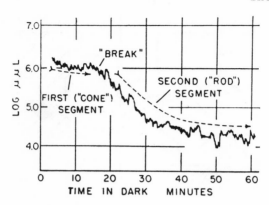

FIGURE 2   *Dark-adaptation curve secured from a bird in 1 hr. The luminance of the stimulus patch, in log micromicro-lamberts, is on the ordinate.*

single peck, are required on key *A* to close the shutter and on key *B* to obtain food. The number of pecks required is varied randomly between one and eight. This increases the time between rewards and prevents the bird from getting a reward simply by pecking the two keys alternately, without attending to the stimulus patch. The time between rewards is further increased by introducing an interval after each reward during which no amount of pecking can close the shutter. The duration of this interval varies randomly about a mean of 7 sec.

When training is nearly complete, a final feature is added to the procedure: the luminance of the stimulus patch is put under the control of the bird's responses during the intervals between rewards. Each peck on key *A* reduces the luminance of the patch by a small amount, while each peck on key *B* increases the luminance of the patch. A pen continuously records these luminance changes. When the bird has learned to perform consistently under these conditions, the collection of threshold data can begin. Experimentation continues indefinitely without further alteration of procedure.

An account of a typical experimental session will serve to illustrate how the bird's threshold is traced. At first, the stimulus patch is brightly lighted, and the trained bird pecks only key *A*. The bird continues to peck key *A* until the patch becomes so dim that it falls below the bird's absolute threshold. Because the pigeon cannot distinguish this "dim-out" of the patch from the true "black-out" caused by the closing shutter, it begins to peck key *B*. But pecking key *B* increases the luminance of the patch, so in a short time the patch again becomes visible to the bird. When this happens, the bird switches its pecking back to key *A*, causing the stimulus to dim and to disappear as before. This process continues indefinitely; the bird alternately pecks keys *A* and *B*, and the stimulus fluctuates up and down across the bird's absolute threshold. The continuous record of the stimulus luminance traces the bird's absolute threshold through time. The randomly spaced rewards, when pecks on key *A* close the shutter and pecks on key *B* bring food, interrupt the continuity of this threshold record frequently but for only a few seconds.

During the first portion of an experimental session, the recording pen traces the pigeon's dark-adaptation curve. A reproduction of such a curve in a 1-hr session is shown on appropriate coordinates in Fig. 2. Before this particular session, the bird had spent 1 hr in darkness, followed by 10 min in a box with white walls at a luminance of 22 millilamberts.

REFERENCES AND NOTES

1. B. F. Skinner, *Am. Psychologist* 8, 69 (1953).
2. G. v. Békésy, *Acta Oto-Laryngol.* 35, 411 (1947).
3. This research was supported in part by contract N5ori07663 (project NR140-072) between Harvard University and the Office of Naval Research, directed by Floyd Ratliff. It represents part of a thesis submitted to the Department of Psychology, Harvard University, in partial fulfillment of the requirements for the Ph.D. degree. I am indebted to Ratliff for his constant interest and helpful advice. Present address: National Institute of Mental Health, Bethesda, Md.
4. C. B. Ferster, *Psychological Bull.* 50, 263 (1953).

STIMULUS GENERALIZATION AS SIGNAL DETECTION IN PIGEONS

Donald S. Blough

Modern psychophysics may clarify our thinking about the stimulus control of animal behavior (*1*). Conversely, animal subjects might supply data necessary to test psychophysical hypotheses. Unfortunately, most experiments with animals are concerned with transient phenomena, whereas psychophysics deals with the steady state; many animal experiments yield response rates to prolonged stimuli, while psychophysics favors choice responses to brief stimuli. This experiment effects a compromise by putting the response rate of an animal in a form suitable for signal detection analysis. A pigeon's response during a 30 second trial shows its "degree of certainty" that a reinforced stimulus was present on that trial. From such ratings, existing procedures yield relatively well-defined receiver-operating characteristic (ROC) functions (*2*).

Three White Carneaux pigeons with a long history of discrimination training were the subjects. Each pigeon, in a darkened chamber, pecked at a plastic disk upon which appeared a bright spot (0.95 cm in diameter). A 250 mm grating monochromator supplied light for this spot through a fiber-optics light guide. The stimulus assumed one of 12 wavelengths (570 to 592 nm in 2 nm steps), each with a half-width dispersion of 6.6 nm. The stimuli were uncorrected for brightness; over this range, brightness probably varied little for the pigeons (see *3*).

After several weeks of training, experimental data were collected for 28 days. Each daily session comprised a 2 hour series of 30 second presentations of the stimulus with 3 second dark periods between these presentations. The key also went dark during reinforcement and for 0.6 second after each peck. On some trials, with 582 nm on the key, pecks intermittently brought reinforcement of 3 second access to mixed grain. Such reinforced trials were mixed with unreinforced "test trials" in a semirandom sequence as follows. Each session began with four reinforced trials followed by 13 stimulus sequences presented serially. The 16 stimuli in each sequence included four reinforced trials of 582 nm

From *Science*, 17 November 1967, 158, 940–941. Copyright © 1967 by the American Association for the Advancement of Science. Reprinted with permission of the author and the publisher.

and 12 test trials in random order, with each test wavelength appearing once. The data below came from responses made in the 12 test trials on the last 12 stimulus series. Although 582 nm was the reinforced stimulus, it also appeared as one of the unreinforced test stimuli. Responses to reinforced trials and to the first complete series each day are omitted from this analysis.

A LINC digital computer (4) controlled the experiment and recorded responses. One reinforcement was delivered, on the average, on each reinforced trial. A peck produced reinforcement only if it followed the preceding peck by an interval least frequently emitted by the pigeon. This schedule is designed to generate a moderate, stable rate of response (5). In two birds, performance over the 28 days was quite stable; the third bird showed a trend toward sharper stimulus control, and so its data were not fully analyzed.

We may consider the test stimuli as signals whose strength increases as their wavelength departs from the reinforced value of 582 nm. The response rate decreases as the bird becomes more certain that the stimulus is not 582 nm. A peck means that the stimulus does not differ from 582 nm. This is the reverse of the usual system, because *fewer* responses mean detection of a difference. To derive a point on the ROC curves for test stimuli, we reduce the bird's response rate on a given trial to a simple "yes" or "no"; by redefining "yes" and "no" many times, we get many points. For example, we may take ten or fewer pecks to mean "yes, the stimulus differs from 582 nm" and more than ten pecks to mean "no, the stimulus does not differ from 582 nm." We then compute the relative frequency of this "yes" response to 582 nm and to each test wavelength. These values are the abscissa and the ordinate, respectively, of a point on the ROC curve for each test wavelength. The changing of the definition of "yes" to 11 or fewer pecks provides another point on the curve (2).

Data from one bird appear in Fig. 1, A — C. Total response output was precisely controlled by stimulus wavelength (Fig. 1A). The curve is comparable to many wavelength generalization functions, but, because of the differential reinforcement, it is much sharper than curves from the usual transient extinction test (6). Data from the same bird are next plotted according to the rating procedure (Fig. 1B). The functions are well defined, as those derived from human ratings are, and they are somewhat asymmetric with respect to the coordinate axes. Figure 1C reproduces the ROC curves on coordinates scaled according to a normal probability transform; Fig. 1D shows comparable data for

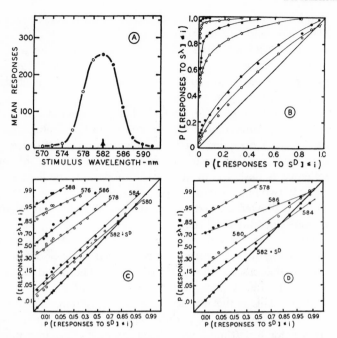

FIGURE 1   *Data from 28 sessions: (A), (B), and (C) results from one bird, (D) results from a second bird. (A) Generalization gradient around 582 nm, the reinforced wavelength (S^D); (B) ROC functions for the six stimuli nearest 582 nm; (C) same functions plotted on double probability coordinates. (D) Functions comparable to those in (C), but for a second bird. Axes in (B), (C), and (D) represent relative frequencies estimating the probability that a given number (i) of responses or fewer were made to the stimulus in question.*

the second bird with a stable performance. In theory, if the sensory events underlying the data have a Gaussian distribution, the ROC functions here should be straight lines. They are reasonably straight, but they reflect the asymmetry of Fig. 1B in failing to lie parallel to the diagonal. This failure indicates that the distributions along the two axes have unequal variance.

The form of this experiment is derived from animal studies in generalization; it is perhaps needlessly complex from the point of view of detection theory. For example, the test wavelengths are divided into two classes, one on each side of 582 nm. This probably yields two functionally discrete detection tasks, a conclusion supported by the somewhat different slopes of the ROC functions from the two sides (Fig. 1D). A second complexity is suggested by the common observation that generalization gradients sometimes come to a peak at one or the other side of the reinforced stimulus. One might say that the bird is uncertain not only that a test stimulus is 582 nm, but also that 582 nm is indeed the stimulus being reinforced. This additional uncertainty may account for the fact that the ROC functions for 584 and 580 nm are "too close" to the diagonal in Fig. 1. Signal detectability analysis is valuable for helping to make such aspects of the generalization experiment explicit, though further work is needed to clarify the situation. Evidently, the generalization gradient, like the usual psychometric function, confounds the subject's "criterion" with its "sensitivity." As in experiments with human subjects, detectability analysis may enable us to measure these factors independently.

REFERENCES AND NOTES

1. M. H. Hack, *Science* 139, 758 (1963); J. A. Nevin, *J. Exp. Anal. Behav.* 7, 169 (1964); M. Rilling and C. McDiarmid, *Science* 148, 526 (1965); C. M. Boneau and J. L. Cole, *Psych. Rev.* 74, 123 (1967).
2. D. M. Green and J. A. Swets, *Signal Detection Theory and Psychophysics* (Wiley, New York, 1966).
3. D. S. Blough, *J. Opt. Soc. Amer.* 47, 827 (1957).
4. W. A. Clark and C. E. Molnar, *Ann. N.Y. Acad Sci.* 115, 653 (1964).
5. D. S. Blough, *J. Exp. Anal. Behav.* 9, 581 (1966).
6. H. S. Terrace, in *Operant Behavior: Areas of Research and Application*, W. K. Honig, Ed. (Appleton-Century-Crofts, New York, 1966), chap. 7.
7. Supported in part by PHS grant MH-02456. I thank Mrs. P. Blough for her assistance.

4. MEASUREMENT OF SENSATION

A. Can the Magnitude of Sensation Be Measured?

As we have seen, Fechner sought to measure the magnitude of sensation. He was severely criticized for his efforts, both because his psychophysical law (the Weber-Fechner law) was inaccurate and because he sought to measure what some scientists thought to be unmeasurable. Not everyone disagreed with Fechner, and many of his critics disagreed with each other. The controversy that developed still remains unsettled. The selections in this section reveal some of the details of that controversy.

One of Fechner's critics was James McKeen Cattell, who, it may be remembered, rejected the notion that differential discrimination is discontinuous or steplike. He looked upon the so-called just noticeable difference as a measure of the variability of discrimination or as a "measure of the error of observation." His attitudes on discrimination led him to reject also the use of the just noticeable difference as a unit of sensation magnitude. In the final pages of "On Errors of Observation" he examined some other ways of measuring sensation and found all of them wanting; he concluded that psychophysics was not able to measure the intensity of sensation. Cattell consequently eschewed his interest in sensation and restricted his own psychophysical experiments to the capacity of observers to make correct responses to stimuli (e.g., to make accurate discriminations among stimuli and accurate judgments of the physical relations among stimulus-objects).

Cattell's position on the measurement of sensation was

much more conservative than the positions of two other critics of Fechner: William James and E. B. Titchener. James, in Psychology: Briefer Course, *and Titchener, in* Experimental Psychology, *both maintained that sensations do not possess magnitude and hence do not themselves admit to measurement. James and Titchener did not abandon sensation, but argued that each sensation is a unique and indivisible unit, different in kind from every other sensation. In place of the measurement of sensation magnitude they offered measurement of the difference or distance between sensations along hypothetical psychological continua.*

In "The Stimulus Error" E. G. Boring argued in favor of "mental measurement." He did not pass judgment on whether it is more valid to measure sense-distance or the magnitude of sensation, but he stood firmly against Cattell's "psychology of capacity." He warned that if the psychology of capacity did not make room for the variable of sensation it would find that it could not always obtain the unequivocal correlations between stimulus and response that it sought.

The points of view represented in the controversy over the measurement of sensation also manifested themselves in attitudes on what is and what is not an acceptable type of judgment. Few would deny that under most circumstances observers can make valid sensory judgments of "equal" or "unequal," "same" or "different," "greater than" or "less than." That is, few would deny that observers can make the judgments required by the classical psychophysical methods. Adherents to the psychology of capacity would accept such judgments only when they were made with respect to stimulus-objects, while other psychologists would accept them only when they were made with respect to sensations or sense-distances. Nevertheless, virtually everyone agreed that such judgments did not exceed the conceptual or perceptual abilities of the normal observer. There was much less agreement, however, whether observers can make valid judgments of interval or ratio relations among sensations or stimuli. Judgments of interval relations included "bisection" and "equisection," and judgments of ratio relations included "fractionation" and "doubling." Those who believed that observers should be required to judge stimulus-objects would allow interval or ratio judgments only when the observer was familiar with the physical scale customarily used to measure the stimulus; the observer might then be expected to produce judgments that were proportional to the objective relations among the stimuli. Those who believed in the measurement of sense-distance might allow judgments of the interval relations among sensations. Here, the observer was cautioned not to base his judgments on what he knew about the objective relations among the stimuli but instead to base them exclusively on his sensations.

It may not be necessary to require direct judgments of intervals between sensations in order to measure sense-distance. According to this view, a measure of sense-distance can also be derived from ordinal judgments, such as those obtained by the method of constant stimuli, if it is assumed that a just noticeable difference provides a unit of sense-distance. This assumption is analogous to Fechner's: a just noticeable difference constitutes a unit of sensation magnitude. Titchener preferred the former assumption, although he did believe that direct judgments (e.g., bisection) of the distance between sensations were possible.

Titchener's notion that sense-distances could be judged directly was not accepted unanimously even among those who believed the measurement of sense-distance to be legitimate. Some claimed that the task was generally too difficult for the observer. Similarly, among those who accepted the measurement of the magnitude of sensation some did not accept the validity of judgments of the interval or ration relations among sensations. Fechner fell into the latter group, as this comment shows: "The immediate judgment we can make in this context . . . is only one of more or less, or one of equality, not one of how many times, which true measurement demands and which it is our purpose to derive."[1] In spite of numerous objections, the procedures of direct judgment continued to be used. These procedures recommended themselves by their face validity and by the finding that observers typically executed

[1] G. Fechner, *Elemente der Psychophysik*, I, 1860. (See G. Fechner, *Elements of Psychophysics*, I, translated by H. E. Adler, and edited by D. H. Howes and E. G. Boring, 1966, p. 47.)

*the judgments without much difficulty. Moreover, they allow
the experimenter to avoid the assumption that the just noticeable difference is a realistic unit of either sense-distance or
sensation magnitude.*

*The question of whether or not sensation can be measured
turns out to be a difficult one. Boring pointed out that there is
evidence that observers can make judgments about their sensations and need not restrict their judgments to relations
among stimulus objects. History has shown, however, that
evidence on this matter is not strong enough to convince all.
Similarly, research into the nature of judgment has not established clearly whether there are limits on the capacity of observers to judge the relations among sensations. In the next
section we will see that the kind of judgment sought from an
observer can influence dramatically the results of an experiment. This finding complicates the picture further.*

SENSATIONS ARE NOT COMPOUNDS

William James

Sensations are not compounds. The fundamental objection to Fechner's whole attempt seems to be this, that although the outer *causes* of
our sensations may have many parts, every distinguishable degree, as
well as every distinguishable quality, of the *sensation itself* appears to
be a unique fact of consciousness. Each sensation is a complete integer.
"A strong one," as Dr. Münsterberg says, "is not the multiple of a weak
one, or a compound of many weak ones, but rather something entirely
new, and as it were incomparable, so that to seek a measurable difference between strong and weak sonorous, luminous, or thermic sensations would seem at first sight as senseless as to try to compute mathematically the difference between salt and sour, or between headache
and toothache. It is clear that if in the stronger sensation of light the

Reprinted with permission of Holt, Rinehart, and Winston, Inc. from *Psychology: Briefer
Course*, 1892, pages 23–24.

weaker sensation is not *contained*, it is unpsychological to say that the former differs from the latter by a certain *increment*."[1] Surely our feeling of scarlet is not a feeling of pink with a lot more pink added; it is something quite other than pink. Similarly with our sensation of an electric arc-light: it does not contain that of many smoky tallow candles in itself. Every sensation presents itself as an indivisible unit; and it is quite impossible to read any clear meaning into the notion that they are masses of units combined.

There is no inconsistency between this statement and the fact that, starting with a weak sensation and increasing it, we feel "more," "more," "more," as the increase goes on. It is not more of the same *stuff* added, so to speak; but it is more and more *difference*, more and more *distance*, from the starting-point, which we feel. In the chapter on Discrimination we shall see that Difference can be perceived between simple things. We shall see, too, that *differences themselves differ* — there are *various directions of difference;* and along any one of them a series of things may be arranged so as to increase steadily in that direction. In any such series the end differs more from the beginning than the middle does. Differences of "intensity" form one such direction of possible increase — so our judgments of more intensity can be expressed without the hypothesis that more units have been added to a growing sum.

INTRODUCTION: MENTAL MEASUREMENT

Edward Bradford Titchener

1. MEASUREMENT

Whenever we *measure*, in any department of natural science, we compare a given magnitude with some conventional unit of the same kind, and determine how many times the unit is contained in the magnitude.

[1] *Beiträge zur exp. Psychol.*, Heft 3, p. 4.

Reprinted with permission of the Macmillan Company from *Experimental Psychology: A Manual of Laboratory Practice*, Vol. II, Quantitative, Part 1, Student's Manual, 1905, pages xix–xxxvii.

Let P be the magnitude to be measured, and p the unit in terms of which it is to be expressed. The result of our measurement of P is the discovery of the numerical ratio existing between P and p. We state this result always in terms of an equation: $P = (x/y)p$. The object of measurement, then, is the giving of such values to x and y that the equation may be true.

When we say, *e.g.*, that Mt. Vesuvius is 4200 ft. high, we mean that the given linear magnitude P, the distance from sea level to the topmost point of the volcano, contains the conventional unit of linear measurement, 1 ft., four thousand two hundred times: $P = {}^{4200}\!/_{1}\, p$ When we say that an operation lasted 40 minutes, we mean that the given temporal magnitude, the time occupied by the operation, contained the conventional time unit, 1 min., forty times: $P = {}^{40}\!/_{1}\; p$. When we say that an express package weighs three quarters of a pound, we mean that the package, laid in the scale pan, just balances the sliding weight when this is placed at the twelfth short stroke beyond the first long stroke or zero point of the bar, — the distance between any two long strokes giving the conventional unit 1 lb., and the distance between any two short strokes the conventional sub-unit 1 oz. $= \frac{1}{16}$ lb.: so that $P = \frac{3}{4}\, p$ in terms of lb., or $P = {}^{12}\!/_{1}\, p$ in terms of oz. In the same way, we might say that the height of Mt. Vesuvius is ${}^{4200}\!/_{5280}$ mile; or that the time of the operation is ${}^{40}\!/_{60}$ hr.

These instances show — what must always be borne in mind — that the unit of measurement is conventional. Its choice is simply a matter of practical convenience. Scientific men are now generally agreed that the unit of space shall be the 1 cm., the unit of time the 1 sec., and the unit of mass the 1 gr.; so that the unit of mechanical energy is the amount contained in a body of 1 gr. moving through 1 cm. in 1 sec. There is, however, nothing absolute and nothing sacrosanct about these units. Our measurements would be every bit as valid, just as much true measurements, if we took as units the pace or span or cubit, the average time of a step in walking or of a respiratory movement, the ounce or pound. The metric system makes calculation easy, relates the three fundamental quantities in a very simple manner: but that is its sole, as it is its sufficient claim to acceptance.

The prototype of all measurement is linear measurement in space. We can literally superpose one portion of space upon another, for purposes of measurement: we can hold the compared portions together for as long a time as we like; we can shift the one portion to and fro upon the other. The linear space unit is thus the most easily manipulated of all units of measurement. Hence there is a tendency, in natural science, to reduce all quantitative comparisons to the comparison of spatial magnitudes. We compare masses, with the metric balance, by noting the deflections of the pointer. We measure the intensity of an electric current by noting the deflections of the galvanometer needle. We measure rise and fall of temperature by the rise and fall of mercury in the thermometer. We determine the period of a tuning fork by the graphic method. It is, moreover, with spatial measurements that we are chiefly concerned in everyday life. We are all, to some extent, practised in the estimation of space magnitudes, however helpless we may be when called upon to grade weights or to estimate brightnesses.

Finally, it is to be noticed that every measurement implies three terms, expressed or understood. In measuring the height of Mt. Vesuvius we had the zero point, or sea level; the highest point of the mountain; and the point lying 1 ft. above sea level or 1 ft. below the highest point. In measuring the time of the operation, we had the beginning and end of the period occupied by it, and the time point lying 1 min. (or 1 hr.) distant from the beginning. In weighing our package, we had the zero point upon the scale bar; the limiting point at which the sliding weight was just counterbalanced; and the mark that lay 1 oz. (or 1 lb.) from the zero point. There are various devices — the introduction of submultiples of the unit, the use of the vernier — for increasing the accuracy of measurement; there are other devices for standardising the conditions (temperature, stress) under which a measurement is made; there are mathematical rules for calculating the "probable error" of a given measurement. These are all refinements of the art of measuring. The essential thing is that we have our three terms: the limiting points of the magnitude to be measured, and a point lying at unit distance from the one or the other limiting point.

The third term, without which measurement is impossible, need not, however, be expressed. Suppose that two black strokes are made upon a sheet of paper, and that you are asked to say how far the one is above the other, or to the right of the other. You reply, without difficulty, "Two inches" or "Five centimetres." But that means that you have mentally introduced a third term: the unit mark, inch or cm., with which you have become familiar in previous measurements. Without this, you could only have said: "The one mark is above the other" or "to the right of the other"; you could not have answered the question "how far." How long is a given stretch of level road? Two hundred and fifty yards? A quarter of a mile? Most people have no mental unit for such a measurement. Either they say "It looks about as long as from so-and-so to so-and-so," — comparing it with a familiar distance; or they make a rough determination by pacing the distance itself. How deep is this well? Very few people can say, even if they can see the water. So a stone is dropped in, and the seconds are counted until the splash is heard. The pace or the familiar distance gives a third term for the measurement of the road; and we know that the distance traversed by the stone in falling is the product of the distance traversed in the first second (about 490 cm. — our third term) into the square of the time. Where there is no such third term, there is no measurement. This rule is universal.

2. MENTAL MEASUREMENT

There can be no question but that, in some way or other, mental processes are measurable. It would be strange, indeed, if the processes of the physical universe, which we know only by means of our sense organs or of instruments which refine upon our sense organs, should be capable of measurement, while the sensations of mental science were not: if all measurement in the physical sciences should tend towards spatial, *i.e.*, visual measurement, while yet the visual sensations themselves were unmeasurable. That apart, however, we have only to appeal to introspection to see that our mental processes furnish the raw material of measurement. Sensations differ more or less in quality: a given tone lies higher in the scale than another, a given green is more yellow than another. They differ in intensity: a noise may be louder than another noise, a brightness stronger than another brightness. They differ in duration: the taste of bitter lasts longer than the taste of sweet, the visual after-image lasts longer than the auditory. They differ in extent: one red is larger, one pressure spread more widely than another. These differences are given with the sensations; they obtain whether or not we know anything of the stimuli which arouse the sensations; we have evidence, in the history of science, that they were remarked and utilised long before the stimuli were known or measured. But if we have differences of more and less, it is only necessary to establish the unit, the third term, in order to convert difference into measured difference.

This establishment of the unit is, however, no small matter. We have said that the units of physical measurement are conventional. On the other hand, the units of modern physics are accurate, objective, universal. It is a far cry to these units — the cm., the sec., the gr. — from such things as the day's journey, the barley-corn, the chaldron. The difficulty of choosing the unit, and of standardising it when chosen, is much greater than might at first thought be supposed, and can be fully appreciated only by one who has followed historically, step by step, the development of scientific theory and practice. What holds in this regard of physics holds also of psychology. Moreover, the psychologist is at a peculiar disadvantage, in that there is no natural unit of mental measurement. The human body affords the natural units of linear measurement: foot, pace, cubit, span. The height of the sun in the heavens, the alternation of day and night, the changes of the moon — these are all natural units of time measurement. Units of weight are furnished by convenient natural objects (grain, stone) or by the average carrying power of man or animal (pack, load). There are no such obvious points of reference in psychology. Once more: physics is able to relate and combine its units, to reduce one to another, to express one in terms of another; so that the formula for mechanical work, *e.g.*, has the form

$$\frac{M \cdot L^2}{T^2},$$

where M represents mass measured in gr., L length of path measured in cm., and T time measured in sec. This sort of interrelation is forbidden by the very nature of mental processes, every group of which is qualitatively dissimilar to every other group. Hence there can be no single unit of mental measurement, no generalisation of the units employed in special investigations.

Here, then, are difficulties in plenty. And there can be no question but that these, the intrinsic difficulties, are largely responsible for the tardy advent of measurement in psychology, and for the doubts and controversies and confusions that have arisen since the methods of psychological measurement were formulated. The formulation itself dates only from 1860, when Gustav Theodor Fechner (1801–1887), gathering together scattered observations from physics and astronomy and biology, summing up elaborate investigations of his own, putting his physical, mathematical and psychological knowledge at the service of mental measurement, published his *Elemente der Psychophysik*. Fechner is the founder, we might almost say the creator, of quantitative psychology, and the modern student who will understand the principles and methods of mental measurement must still go to school with Fechner.

There are, however, other and extrinsic reasons for the late development of a quantitative psychology. If we are to have a satisfactory system of mental measurements, we must (as will appear later) rely largely upon the results of physical and physiological research; and, while physics has been securely established for some centuries, modern physiology may be said to date from the second quarter of the nineteenth century. Moreover, there is a sharp line of division in popular thought — a line drawn for the modern world by Descartes — between the natural and the mental sciences; the former seem to be quantitative and measurable, the latter qualitative and unmeasurable. This "common sense" point of view has all the weight and inertia of a settled tradition. Nay more: at the beginning of the nineteenth century it had received strong reinforcement from the philosophical side. Immanuel Kant (1724–1804) — not a mediæval philosopher, but the author of the *Critique of Pure Reason* and one of the most influential thinkers of modern times — declared roundly in 1786, and found no reason later to change his opinion, that psychology could never attain the rank of a true science. Something was done towards breaking up this dogma by the psychological work of Johann Friedrich Herbart (1776–1841). Herbart is, however, as weak in fact as he is strong in theory. So that, simple as the idea of mental measurement appears to us, who come after Fechner, we need not read far in the psychological literature of the early nineteenth century to realise how difficult it was, before Fechner, even seriously to entertain the idea, to dwell upon it as practicable, as anything more than a bit of daring speculation. The path of scientific progress is littered with brilliant suggestions: it is so easy to suggest, and so hard to grasp the suggestion, to work it out, to invent the methods for turning it into fact! Fechner not only had the idea, the inspiration of mental measurement, but he spent ten laborious years on its actual accomplishment.

There is one mistake, so natural that we might almost call it inevitable, which has sorely delayed the advance of quantitative psychology. It is a mistake with regard to the object of measurement, the mental magnitude. We have seen that every measurement requires three given terms; so that the physical quantity or magnitude is not, so to say, a single term, but rather a distance between terms, a section of some stimulus scale. We are apt to say, carelessly, that we have measured "the highest point" of Mt. Vesuvius, when we have in reality measured, in terms of our arbitrary unit, the distance between its lowest and highest points. It is not the point that is the magnitude, but the distance between points. So with sensations: we are apt to think of a brightness or a tone of given intensity as a sensation magnitude, as itself measurable. Now the stimulus is measurable: we can measure, in terms of some unit, the amplitude of vibration of the ether or air waves: we have our three terms to measure with. But the sensation, the brightness or the tone, is just a single point upon the sense scale, — no more measurable, of itself, than is "the highest point" of Mt. Vesuvius. The only thing that we can measure is the distance between two sensations or sense points, and to do this we must have our unit step or unit distance.

Let us take some instances. Suppose that two rooms of equal dimensions are illuminated by two ground glass globes, the one containing five and the other two incandescent lights of the same candle-power. We can say, by eye, that the illumination of the first room is greater than that of the second. How much greater, we cannot possibly say. Even if the globes are removed, so that we can count the lights, we cannot say. The stimuli stand to one another in the ratio 5 : 2. But the corresponding sensations are simply different as more and less, the one a "more bright" and the other a "less bright." The brightness of the lighter room does not contain within it so and so many of the brightnesses of the darker room. Each brightness is one and indivisible. What we have given is rather this: that on the scale of brightness intensities, which extends from the just noticeable shimmer of light to the most dazzling brilliance that the eye can bear, the illumination of the one room lies higher, that of the other room lower. There is a certain distance between them. If we can establish a sense unit for this distance, we shall be able to say that the greater brightness is, in sensation, so and so many times removed from the lesser brightness; just precisely as the top of the mountain, in terms of the 1 ft. unit, is 4200 times removed from the bottom. Neither of the two brightness sensations is itself a magnitude. The magnitude is the distance which separates them on the intensive brightness scale.

Again: we can say by ear that the roar of a cannon is louder, very much louder, than the crack of a pistol. But the cannon roar, as heard, is not a multiple of the pistol crack, does not contain so and so many pistol cracks within it. What we have given is that, on the scale of noise intensities ranging from the least audible stir to the loudest possible crash, the cannon roar lies very high, the pistol crack a good deal lower. Neither noise, in itself, is a magnitude; both alike are points, positions, upon an intensive scale. The magnitude is the distance between them. With a sense unit of noise distance established, we can measure this given distance, as before.

It was said above that the mistaking of the single sensation for a magnitude is so natural as to be almost inevitable. We are constantly confusing sensations with their stimuli, with their objects, with their meanings. Or rather — since the sensation of psychology has no object or meaning — we are constantly confusing logical abstraction with psychological analysis; we abstract a certain aspect of an object or meaning, and then treat this aspect as if it were a simple mental process, an element in the mental representation of the object or meaning. What is meant will become clear at once, if we take a few instances. We do not say, in ordinary conversation, that this visual sensation is lighter than that, but that this pair of gloves or this kind of grey note-paper is lighter than this other. We do not say that this complex of cutaneous and organic sensations is more intensive than that, but that this box or package is heavier than this other. We do not even say, as a rule, that this tonal quality is lower than that, but rather that this instrument is flat and must be tuned up to this other. Always in what we say there is a reference to the objects, to the meaning of the conscious complex. It is not grey, pressure, tone, that we are thinking of; but the grey of leather or paper, the pressure of the box, the pitch of the violin. Now the stimuli, the physical processes, are magnitudes or quantities. What is more natural, then, than to say that the corresponding grey or pressure or tone is also a magnitude or a quantity? What is more natural than to read the character of the stimuli, of the objects, into the "sensations" with which certain aspects of stimulus or object are correlated? At any rate, this is what Fechner did. Fechner had an inkling of the truth; he knew that sense-distances are magnitudes, and every now and then he seems to look upon the single sensation as merely the limiting point of a distance, *i.e.*, as a position upon some sense scale. But his teaching is that the sensation as such is a magnitude. "In general," he says, "our measure of sensation amounts to this: that we divide every sensation into equal parts, *i.e.*, into the equal increments out of which it is built up from the zero point of its existence, and that we regard the number of these equal parts as determined by the number of the corresponding . . . increments of stimulus . . . just as if the increments of stimulus were the inches upon a yard-stick." This is wrong. No sensation is a sum of sensation-parts or of sense-increments; no sensation is a measurable magnitude. Fechner has transferred to sensation a point of view that is right for stimulus, but that introspection refuses to recognise in psychology.

3. AN ANALOGY

The passage which we have just quoted from Fechner reads in full as follows: "Our measure of sensation amounts to this: that we divide every sensation into equal parts, *i.e.*, into the equal increments out of which it is built up from the zero point of its existence, and that we regard the number of these equal parts as determined by the number of the corresponding variable increments of stimulus which are able to arouse the equal increments of sensation, just as if the increments of stimulus were the inches upon a yard-stick." Notice that Fechner speaks of the *variable* increments of stimulus which arouse the *equal* increments of sensation. This means, in our own terminology, that equal sense-distances do not correspond always to equal stimulus magnitudes: to obtain equal sense-distances, under different conditions, we must vary the magnitude of the corresponding stimuli. The fact is important: it is also obvious. Go into a small darkened room, and light a candle. There is an immense difference in the illumination of the room. The physical magnitude, the photometric value of the candle, corresponds to a very wide distance upon the scale of subjective brightness intensities. Light a second candle. There is a difference in the illumination, and a marked difference; but it is nothing like so marked as the first difference. The same physical magnitude, then, corresponds now to a lesser sense-distance. Light a third candle, and a fourth, and a fifth. A point will soon come at which the introduction of another candle makes hardly any appreciable difference in the illumination. The same physical magnitude now corresponds to a minimal sense-distance.

Facts of this sort recur in all departments of sense, and it is part of the business of quantitative psychology to take account of them, and to sum them up in a numerical formula. What precisely the programme of quantitative psychology is in this field, what the facts are with which it has to deal, and how these facts are to be grouped under laws, we shall best understand by help of an analogy from physics. The analogy was first suggested by J. R. L. Delbœuf (1831–1896), late professor in the University of Liège, — a psychologist of great originality, to whom we owe the conception of mental measurement set forth in § 2,[1] — and has been worked out in detail by H. Ebbinghaus (b. 1850), professor

---

[1] *Revue philosophique*, v., 1878, 53; *Examen critique de la loi psychophysique, sa base et sa signification*, 1883, 104 f.

in the University of Breslau and editor of the *Zeitschrift für Psycho-logie und Physiologie der Sinnesorgane*.[2]

If a magnetic needle be suspended at the centre of a circular coil of wire, and an electric current be sent through the wire, the needle is deflected from its position of rest. Suppose that we are seeking to dis-cover the law of this deflection, to find a general expression for the movement of the needle under the influence of currents of different strength. We send a current of so and so many amperes through the coil, and measure the angle of deflection upon a circular scale; then we send through a current of so and so many more amperes, and measure again; and so on. We find that the needle moves farther and farther, as the current is made stronger and stronger. But we find also that the angle of deflection is not simply proportional to the strength of current. If we increase the strength of current by equal amounts, the deflection of the needle becomes progressively smaller and smaller. And however strong we make our current, the needle will never make an excursion of 90°. The mathematical expression of the relation is very simple. If a is the number of amperes in the current, k a constant, and θ the angle of deflection, then $a = k \tan. \theta$.

Let us now, instead of taking determinate strengths of current, change the strength of the current continuously, and let us watch the behaviour of the needle. We find the same law in operation; but it is crossed by a second law. If the needle is hanging steady, whether at the zero point of its scale or at any other point at which it is held by the current in the coil, and we increase the current very slowly, we get at first no movement at all. During this period, while the needle remains stationary, our law of correlation is, apparently, not fulfilled; and the greater the increase of the current before movement sets in, the greater, of course, is the apparent deviation from the law. Presently, however, when the current has been increased by a certain amount, the needle goes with a little jump to the position which the law of cor-relation requires. And as we continue slowly to increase the strength of the current, the phenomenon is repeated, until the limit of the needle's excursion is reached. The law of correlation is not really in abeyance; it is crossed or masked by another law.

We have, then, two things before us. On the one hand, the needle is a magnetic needle, and the amount of its deflection is a continuous function of the current in the coil. On the other hand, the needle does

not move without friction; so that we obtain, under the conditions of
our second experiment, not a continuous movement of the needle, but
a discrete movement, a series of jerks. It is one and the same needle
that moves, and one and the same movement that it makes; but the
single needle is at once mechanical and magnetic, and the single movement gives evidence of the operation of two distinct laws.

4. THREE PROBLEMS OF QUANTITATIVE PSYCHOLOGY

We cannot argue from the behaviour of a magnetic needle to the behaviour of our sensations. Nevertheless, the analogy serves to give us
our bearings in the matter of sense measurement. We will take, first,
the facts of sensation that correspond to the phenomena of friction in
the needle.

1. The perfect sensation has four attributes: intensity, quality, duration, extent. Every one of these attributes of sensation is correlated
with some property of stimulus. Not every value of stimulus, however,
is capable of arousing the corresponding sensation. Just as the current
must be increased by a certain amount, whether from zero or from
some positive magnitude, to produce a deflection of the stationary
needle, so must the stimulus in every case reach a certain magnitude,
if it is to set up a sensation.

Take intensity. Some lights are too faint to be seen; there are stars,
e.g., that even on the darkest night remain invisible to the naked eye.
Some sounds are too faint to be heard; we may be sure, from his ges-
tures, that our friend is shouting to us, but we are too far off to hear his
voice. Some pressures are too weak to be sensed; we have no knowledge of the flake of cigar ash that falls upon our hand. Some tastes are
too weak to be sensed; a draught of water which proves, on chemical
analysis, to hold various salts in solution, may yet be entirely tasteless.
Some smells are too weak to be sensed; we get no sensation from an
exposure of 1 mm. of black rubber tubing on the olfactometer. One of
the things that we have to do, then, is to determine the least intensity
of stimulus, in the different sense departments, that will arouse a noticeable sensation. What is the faintest light that we can see? The least
sound that we can hear? The lightest weight that we can feel? And so
on.

Again: some differences of stimulus intensity are too small to be remarked. If a few lights go out in a brilliantly lighted ballroom, the illu-

mination is not sensibly diminished. If an orchestra is playing, and a belated second violin suddenly joins his fellows, the volume of sound is not sensibly increased. If we lift, blindfold, two glasses of water, from one of which a teaspoonful has been taken, we cannot say which is the heavier. If we put five lumps of sugar into our coffee, we shall hardly make it sweeter by adding a sixth. If we have spilled a bottle of eau de Cologne on the carpet, we shall not notice the little that our guest has poured on her handkerchief. Another thing to do, therefore, is to determine the least increase or decrease of stimulus intensity, in the different sense departments, that will make a noticeable change in the intensity of a given sensation, that will shift it a minimal distance up or down upon the intensive scale.

The same thing holds of quality. There is a lower limit to the tonal scale and to the band of spectral colours; the air waves and ether waves must reach a certain frequency of vibration before they set up the lowest audible tone and most extreme spectral red. Moreover, although we can distinguish several tones within the musical semitone, and many more than Newton's seven colours in the spectrum, still, not every change of vibration frequency produces a change of sense quality. We cannot distinguish an a^1 of 440 vs. from one of 440.1 vs.; we cannot distinguish a blue of 465mμ from one of 464.5mμ.

The same thing holds of duration. If a strip of spectral green be exposed, under certain experimental conditions, for a very short time, it is seen merely as a grey. If the time of exposure be made a little longer, it is seen as bluish grey. If the time be still further increased, the bluish grey becomes a distinct blue. Finally, with still greater increase, the green is seen as green. Similarly, if the a^1 be sounded for only ¼₄₀ sec., so that a single v. reaches the ear, we hear not a tone but merely a noise. As the duration of stimulus is increased, the tonal quality becomes clear. If pairs of clicks are sounded, in rapid succession, a practised observer can distinguish a pair separated by 0.3 sec. from a pair separated by 0.303 sec. But the same observer cannot distinguish a separation of 0.3 sec. from a separation of, say, 0.301 sec.

Finally, the same thing holds of extent. Two stars, whose apparent distance is less than 30″, are always seen as a single star. Cut a square of blue paper, with sides of 1 mm., and paste it on a white card. Walk backwards from the card: at a distance of about 3 m. the colour of the blue disappears. At certain parts of the skin, pressures of quite considerable area are sensed as mere points. Again: a strip of red, 10 cm. long, cannot be distinguished from a similar strip, 10.05 cm. long, laid in the same straight line with it. In pressure experiments at certain regions of the skin it is necessary to increase the diameter of the stimulus from 2 to 25 mm., in order to obtain a noticeable difference of extent.

2. Further: our magnetic needle will never make an excursion of 90°, whatever the intensity of current that we employ. In the same way, the sense organs refuse to mediate sensation when the stimulus has passed a certain maximal value. We cannot hear "tones" of 100,000 vs. in the 1 sec.; we cannot see "colours" beyond the extremest violet of the spectrum. Noises of maximal intensity stun or deafen us. If a tone or pressure is continued beyond a certain time limit, we cease to hear and feel; the organ gives out, becomes fatigued and exhausted. If visual stimuli are presented at certain distances from the fovea, they are not seen; the extent of the field of vision is limited. Here, then, is a second principal problem: the determination of the highest value of stimulus that is still effective for sensation.

3. Thirdly, we will take the facts of sensation that correspond to the law of angular deflection in the tangent galvanometer. Sensation, under all its four aspects, is a continuous function of stimulus. True, a continuous gradation of stimulus will, under certain conditions, give us a discrete sense scale. But that is simply because the nervous structures involved offer resistance to the incoming disturbance, and so produce the phenomena of "friction." What, now — apart from friction — is the law of correlation of stimulus and sensation?

Let us pause, for a moment, before we try to answer this question, and look back upon the path that we have already travelled. It should be clear that we have not as yet entered upon our proper task of mental measurement. We have talked of measuring the stimulus that can just arouse a sensation; the stimulus that can just evoke a change in sensation, *i.e.*, that corresponds to a minimal sense-distance; and the stimulus that can still just arouse a sensation. All the measurements so far discussed, therefore, are physical, not psychological. Our present problem requires us to measure sensation.

Measurement demands three terms. Suppose, then, that a sense-distance is given: say, a distance of sound intensity. We have two sharply defined noises, of markedly different intensity, chosen from the middle portion of the intensive scale: we are to apply measurement to this noise distance, we are quantitatively to estimate it. How shall we begin? Well, we can measure it, in terms of an arbitrary unit, simply by halving it. We can ask, and seek methodically to answer the question: What noise intensity lies midway, for sensation, between the two given noises? In other words: At what point, upon the intensive noise scale, is the given noise distance divided into two sensibly equal noise distances? Having determined this point, the middle noise intensity — which we can do with practice, by help of one of the metric methods — we may go on to ask: What point upon the scale lies as far above the upper point of our given distance as this lies above the middle point that we have just determined? And again: What point lies as far below the lower point of the given distance as this lies below the middle point? These two new points established, we can say that the whole noise distance which we have so far explored is the fourfold of our arbitrary unit, the half of the original distance. The procedure can then be continued above and below, until a wide range of noise intensities has been measured; *i.e.*, until a considerable section of the intensive scale has been marked off in equal sense divisions.

A diagram will simplify matters. Let the horizontal line in Fig. 1 represent the continuous scale of sensation intensity in the sphere of noise. We have given the two noises, the two sense points, m and o. Our first task is to determine the noise n that lies midway, for sensation, between m and o. That done, we can take the distance no as given, and increase the intensity of o till we reach a point p such that $no = op$. Again, we can take mn as given, and decrease m till we reach a point l, such that $lm = mn$. The sense-distance lp is then four times the sense unit $lm = mn = no = op$. And we can evidently go on to determine $q, r, \ldots$ and $k, j, \ldots$ in the same manner.

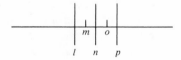

FIGURE 1

All that we now have to do, in order to formulate our law of correlation, is to write the corresponding stimulus values by the side of the unit sense-distances. We have already seen that equal stimulus magnitudes do not correspond to equal sense-distances, *i.e.*, that the law of correlation does not take the form of a simple proportionality of the two. We shall now discover what other and less simple relation obtains.

The correlation has been worked out with some degree of fullness for brightnesses, partially for noises, and a formula has been found which satisfies the results in both cases. Where, however, the stimuli must be presented to the observer successively (sounds, lifted weights, temperatures, smells, etc.) the procedure is, naturally, much more difficult and uncertain than it is where they can be presented simultaneously (brightnesses). By the time that the third stimulus comes, the observer may have "forgotten" the distance that separated the second from the first; or the presenting of the second distance may itself drive the first distance out of clear consciousness. Hence we are led to look round for another method. Besides, there is the question of the unit. It is not satisfactory to start out with an arbitrary sense-distance, and take the half of it as our provisional unit. It would be far better if we could find a definite unit, to be employed by all investigators alike. Is there another method of working, and can we discover such an unit?

Suppose that a brightness or a noise is given, and that we seek to determine the just noticeably brighter brightness, or the just noticeably louder noise. The experiment is identical with one of our "friction" experiments; and its result is the ascertainment of a just noticeable sense-distance. Let us perform it at various points of the sense scale, so that we get the stimulus values corresponding to the distances ll', $l'l''$, . . . mm', $m'm''$, . . . nn', $n'n''$, . . . etc. Now these are all least distances, minima of sensible distance. Are they not, then, equal distances? And, if they are equal, may we not take them as the units of sense measurement?

That least steps, at various parts of the sense scale, should also be equal steps is by no means self-evident. A given difference between sensations might be the least perceptible difference, and yet, when compared with another least perceptible difference from another part of the scale, might be larger or smaller than this other. The equality of just noticeable differences must, then, be proved: it cannot be assumed. The appeal lies, directly, to introspection; indirectly, to the results of experiment. Fechner asserted, on the basis of his own introspections, that all just noticeable differences of sensation are sensibly equal. The statement is made positively, and Fechner was an exceedingly careful and eminently practised experimenter. Still, this evidence needs to be supplemented: judgments of just noticeable difference are far from easy, and one might deceive oneself in the matter. Further evidence is, however, forthcoming. The course of stimulus, over against the least distances of noise and brightness, is precisely the same — is summed up in the same formula — as it is over against the larger sense-distances with which we have been dealing. Moreover, the formula which connects stimulus magnitude with least sense steps has the same form in other sense departments (pressure, lifted weights, tone, smell) that it has in the cases of noise and brightness. We can hardly doubt then, that the proposition "All just noticeable differences of sensation are equal sense-distances" is correct. And so we have our new method and our common unit of sense measurement.

We have our unit of measurement, that is to say, for intensity of sensation: for, so far, we have been speaking only of intensity. Does the same thing hold of quality, duration and extent that holds of intensity?

No: matters are more complicated. In the case of tonal pitch, e.g., it seems that one and the same formula would naturally (in bare sensation) cover both just noticeable differences and the halves of larger tonal sections or distances. Only, when we are asked to bisect a tonal distance, we are not in the domain of bare sensation; we fall under the influence of musical training and tradition, and the results of our experiments are thus obscured. Æsthetics has cut across psychology. Again: when we are determining the jnd of visual extent, we get one formula for the correlation of stimulus and sensation; when we are comparing visual extents as wholes, we get another and a different formula. There is good reason for this result: the conditions of judgment are very different in the two cases. Here it is psychology that cuts across psychology; the one set of experiments brings out one law, the other set brings out another. The same thing seems to be true of durations; though in this case the conditions of judgment are still more complicated, and experiments have not been made in sufficient number to allow of any general formulation. The facts will come out later, as we perform the experiments. What is important to remember now is that quantitative psychology sets us certain definite problems of mental measurement, and that we are able in theory to solve all these problems — even if they have not yet been all solved in fact — by help of our metric methods and our unit of sense-distance.

There is one point in the above discussion which may have puzzled the reader. We made a sharp distinction between the phenomena of friction (the needle as mechanical) and the phenomena of correlation (the needle as magnetic). Yet, in determining our unit of mental measurement, i.e., our unit of correlation, we have had recourse to one of the friction experiments. There is, however, no real confusion. The fact that the needle remains stationary for a little while, as the strength of current is slowly and continuously increased, is a fact of friction; but when the needle moves, it moves in obedience to the law of correlation, it moves as a magnetic needle. In psychology, we use the fact of friction as a means to our end, which is correlation; we do not use it for its own sake. Suppose that we gave a quickly changing continuous stimulus, like the tone of a siren-whistle, which rises from bass to treble: we should get a corresponding continuous change in sensation; we should hear what we call, loosely, a "rising tone." How could this continuously changing sense-continuum help us towards mental measurement? How could it give us a correlation of stimulus with single sensation quality? How could it give us the unit sense-distance? To measure, we must have a discrete series of sensations, in which each term is equidistant from its neighbours before and after. We obtain this series by increasing our stimulus very slowly, so that sensation follows it, not continuously, but in little jerks. We owe the jerkiness of sensation to the fact of friction; but the space moved over at every jerk corresponds to a just noticeable sense-distance, *i.e.*, if our reasoning is correct, to a sensation unit.

That there are gaps and discrepancies, even in this first part of the programme of quantitative psychology, ought not to be surprising. Think of colours and tones. The stimulus magnitudes progress uniformly from less to greater in both sense departments. But tones form one single series, while the colours correlated with homogeneous light form no less than four (three complete, and one incomplete) series.[3] Think, again, of the difference between a duration, say, of 0.5 sec., which we can take in as a whole, as "a" duration, and a duration of 5 min., which we can estimate only by means of the number and variety of the ideas and perceptions which "fill" it. Here are differences on the objective side. On the subjective, remember that a science does not advance according to a prearranged logical plan, but unevenly, as the interests of individual workers or the claims of practical utility dictate. Fechner was chiefly interested in the intensive aspect of mental processes, and among mental processes in sensation. His example has led other enquirers to give a disproportionate amount of attention to the laws of sensation intensity. It was a practical question, again, the question of the "personal equation" in astronomical observations, that

[3] See vol. i., S. M., 3, 31; I. M., 7 f. 55.

put reaction times in the forefront of experimental psychology. Further, at the inception of a science, problems will be wrongly — or, at any rate, inadequately — formulated. Hence much of the work done, *e.g.*, upon what were formerly called the "space sense" and the "time sense" is not available for our present purposes. It is concerned rather with perception than with the sensation attributes of duration and extent. All these factors, objective and subjective, combine to make quantitative psychology a ragged group of facts and methods rather than a well-rounded system. The rounding will come with time. . . .

ON ERRORS OF OBSERVATION

James McKeen Cattell

. . . I wish to notice the relation between the error of observation and the estimation of mental intensity. It has commonly been assumed that the variable error and the probable error (or h in Germany) are proportional to the just noticeable difference. The just noticeable difference has further been used to measure the intensity of sensation. The just noticeable difference is thus used ambiguously, on the one hand as a difference equally likely to be correctly perceived, on the other hand as a difference accompanied by an apparently equal increment in sensation. I entirely question the application of the error of observation to the measurement of the intensity of sensation. Supposing the intensity of sensation to be measurable, it may increase as the stimulus or (conceivably) as the logarithm of the stimulus, while the error of observation may be any other function of the stimulus.[1] When it is evident that the error of observation may be increased or decreased in many ways without greatly altering the apparent intensity of sensation, I cannot understand how it has come to be used as a unit suitable for measuring the intensity of sensation. The error of observa-

From *American Journal of Psychology*, 1893, 5, 285–293. Pages 292–293 reprinted with permission of the University of Illinois Press.

[1] This was noticed by G. E. Müller in 1879 (*Zur Grundlegung der Psychophysik*, p. 79–80).

tion is a physical quantity, a function of the intensity, area, duration, etc., of the stimulus, of the condition of the nervous system, and of the faculties, training, attention, etc., of the observer. That it should increase with the magnitude of the stimulus, and tend to increase as the square root of the magnitude, seems to me a natural consequence of the summation of errors. But I see no necessary connection between the supposed fact that the error of observation increases in direct proportion to the stimulus and the consequence which has been drawn from it that the intensity of sensation increases as the logarithm of the stimulus.

The measurement of the intensity of sensation is not out of the question because the error of observation cannot be used as a unit. The attempt is made to accomplish this when for different intensities sensations are adjusted midway between two others, when they are made apparently half or double others, or, lastly, when they are made just greater or less than others in the sense that the difference in sensation is apparently equal. The question here is whether we do in fact judge differences in the intensity of sensations, or whether we merely judge differences in the stimuli determined by association with their known objective relations. I am inclined to think that the latter is the case. I find it comparatively easy to adjust one time, length of line or weight midway between two others, much more difficult to judge when one light or sound is midway between two others, and almost impossible to judge one temperature or pain midway between two others. The difficulty of making a decision increases as the objective relations are less familiar, and I believe that my adjustment is always determined by association with the known quantitive relations of the physical world. With lights and sounds, association might lead us to consider relative differences as equal differences, and the data would be obtained from which the logarithmic relation between stimulus and sensation has been deduced. With the force, extent and time of movement, Prof. Fullerton and the writer have shown that our estimates tend to follow the objective relations. But, in any case, if we merely judge the relations of objective magnitudes by association, we have no basis whatever for determining a relation between physical energy and mental intensity.

I conclude, consequently, that we cannot measure the intensity of sensation and its relation to the energy of the stimulus either by determining the error of observation or by estimating amounts of difference. The most natural assumption would seem to be that the intensity of sensation increases directly as the energy of the brain changes correlated with it. The relation between the energy of the brain changes and the physical stimulus is a physiological question. This conclusion does not mean, however, that psycho-physical research is valueless. On the contrary it is an important contribution to the science of psychology, whence its application will be extended to physical science, to art, to medicine, to pedagogy and in other directions.

THE STIMULUS-ERROR

Edwin G. Boring

The purpose of this paper is to discuss the "stimulus-error," to indicate something of its history (though limits of space will preclude more than a bare outline), to add something by way of definition (since definition has remained implicit and there are some who do not understand this term), to enquire, at the level of the scientific experiment, into the significance of the attitude which is thus styled an "error" (relying as much upon experimental observation and as little upon epistemological conviction as is possible), and to arrive, if may be, at an evaluation of the stimulus-error or stimulus-attitude in its relation to the psychology of the present day. This is not so large an order that it does not need filling. Some psychologists put out of court experiments that involve the stimulus-error; others refuse to see any "error" at all and discount the works that stress this "merely epistemological" distinction. And when we seek a sanction for the one view or the other, we are at a loss whither to turn, for the "stimulus-error," although it has a long

From *American Journal of Psychology*, 1921, 32, 449–471. Reprinted with permission of the University of Illinois Press.

The present paper is the outcome of a promise to deal specifically with the nature of the stimulus-error, especially with its relation to psychological measurement and psychophysics. *Cf.* the discussions of the present writer in "The logic of the normal law of error in mental measurement," *Amer. J. Psychol.*, 1920, 31, 1–33, esp. 27ff.; and in "The control of attitude in psychophysical experiments," *Psychol. Review*, 1920, 27, 440–452, esp. 447f., 449 and note.

history, has been left to make its way without any very formal introduction.

THE STIMULUS-ERROR

Undoubtedly much of the confusion and disagreement has been
brought about by the term itself: "stimulus-error." It implies something
that is right and something that it wrong, defending one position and
impugning another. It serves, and was intended, to throw two positions
into contrast, to insist upon an important distinction that is often overlooked; yet does not stop with definition, but goes on to pass a judgment. In this dual function of the phrase there has been both an advantage and a disadvantage. To those who accept both the implied
distinction and the explicit evaluation the notion has been exceedingly
useful, for it has enabled them, not only to separate the methodological
sheep from the goats, but also to dispense with the goats — a telescop-
ing of procedure that is convenient and economical. On the other
hand, those psychologists who have staked their fortunes on the goats of
stimulus are not to be reformed by being found in the way of the
"stimulus-error." They simply deny the "error" and in so doing miss
the more fundamental distinction between opposing positions that
must be made out before judgment can be passed upon either. We
ourselves must not be thus misled, whatever our ultimate judgment
may be.

This implied opposition, which we must now bear clearly in mind,
is the fundamental opposition in psychology — or between psychologies — of mental process and meaning, of content and object, of
Beschreibung and *Kundgabe*. Titchener, who is responsible for the
term "stimulus-error," puts the case thus:

> We are constantly confusing sensations with their stimuli,
> with their objects, with their meanings. Or rather — since the
> sensation of psychology has no object or meaning — we are
> constantly confusing logical abstraction with psychological
> analysis; we abstract a certain aspect of an object or meaning,
> and then treat this aspect as if it were a simple mental process,
> an element in the mental representation of the object or mean-
> ing. . . . We do not say, in ordinary conversation, that this
> visual sensation is lighter than that, but that this pair of gloves
> or this kind of grey paper is lighter than this other. We do not
> say that this complex of cutaneous or organic sensations is

more intensive than that, but that this box or package is heavier than this other. We do not even say, as a rule, that this tonal quality is lower than that, but rather that this instrument is flat and must be tuned up to this other. Always in what we say there is a reference to the objects, to the meaning of the conscious complex. It is not the grey, pressure, tone, that we are thinking of; but the grey of leather or paper, the pressure of the box, the pitch of the violin. . . . What is more natural than to read the character of the stimuli, of the objects, into the "sensations" with which certain aspects of the stimulus or object are correlated? . . . This is what Fechner did. . . . [He] transferred to sensation a point of view that is right for stimulus, but that introspection refuses to recognize in psychology.[1]

We commit the stimulus-error if we base our psychological reports upon objects rather than upon the mental material itself, or if in the psycho-physical experiment, we make judgments of the stimulus and not judgments of sensation. At the more complex levels we may make a similar error, a "meaning-error," which consists of describing objects, reporting meanings, stating *Kundgabe*, instead of describing mental process or giving *Beschreibung*. We can not, however, in this paper, extend the discussion to include this complex level, but must content ourselves with the conviction that whatever applies in the controversy between judgment of stimulus and judgment of sensation, applies also to introspection and its rival, the statement of meaning. We may concede that the psychophysical experiment in its simplicity represents the ideal ultimate in the psychological experiment, where control of conditions and adequacy of observation are maximal; and that we should be glad to reduce all psychological observation to this degree of rigor at least. At any rate any extension of this discussion to the "higher" processes must wait, for the history and application of the

[1] E. B. Titchener, *Experimental Psychology*, II, i, 1905, p. xxvif.; *cf. Text-book of Psychology*, 1910, 202f. Titchener first uses the term stimulus-error = "R-error" in *Exper. Psychol.*, II, ii, 1905; see pp. lxiii, 198f., 203ff., 207, 219, 223, 230f., 262, 450. For Titchener's further use of the term, see *Text-book*, pp. 218, 350, 398 note, 522. J. v. Kries characterized the objectifying attitude as a "source of error:" "Wenn mann aber diese Quelle des Irrthums ausschliesst und möglichst an den objectiven, als Reiz dienenden, Vorgang gar nicht denkt. . . ." *Vtjschr. f. wiss. Philos.*, 1882, 6, 275, and Titchener seems to refer to this discussion as a sanction for the term "stimulus-error."

stimulus-error are at the level of psychophysics, and the interpretation of the "stimulus-error," up to which we are leading, shows most clearly here.

THE QUANTITY OBJECTION
AND THE STIMULUS-ERROR

It is not surprising that a psychophysics, which seeks to establish the relation between the mental and the physical, should emphasize the distinction between sensation and stimulus. What is surprising is that the opponents of psychophysics should have raised this very distinction for the confounding of psychophysics and should have claimed that the psychophysical relationship (the logarithmic relation of the Weber-Fechner law) was an artifact created, not by the attempt of the psychophysicist to distinguish between sensation and stimulus, but by his confusion of the two. Yet such is the substance of the "quantity objection" to psychophysics, which had later to be met with the psychological sense-distance by Müller, Titchener, and others, who thus turned the tables and brought the argument for the distinction between mental and physical material to the support of a Fechnerian psychophysics. This was a long and tedious battle, and one might have expected that the resultant emphasis upon the two-fold nature of psychophysics would have determined the psychophysical universe for a time. On the contrary, however, the confusion between sensation and stimulus persisted. Cattell was fathering a psychology of the stimulus, and it was in the tradition of the work of Fullerton and Cattell that Urban did his experiments. Now that behaviorism has come into vogue, it is not apparent that we do not have two kinds of psychophysics — a psychophysics of process that gives, as Fechner wanted, the correlation between mental and physical data, and a psychophysics of behavior that seeks to identify response with its stimulus. That this psychophysics of stimulus-and-response needs also, if it is to be scientific, to take account of the error that has been called the "stimulus-error" is the thesis of the present paper; but the thesis must wait upon the perspective of the preface.

A clear recognition of the distinction between mind and body, between consciousness and objects, was the key-note of Fechner's position. There was for him at least this dualism in the universe, which may be regarded from one standpoint or the other. The case is not unlike, Fechner argued, the Ptolemaic and Copernican worlds. The geocentric and heliocentric solar systems are different systems, and we may at pleasure take either point of view that we choose. The worlds remain distinct. Or the matter is like a circle, which may be viewed from the inside or the outside. In the one case we see only concavity, in the other only convexity. Such a dualism can be resolved only by the law of relationship that holds between its two aspects, and, just as the relationship between concavity and convexity can be stated geometrically for the circle, so the logarithmic law resolves the dualism of mind and body. There is no doubt, therefore, that Fechnerian psychophysics stands or falls according to its success in distinguishing between measurements of mind and measurements of body, or between sensation and the object of sensation, the stimulus.[2]

The vigorous opposition that developed to Fechner's psychophysics took its stand firmly upon the distinction between mind and body, but denied the possibility of a quantitative correlation between the two on the ground that mind was not possessed of magnitude and that mental measurement was an impossibility. This argument came to be known as the "quantity objection" and was the main source of opposition to quantitative psychology in the eighties and nineties of last century. Introspection, the objection runs, does not show that a sensation of great magnitude ever contains other sensations of lesser magnitude in the way that a heavy weight may [supposedly] be made up of a number of smaller weights. "Our feeling of pink," said James, "is surely not a portion of our feeling of scarlet; nor does the light of an electric arc seem to contain that of a tallow-candle in itself."[3] "This sensation of 'gray,' " remarked Külpe, "is not two or three of that other sensation of 'gray.' "[4] "A blue surface," Ebbinghaus commented, "is something other than a green, but the latter has in itself, apart from memory of the colors, nothing of the doubleness or threefoldness of the green. . . . A low tone sounds different from a high tone, and in like manner a loud tone different from a soft."[5] In other words increase of magnitude in no sense means increase of complexity. A sensation is just itself no matter what its degree. The tone produced by many instruments in unison is not of itself composed of more units than is the tone from a single string, nor is the tone of many vibrations per second more

[2] G. Th. Fechner, *Elemente der Psychophysik*, esp. 1889, I, 1–12.

[3] W. James, *Principles of Psychology*, 1890, I, 546.

[4] O. Külpe, *Outlines of Psychology*, tr. 1896, 45.

[5] H. Ebbinghaus, Z. f. Psychol., 1890, 1, 323.

complex than the tone of few vibrations. In this form the objection seems obvious enough. Sensational magnitude is certainly not multitude, and intense sensations are not integrated of more sensory stuff than are weak.[6] How then was psychophysics to defend itself?

Its immediate defense was a display of the factual material. Here were the experimental measurements. If they were not observations of the magnitudes of sensation, what were they?

To this question the raisers of the "quantity objection" replied that psychophysicists had created an artificial mental magnitude by a confusion of the sensation with the stimulus, that is to say, they had committed in their experimental work the "stimulus-error." This was a serious charge against a discipline that depended for its existence upon a sharp distinction between the mental and the physical. Let us see how the accusers dared to raise it.

Von Kries put the matter clearly:

> An illusion is thus very easily brought about by the fact that one tends in general to estimate objective values (measurable in objective terms) according to the sensation. If one, however, excludes this source of error, and in so far as possible thinks not at all of the objective process serving as a stimulus, then one must necessarily admit that a quantitative relation does not exist between the different parts of an intensive series. This fact is most obvious to us when we do not attempt objectification as, *e.g.*, in pain. Whatever it is called, a pain exactly ten times as strong as another does not admit of such absolute statement.[7]

Ebbinghaus, somewhat later, was even more explicit:

> In general one designates the brightness of a flame or a surface as 10 or 12 times another brightness, and could just as easily, it appears, designate a loud tone as the double or treble of a soft tone. But what occurs here is no longer an immediate sensation or an immediate judgment of sensations, but depends

---

[6] Titchener mentions as raising the quantity objection: G. E. Müller in 1878, Exner in 1879, Stadler in 1880, Zeller in 1881, Boas and F. A. Müller in 1882, Stumpf in 1883, Tannery in 1884, Elsas in 1886, Grotenfelt in 1888, James, Münsterberg, and Ebbinghaus in 1890, Sully in 1892, Külpe in 1893, Wahle in 1894, Meinong in 1896, Höfler in 1897, and Lehmann in 1902. See Titchener, *Exper. Psychol.*, II, ii, pp. xlviii–lxiii.

[7] I. v. Kries, *loc. cit.*

upon the introduction of experiences. We can readily experience, and we do every day experience, the fact that the arousal of a brightness or a loudness depends upon a diversity of just those physical things or processes that in limited number call forth the impression of darker or softer. In order to have an impression of greater brightness for a surface, one can increase the number of gas-flames illuminating it; in order to strengthen a tone, one multiplies the instruments carrying it. Such experiences with respect to the causes of sensations we have always in immediate view, and we believe that we have the numerical characteristics that always attach to the one occurring without anything further in the other. It is psychologically difficult to get rid of them, just as it is difficult not immediately to see in a grass-green apple its sourness. But if one succeeds in the perfectly possible separation of the thought context, then it is clear that, as the bare visual impression of an apple has no sourness in it, similarly the bare impression of brightness does not consist of the multiplicity of candles upon which, of course, it frequently depends.[8]

We have already seen what, fifteen years later, Titchener had to say in the same vein and how, although defending mental measurement, he makes the charge of the stimulus-error against Fechner. And there were many others.

Exner put forward the general argument in 1879;[9] and Boas in 1882.[10] Tannery said in 1883: "It is the objective study of the excitation and its variations that leads to this definition of number that measures the sensation. At bottom it is by excitation that sensation is defined."[11] On epistemological grounds both F. A. Müller[12] and Meinong[13] concluded that mental magnitudes, unlike physical, were indivisible. And long before any of these, Brentano, the father of modern intentional psychology, had said: "If one measures, as Fechner did, the intensities of colors, tones, etc., then one is measuring the intensities of physical

[8] H. Ebbinghaus, op. cit., 323f.; cf. Grundzüge der Psychologie, I, 1905, 71–79.

[9] S. Exner, Hermann's Handbuch der Physiologie, 1879, II, ii, 242.

[10] F. Boas, Pflüger's Arch., 1882, 28, 568f.

[11] J. Tannery in J. Delboeuf, Éléments de psychophysique, 1883, 138.

[12] F. A. Müller, Das Axiom der Psychophysik, 1882, 46–56.

[13] A. Meinong, Z. f. Psychol., 1896, 11, 81–133, esp. 96ff.

phenomena. The color is not the seeing, the tone is not the hearing, the warmth is not the sensing of warmth." [14]

Nevertheless this still seems a surprising charge to bring against Fechnerian psychophysics. If the fundamental task of psychophysics is the discovery of the relationship between the hitherto unrelated body and mind, is it not astonishing that psychophysics should have confused the two, the two whose very separateness was the *raison d'être* of psychophysics? Yet the critics stuck to the point and were at pains to show the readiness with which these incommensurables did duty, the one for the other. Ward, pointing out that the psychophysical limen expressed in terms of stimulus was physical quantity, concluded: "There is no trespass harder to avoid than that across the lines dividing the subjective and objective aspects, and none more disastrous to the offender." [15] Other writers urged the same point, and Külpe even brought the prevalence of objectification into an experimental study.[16] It is no wonder then that objectification was thought of as a source of error and that Titchener coined for it the term "stimulus-error."

THE ANSWER TO THE QUANTITY OBJECTION

The fundamental and final answer to the quantity objection was Weber's law: $S = k \log R$. In so far as the relationship had been observed, no amount of explaining could explain it entirely away. It might be that the function was not exactly logarithmic or that it held only within certain limits; it might not be certain just what was the nature of S, or of R; but the unescapable fact was that there were an S and an R, which were covariant, and which were not identical since the mode of variation of the one was not the mode of variation of the other. To charge the stimulus-error and say that S was contaminated by R was not enough, since the confusion of S with R was not enough to explain the discovery of this difference in variation. The psychophysicists, therefore, had the stronger position, and had only to show where the difference actually lay. There seem to be five ways of accounting for the difference and thus of establishing psychophysics.

1. Systematically one may argue for a physiological interpretation

[14] F. Brentano, *Psychologie vom empirischen Standpunkte*, 1874, I, 91.

[15] J. Ward, Mind, 1876, O. S. 1, 460.

[16] O. Külpe, Ueber die Objectivirung und Subjectivirung von Sinneseindrücken, *Philos. Stud.*, 1902, 19, 508–556.

of Weber's law, as Müller did.[17] Excitation varies somewhat as does the logarithm of the stimulus. No one doubts that excitation may have magnitude, and thus the quantity objection is met. Moreover the logarithmic relation between physical dependents is not unknown.[18] Excitation, however, does not happen to be open to immediate observation, so we must observe its correlate sensation. We deal therefore with stimulus and sensation, which we must keep apart, avoiding the stimulus-error; and we escape from the formal objection that sensation does not have magnitude by making it a mere qualitative indicator of excitation which must have magnitude.

2. Wundt's psychological interpretation of Weber's law meets the quantity objection by the introduction of *Merklichkeitsgrade*. Sensations do not have magnitude, but if they did the matter would be irrelevant to psychophysics. It is apperception that gives a quantitative aspect to mind; there are degrees of noticeableness to sensations or to the differences between them.[19] The sensation scarlet is not more than the sensation pink, but is more noticeable than the pink; and the difference between a scarlet and a pale pink is more noticeable than the difference between the scarlet and a rose. To introspection it is just as obvious that apperception has degree as it is obvious that sensation has not, and it is between these *Merklichkeitsgrade* and the physical values of the stimulus that the logarithmic law holds.

3. What was Fechner's answer to the quantity objection? To deny the stimulus-error, which the quantity objection implies. In the *Revision* he wrote:

> One must take care not to try to count relations that exist in the physical realm between physical units as existing within the mental province because they can be grasped only by the mind; for in so doing one loses the ground for distinction between the two provinces. Even the physical, within which the relations exist, must be grasped by our minds in order to exist for us and to be spoken about. Yet we discriminate on the basis of this community between outer and inner phenomena as be-

---

[17] G. E. Müller, *Zur Grundlegung der Psychophysik*, 1878, 224–403.

[18] Müller, *loc. cit.;* Ward, *op. cit.*, 452–466; Titchener, *op. cit.*, II, ii, 66f. The autocatalytic theory is more recent: T. B. Robertson, *Monist*, 1909, 19, 372ff., 384f.

[19] Wundt's theory passed through successive stages and no brief statement does it justice. For summary and discussion, see Titchener, *Exper. Psychol.*, II, ii, pp. lviff., lxxivf., lxxxff., 69f.; for summary and genesis, p. lxxxii, note.

tween two provinces, and have to distinguish properties as belonging in the one or the other, not merged with each other or interchangeable, as might sometimes seem to be the case under a philosophical point of view. At any rate psychophysics takes this point of view and thus avoids confusion. Whenever something like a relation, a change, a difference, a unity, or a fusion, *etc.*, appears as characterizing the physical or psychical world, it is abstracted from the province of the one or the other, or it is counted into the one or the other province; it may occur just as readily in psychology as in natural science. Hence it is perfectly possible that the pitches should be represented in one province by something in the other province without our identifying the two. The relations of periodicity between vibrations, which occur as the psychophysical representatives of melodic and harmonic sensations, are the most obvious; the one is something very different from the other.[20]

In other words it is all in our point of view. We can judge the stimuli or we can judge the sensations; and, according as we do the one or the other, we constitute for ourselves the physical or the mental world. It is nonsense to assume that, because we make judgments of physical phenomena in building up natural science, this natural science is a science of judgments and therefore mental. The two are distinct, and the discovery of the difference that is summarized by Weber's law attests the distinction.

To the writer of this paper it seems that Fechner's argument, turned a different way, becomes at least as invincible as any of the other ways out of the difficulty. The trick for escaping the force of the quantity objection, when directed against mental phenomena, is to turn it upon the stimuli themselves. Suppose sensations of weight do not under observation exhibit magnitude; what of the physical weights themselves? To physical observation ten grams is *a* weight and one gram is *a* weight; it is only in common sense, which is assuredly not physics, that ten grams is ten one-gram weights. Because physical phenomena, like mental, are referable to objects, is no excuse for reading the objects into them. Physical weight is as little the number of objects in the scale-pan as mental weight is the number of weights in the hand. The physical quantity is just as simple and unitary as the mental, and if sensation

<hr>

[20] Fechner, *Revision der Hauptpunkte der Psychophysik*, 1882, 5f.

lacks magnitude so must stimulus. We can hardly, however, deny measurement to physics, and it thus appears that the quantity objection is not valid either against the measurement of sensation.[21]

4. Undoubtedly the most general way of meeting the quantity objection while saving mental measurement is by the substitution of the sense-distance for the sensation magnitude. Historically this conception dates from Delboeuf's *contraste sensible*. It is not necessarily incompatible with any of the foregoing accounts of mental measurement and is endorsed essentially by Wundt, Boas, Stumpf, Ebbinghaus, James, Meinong, Höfler, Stout, and G. E. Müller.[22] It is the basis of Titchener's quantitative psychology, where it finds its clearest exposition.[23]

This position holds that sensations, although they do not possess magnitude, may lie within a continuum, and that, although we can form no quantitative estimate of any sensation, we can nevertheless estimate the relative degree of separateness of two sensations within the continuum. Sensations are simply themselves and are not summed of various numbers of increments; the distances between these sensations, however, do vary and can be estimated in amount. The simplest case of mental measurement occurs when, for a series of three sensations, A, B, and C, occurring in a continuum, we estimate the sense-distance AB as equal to the sense-distance BC. Here we have measurement, for we have laid off the unit AB = BC twice in the distance AC, and it is the correlation of such estimated sense-distances with the corresponding values of stimulus that gives Weber's law.

5. All the foregoing modes of meeting the quantity objection are successful without sacrificing the possibility of mental measurement; the fifth mode of defense consists in joining the enemy. We can give up the measurement of mind, substituting the measurement of sensitivity or of capacity-for-discrimination. Fullerton and Cattell give us our orientation here.

---

[21] The more thorough exposition would show that magnitude and measurement are systematic matters and are not found immediately at the observational level of science. The confusion is not unlike that of the systematic "sensation" with the observational "attribute": *cf.* Sensation and system, *Am. J. Psychol.*, 1915, 26, 258–267, where Titchener makes this point. On the other hand, it is hardly fair to physics to say: "No sensation is a sum of sensation-parts or of sense-increments; no sensation is a measurable magnitude. Fechner has transferred to sensation a point of view that is right for stimulus, but that introspection refuses to recognize in psychology:" Titchener, *Exper. Psychol.*, II, i, p. xxvii.

[22] *Cf.* Titchener, *op. cit.*, II, ii, p. cxxxiii.

[23] Titchener, *op. cit.*, II, i, pp. xxi–xxvii; ii, pp. cxvi–cxliv.

They declare, in the first place, that both sensation magnitudes and sense-distances are undiscoverable:

> If an observer can, in fact, estimate quantitative amounts of difference in sensation, apart from association with known quantitative differences in the stimuli, a relation between mental and physical intensity can be determined. The writers, however, agree in finding that they cannot estimate such quantitative differences in sensation in a satisfactory manner. We can indeed say when one weight seems approximately double another, but this is doubtless because we have often lifted first one volume, and then two, and the like. But we cannot say when one sound seems twice as loud, or one day twice as hot as another. We have made experiments to see how nearly different observers would agree in adjusting one shade of light midway between two others, and have found hesitation in coming to a decision and great divergence of opinion. Most men will think that a just king is happier than a tyrant, but few will agree with Plato in considering him 729 times as happy.[24]

What is left? The observed *stimuli* [25] and errors of observation incurred in observing the stimuli.[26] There is no constant just noticeable difference nor threshold.[27] We have only errors of observation as we fail to observe an actual difference in the stimuli or, less often, observe a difference that is not there. These errors can be treated under the ordinary calculus of probabilities and follow the normal law of error.[28] The amount of the average error is always determinable and it increases with the magnitude of the stimulus.[29] It is the law of the dependence of the average error of observation upon the magnitude of the stimulus that Weber's law seeks to state, although the mathematical form of Weber's law is actually incorrect.[30]

Such a quantitative psychology of error is of necessity a psychology of capacity[31] — of the capacity of the organism to respond correctly to

---

[24] G. S. Fullerton and J. McK. Cattell, *On the Perception of Small Differences*, 1892, 20.

[25] Fullerton and Cattell, *op. cit.*, 9ff., 20, 153, *etc.*

[26] Fullerton and Cattell, 14ff.; Cattell, *Am. J. Psychol.*, 1893, 5, 287ff.

[27] F and C, 11, 150; Cattell, 288f.

[28] F and C, 12ff.; Cattell, 285ff.

[29] F and C, 23ff., 153f.; Cattell, 290ff.

[30] F and C, 24ff., 152.

[31] *Cf.* Titchener, *Exper. Psychol.*, II, ii, p. cxxxiv note.

stimuli. This point of view has since developed into the statistics of mental tests and of behaviorism, which is a psychology of stimulus and response. It is a point of view for which there is no stimulus-error since quantitative judgments can be made only of the stimulus, and it is one that touches other sciences very closely since it concerns itself with observation, the method of every science.[32]

THE TWO PSYCHOLOGIES

Thus it becomes evident that the answers to the quantity objection have divided along the traditional cleft in psychology. We have not only a psychology of datum and a psychology of capacity, but we have quantitative psychologies of datum and of capacity.[33]

The quantitative psychology of datum ["the given"] insists upon a truly mental measurement. When further it correlates these mental measurements it is the true psychophysics. It may answer the quantity objection in any of the first four of the five foregoing ways, because any one of those four insists upon or explains the existence of mental quanta. It is a part of the larger psychology that is variously called structural or introspective, the psychology of process or of *Beschreibung*.

The quantitative psychology of capacity admits the quantity objection and denies — or at least ignores — mental quanta. This psychology sees no distinctively mental measurement, but undertakes the physical measurement of bodily response as a function of the physical quantities of the stimulus. There is no sharp epistemological line discernible between this sort of measurement and other physical measurement, and it thus meets the requirement of modern behaviorism that psychology interpenetrate physical science without sensible demarcation.[34] The psychology of capacity is also the psychology of mental tests [35] and of Urban's psychophysical experiments.[36]

[32] F and C, 9; Cattell, 285.

[33] *Cf.* O. Külpe, *Vorlesungen über Psychologie,* 1920, 5ff.; Titchener, *Am. J. Psychol.,* 1921, 32, 108–120.

[34] J. B. Watson, *Psychol. Rev.,* 1913, 20, 177; *J. Philos., etc.,* 1913, 10, 427; *Psychology,* 1920, vii.

[35] See note 31 above.

[36] The present writer has already had occasion to refer to F. M. Urban's position: E. G. Boring, *Am. J. Psychol.,* 1920, 31, 27f., esp. note 77; *Psychol. Rev.,* 1920, 27, 446f. It is well to repeat that no reference is intended here to Urban's later position, which involves an acceptance of the epistemology of Mach and Avenarius; see Ueber einige Begriffe und Aufgaben der Psychophysik, *Arch. f. d. ges. Psychol.,* 1913, 30, 113–152, esp. 113, 124f., with notes; *cf.* also *Am. J. Psychol.,* 1913, 24, 274.

These latter seem strange mates, but the influence of Cattell is apparent in both. If the germ of the tests was in Galton, nevertheless it was Cattell, in the interests of the psychology of individual differences, who planted it in American soil where it has brought forth fruit abundantly. Urban's origin is less apparent. It is trivial to remark that he began his psychophysics in the laboratory that Cattell had founded years before. The evidence is internal and not explicit, but the seeker after information can find it.[37] In the broad, we may add, the psychology of capacity may become a functional psychology and deal, when it is experimental, with *meanings* and *Kundgaben* instead of mental processes and *Beschreibung*.

As a term the "stimulus-error" is the property of the psychology of datum. It characterizes the attitude of the psychology of capacity as being concerned observationally with the stimulus and admonishes against it. Of course the psychology of capacity ignores this admonition, for in making observations of the physical stimulus it is simply fulfilling its self-appointed task. The "stimulus-error" is no valid charge against this psychology, nor does it raise within it a question of right and wrong. No more can be expected of either psychology than that it hold to its premises.

In practice there is a difficulty, however. No matter how distinct the two psychologies may be, psychologists can scarcely hold strictly to the one or to the other. The psychologist of the datum can not be expected to attack a new perception without recourse to judgments of stimulus or of meaning,[38] and statements of meanings moreover may themselves become the object of psychological investigation.[39] As to whether the psychology of capacity might remain wholly faithful to the stimulus it

[37] On psychophysical judgments and random events, compare Fullerton and Cattell, *op. cit.*, 12ff., 23ff., with Urban, *The Application of Statistical Methods to the Problems of Psychophysics*, 1908, 17f. On the meaning of the just perceptible difference, compare F and C, 11, and Cattell, *op. cit.*, 288f., with Urban, *Stat. Meth.*, 70. On mental measurement compare F and C, 20, 152f., and Cattell, 293, with Urban's ignoring of the issue in *Stat. Meth.* [Or could he have thought that Titchener had settled it for the sense-distance? *Cf. Psychol. Bull.*, 1912, 9, 245.] On judgment as directed upon stimulus, compare F and C, 20, and Cattell, 293, with Urban, *Stat. Meth.*, 5, 17, *Psychol. Rev.*, 1910, 17, 27ff. On recording degrees of assurance, compare F and C, 11, 151, with Urban, *Stat. Meth.*, 5ff. On the relation of psychophysics to physics, compare F and C, 151, Cattell, 285, with Urban, *Psychol. Rev.*, 17, 243f.

[38] *Cf.*, *e.g.*, L. B. Hoisington, On the non-visual perception of the length of lifted rods, *Am. J. Psychol.*, 1920, 31, 114–146.

[39] *Cf.*, *e.g.*, H. P. Weld, Meaning and process as distinguished by the reaction method, *Titchener Commemorative Volume*, 1917, 181–208.

is not so easy to say. This attitude is more natural and it is possible to complete entire experiments without once trespassing upon the realm of mental process. On the other hand, the functional psychologies, for all they have to say of the inadequacies of structural psychology, seem usually unable to complete the systematic mental picture alone, and a recent system of behaviorism has drawn unhesitatingly upon the psychology that it seeks to supplant.[40] In general what is fundamental to the one can not be ignored by the other, and on this account the writer of this paper would urge the attention of the psychologist of capacity to the "stimulus-error."

THE EFFECT OF THE STIMULUS-ERROR

If we are now to urge upon the psychology of capacity the avoidance of the stimulus-error, it is a fair demand that we state first the probable penalty that is incurred by a failure to accept our advice. Here we can not stand upon the epistemological ground that psychology observes mental processes and not stimuli, and that judgments of stimulus are therefore *a priori* inadmissible. This historical warning against the stimulus-error does not apply to the psychology of capacity which protests against a scientific dualism and deals by preference with stimulus and response. What we have to show is rather that the stimulus-error works against the establishment of the univocal correlations between stimulus and response that a psychology of capacity demands, that it interferes with the prediction of the response for a given stimulus. Here the ground is broadly scientific: we are dealing with the constancy of experimental conditions and the reproducibility of results.

When we go frankly to the literature, however, asking just what in numerical terms may be the effect in mental measurement of allowing judgments of the stimulus or of instituting them, we meet at first disappointment.

The psychology of datum is set to avoid, rather than to measure, the stimulus-error. It tells us where the stimulus-error is most insidious, *viz.*, in judgments of supraliminal sense distances.[41] We may have trouble with the limens; we are almost sure to have it in comparing large sense-distances. Sometimes a special technique is necessary to avoid the error. In Martius' experiment on the apparent size of objects at different distances from the eye, all the stimulus habits for the esti-

[40] Watson, *Psychology, from the Standpoint of a Behaviorist*, 1919.

[41] *Cf., e.g.,* Titchener, *Textbook*, 218.

mation of the size of objects in everyday life are appealed to, and a special method is required "in removing the initial tendency of the observers to reflect on the actual size of the comparison rod in relation to the standard rod."[42] In Angell's experiment on intensive distances between sounds one would expect concrete reference to the stimulus to enter much less readily; on the contrary, however, the observers tend to judge the height of fall or the angle of fall of the stimulus, and to neglect the mental datum.[43] For this error special remedies are presented. Müller urges that the amount of intensive difference be taken as the *Kohärenzgrad*, the *Leichtigkeit des Kollektivaufgefasstwerdens* of the two sounds.[44] Titchener suggests letting the observer blunder into the stimulus-error and then rescuing him by individualized treatment, his protocols in hand.[45] These experiments are striking cases, but even the psychologists who have no special measures of reform to offer cry out against the evils of judgments based upon secondary criteria, upon associates of the processes judged, or upon surrogate processes.[46] A surrogate, they complain, can even render incommensurables artificially commensurate, as seems to be the case when the intensities of weights and noises are compared in terms of *Spannungsempfindungen*.[47]

Now it is not likely that there could be so much smoke without some fire; yet we are still at a loss to estimate the amount of danger. It would be reasonable for these psychologists of datum to seek to avoid stimulus for no other reason than that they are interested solely in "mind," but it is not to be supposed that the matter would have been taken so seriously had the quantitative results, and Weber's law which is dependent upon them, been unaffected by the kind of judgment given. Indeed this belief came to the surface when Grotenfelt, in defense of Weber's law, accused Merkel of the stimulus-error and inclined to the belief that re-

---

[42] G. Martius, Ueber die scheinbare Grösse der Gegenstände und ihre Beziehung zur Grösse der Netzhautbilder, *Philos. Stud.*, 1889, 5, 601–617, esp. 605f.; *cf.* Titchener, *Exper. Psychol.* II, ii, pp. 262f.

[43] F. Angell, Untersuchungen über die Schätzung von Schallintensitäten nach der Methode der mittleren Abstufungen, *Philos. Stud.*, 1891, 7, 414–468, esp. 438.

[44] G. E. Müller, *Die Gesichtspunkte und die Tatsachen der psychophysischen Methodik*, 1904, 237f.

[45] Titchener, *Exper. Psychol.*, II, ii, p. 198; *cf.* also pp. 203f., 230.

[46] *Cf.* Fechner; *Elemente*, II, 318ff.; H. Neiglick, *Philos. Stud.*, 1888, 4, 41; Angell, *op. cit.*, 438; W. Ament, *ibid.*, 1900, 16, 173; G. E. Müller, *op. cit.*, 241; J. Fröbes, *Z. f. Psychol.*, 1904, 36, 259.

[47] H. Münsterberg, *Beiträge zur experimentellen Psychologie*, III, 1900, 56–122, esp. 98ff.

sults that followed Merkel's law might possibly indicate that they were based upon judgments of stimulus.[48] The data that we wish, however — the comparison in quantitative terms of results of judgments of process — are, in the earlier history of psychophysics, lacking.

(The psychologists of capacity, we may note in passing, are not to be asked for this comparison. Cattell and Fullerton denied the possibility of mental measurement. They can not therefore be asked for its comparison with any form of physical measurement.)

On the basis of recent literature, however, there is something to be said, in answering this question, for the case of lifted weights, and very much to be said for the case of the limen of dual cutaneous impression. We may mention the lifted weights at once and reserve the two-point limen for the next section.

Friedländer undertook a comparative study of lifting weights under different *Einstellungen*.[49] He employed a *"G-Einstellung"* in which the attention was directed upon the lifted object (*Gegenstand*, hence *"G"*), and an *"A-Einstellung"* in which the object was abstracted from (hence *"A"*) and the attention directed upon the sensory aspect of the experience (*Druck-, Spannungs-, Kraftempfindungen*).[50] Here we should expect to find the results we are seeking, for the *G-Einstellung* is the stimulus-attitude, the attitude demanded by a psychology of capacity and called the "stimulus-error" by the psychology of datum; and the *A-Einstellung* in its various forms is the process-attitude which avoids the "stimulus-error." There is not the least doubt that the two attitudes give different results. "Differential sensitivity on the whole is somewhat finer for the G-series" for a standard weight of 500 g., Friedländer tells us, but a standard of 1200 g. may give a finer discrimination under the *A-Einstellung*. The data unfortunately are for one observer only. They are based on too few cases, — 41 series after the practice-effect was presumably constant. The observer did not always succeed in maintaining the required attitude, for the stimulus-attitude was difficult for him (!) and he sought to make his finer discriminations under the *A-Einstellung*. The resultant psychometric functions are not

[48] A. Grotenfelt, *Das Webersche Gesetz und die psychische Relativität*, 1888, 111f.; *cf.* Titchener, *Exper. Psychol.*, II, ii, pp. lxxviiif., 219.

[49] H. Friedländer, Die Wahrnehmung der Schwere, *Z. f. Psychol.*, 1920, 83, 129–210, esp. 187–193.

[50] Pp. 133ff.

smooth ogives; one just barely misses inversion in its central portion.[51]
We are not yet ready, then, to generalize as to the exact effect of attending to the stimulus in making psychophysical judgments. All we
can say is that there is an effect, that a shift in the observational attitude
alters the numerical results significantly. We shall not dare, therefore, if
we wish to predict response from stimulus, to leave attitude out of
account.

My colleague, Professor Fernberger, has recently completed similar
experiments in the Clark Laboratory. He had three observers, and extended his series through many fractions to take account of progressive
practice and to give an adequate number of cases. His resultant ogives
are smooth and regular, and his procedure seemed calculated to yield
all that could be desired methodically. He gets differences for the different attitudes — more striking differences in some cases than Friedländer's. More than this I can not say in advance of the publication of
his results. Perhaps in his final analysis he will discover a generalization,
which is not apparent to casual inspection of the functions and constants. The results indicate unquestionably that an alteration of attitude by instruction may result in an alteration of the psychometric
functions, which is significant in the mathematical sense of being many
times its probable error, but which for a given observer is unfortunately
quite unpredictable. Attitude may be very important even when we
can not say just why.

Fortunately the case of the two-point limen is less mysterious.

THE STIMULUS-ERROR AS EQUIVOCAL CORRELATION

The limen of dual impression upon the skin furnishes the case for which
we are looking. We know, not only that judgments of stimulus may
here make a difference in the quantitative results, but we know further
how great this difference may be and something of its conditions. We

---

[51] In fact it is not even clear that Friedländer's cautious generalization is not in part an
artifact. If we compute the data of Table 10 by Urban's procedure for the *Konstanzmetho-
de*, we get:

	A-Einstellung	G-Einstellung
Av. measure of precision (h)	0.0138	0.0147
Interval of uncertainty (grams)	35.39	37.13
Point of subjective equality (grams)	500.8	509.9

There is not much difference in precision or discrimination by this method. The striking
difference is in the effect of attitude on the point of subjective equality.

are in a position, moreover, to generalize from these facts with some assurance and to assert that the effect of the "stimulus-error," from the point of view of a psychology of capacity, is — under similar conditions, at least — to render the correlations between stimulus and response equivocal and thus to jeopardize the rigor of conclusion that science demands.

We may proceed to the point by reference to the visual schema of the figure reproduced herewith. The diagram is intended merely to assist in the analysis of the factors involved and not as an actual picture of neural or psychophysical fact.

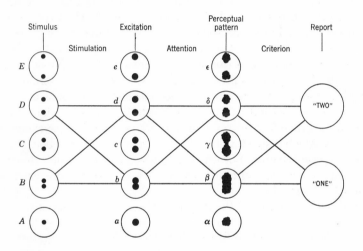

One deals in determining the two-point limen with a series of stimuli, A, B, C, D, E, pairs of stimulus-points at different separations, with perhaps a single point, A, at the extreme of the series. From the work of numerous investigators [52] we know that there is a similar series of perceptual patterns, α, β, γ, δ, ε, which passes, with approximate regularity, from a sharp point to a blunt point, to an oval, to an elongated oval, to a double-paddle, to a dumb-bell, to two separated points. We may best think of these perceptual patterns as the process material of the psychology of datum, but they exist also for the psychology of

[52] G. A. Tawney, *Psychol. Rev.*, 1895, 2, 585–593; V. Henri, *Ueber die Raumwahrnehmungen des Tastsinnes*, 1898, 6; M. Foucalt, *L'illusion paradoxale et le seuil de Weber*, 1910, 122–145; E. J. Gates, *Am. J. Psychol.*, 1915, 26, 152–157; and numerous other references cited in these articles.

capacity as inscrutable "middle terms." Intermediate between stimulus and process we are accustomed to assume some sort of excitatory process, *a, b, c, d, e.* Of these there must also be a series, and knowing little about them, we may picture them as somewhat like the perceptual processes. Finally there is the verbal report which is generally limited experimentally to the words *One* and *Two.* It seems, moreover, that we keep within the limits of scientific good sense if we say that stimulus, excitation, mental process, and report form a dependent series, and that each is the resultant of the preceding.

If now we choose for special consideration the stimuli *B* and *D,* we may note that they most frequently, perhaps, give rise to the dependent series *"B-b-β-One"* and *"D-d-δ-Two,"* but we must note further that cross-connections are possible.

Stimulus gives rise to excitation by way of stimulation. Here variation may tend either in the direction of fusion or of separation. On the forearm, for example, the angular shifting of stimulus toward the longitudinal axis may result in fusion and *D* may give rise to *b;* if the rotation is toward the transverse axis, *d* may follow upon *B.*[53] Location as well as angular orientation also yields these differences. Near the elbow *D* gives *b,* say; a little further down *B* may give *d.*[54] It is also possible that the chance impingement of the stimulus-points upon multiply innervated spots in the skin gives rise to multiple excitation (*B* to *d*) and that the stimulation of less complexly innervated spots may lead to a simpler excitation *(D* to *b).*[55]

At the next phase of our series excitation culminates in perceptual pattern under the selective action of attention. These terms sound strange of course to the psychologist of capacity, but we may ask him to accept them or to find substitutes for them. They stand for factors that affect the correlations with which he is working, and he must take scientific account of them, whatever he calls them.

It is experimentally demonstrable that under inattention potential *Twos* become *Ones;* one stimulating point or the other catches the attention and thus withdraws it, as it were, from the other.[56] The converse occurs in the well-known *Vexirfehler,* the paradoxical judgment, where two points close together or even a single point give a percep-

---

[53] *Cf.* Tawney, *Philos. Stud.,* 1897, 13, 170; *cf.* Boring, *Quart. J. Exp. Physiol.,* 1916, 10, 23.

[54] *Cf.* Henri, *op. cit.,* 26f.; *cf.* Boring, *loc. cit.*

[55] Henri, *op. cit.,* 64ff.; Boring, *op. cit.,* 89–93, esp. 93.

[56] *Cf.* A. Brückner, *Z. f. Psychol.,* 1901, 26, 54f., 60; Boring, *op. cit.,* 88f.

tion of duality. Henri and Tawney referred this phenomenon in part
to attention, and its dependence upon certain suggestive factors seems
to indicate that it is of this order.[57] Griesbach and others supposed that
fatigue reduced the limen,[58] but Friedline has shown that the effect of
fatigue is operative only among the perceptual forms at the lower end
of the series, say α and β. Here fatigue acts in the direction of fusion
and may perhaps be another factor that operates within the attentive
phase.[59] Thus the perceptual pattern is not wholly dependent upon
conditions at the periphery, the mode and place and nature of the stimulation. Certain more central factors also come into play and justify us
in adding to the cross-connections B-d and D-b the connections b-δ
and d-β.

Finally now the perceptual pattern issues in a judgment in accordance with criteria of judgment that have been established. The
available factor here lies in the setting up and the preservation of these
criteria. Left to himself there is no guarantee of what the subject will
do, as the studies of Titchener,[60] deLaski,[61] and Friedline[62] all show.
Perhaps the most normal criteria for sophisticated adult subjects would
be such that the perceptual δ of our chart would lead to the judgment
Two and the perceptual β to the judgment *One*. It is a reasonable inference that McDougall's savages in Torres Straits, under the competi-
tive incentive to do well, assumed such criteria that even our β would
have led to the judgment *Two* for plainly β is larger than the pattern
which a single point most often gives.[63] An overzealous subject can
interpret perceptual patterns lying very low in the series as meaning the
presence of two points upon the skin; in fact, as Friedline has shown,
he can do amazingly well under the influence of both practice and incentive, provided he is not fatigued.[64] On the other hand the sophisti-

[57] Henri and Tawney, *Philos. Stud.*, 1895, 11, 394–405, esp. 403ff.; Tawney, *ibid.*, 1897,
13, 186–198; Henri, *Raumwahrnehmungen*, 61–66.

[58] H. Griesbach, *Arch. f. Hygiene*, 1895, 24, 124ff.; but see the summary in C. L. Friedline, The discrimination of cutaneous patterns below the two-point limen, *Am. J. Psychol.*,
1918, 29, 415–418.

[59] Friedline, *op. cit.*, 411f., 418f.

[60] Titchener, On ethnological tests of sensation, *etc.*, *Proc. Am. Philos. Soc.*, 1916, 55,
206–215.

[61] E. deLaski, On perceptive forms below the level of the two-point limen, *Am. J.
Psychol.*, 1916, 27, 569–571.

[62] Friedline, *op. cit.*, 405–415, esp. 405f., 408f., 411ff.

[63] W. McDougall, *Rep. Cambridge Anthropol. Expedition to Torres Straits*, 1903, II, 189–
193; *cf.* Titchener, *op. cit.*

[64] Friedline, *op. cit.*, 408f., 414f.

cated subjects of the laboratory, and, it may be, therefore the Englishmen, whom McDougall compared with the savages, tend to define *Two* by reference to a perceptual pattern higher in the scale.[65] We should hardly have been bold enough to have predicted this result; to the writer, however, it seems reasonable enough now that it has been pointed out. Is it not to be expected that the savage would try to "do well" by discriminating as finely as possible and that the sophisticated person would try to "do well" by discriminating as accurately and consistently as possible, though less finely? In any case the point is that the acceptance of a criterion is an unavoidable experimental condition in determinations of cutaneous spatial sensitivity, and that the criterion must therefore be controlled, since when uncontrolled it gives uncertain significance to the verbal responses *Two* and *One*. In fact it appears that the apparent limen for cutaneous duality may be very much more than quartered by a variation of criterion, and it seems further that the conflicting results in the literature with respect to the effect of fatigue and the effect of practice upon the limen are to be explained in this way.

This leads to a conclusion. If only the end-terms of stimulus and response are controlled a univocal one-to-one correlation between stimulus and response is not possible. In the terms of the diagram, both the stimuli *D* and *B* may condition the response *Two*. There are eight paths leading to *Two*, four from *D* and four from *B*. If we consider the other factors of the schema, the situation is enormously complicated. There are over a hundred modes of connection from *A*, *B*, *C*, *D*, and *E*, to *Two*. Certainly the actual possibilities must be legion. At this level of work the best we can do is to remain in the dark and to deal with relative frequencies, yet relative frequencies do not yield the predictive correlation that science demands. The only way to get out of the dark would be to study the effect of stimulation, of attention, and of criterion by taking hold of these dependent series at their intermediate points, thus providing ourselves with a more complete knowledge and control of the entire psychophysical situation. Now the psychologist of capacity habitually controls stimulation, the various adjustments of the stimulus to the sense-organ, but the psychologist of datum also controls by instruction both attention and criterion. He does not, to be sure, reach the ideal of 100% certainty in the prediction of the response to a given stimulus, but he is able greatly to increase the pre-

---

[65] McDougall, *op. cit.*, 192 and note; Titchener, *op. cit.*, 211.

cision of these stimulus-and-response correlations. On the other hand, the failure to control the attitudinal factor implied in the acceptance of a criterion, and the attentional factor, again and again results perforce in an equivocal determination of these responses, which is nothing more nor less than a "stimulus-error."

In the psychology of capacity, then, the danger of the "stimulus-error" reduces to the danger that judgments of stimulus will prove scientifically equivocal. Experimentation will show when they are and when they are not. When they are equivocal, the problem is soluble by refinement in the control of conditions. The modern technique for the control of attention and attitude is a method that satisfies scientific standards of accuracy of prediction better than any available substitute. To shut our eyes to this technique in the absence of a substitute would be to refuse to accept scientific methods that have already yielded practical results. Certainly if the psychologist of capacity is to be a successful experimenter, joining hands with the biologist and physicist, he must in some way take account of all the means of experimental control that have been demonstrated as essential to the securing of accuracy.

SUMMARY

Scientific psychology in its inception assumed a distinction between mind and matter and the separate existence of observable mental data and observable physical data. Fechner's psychophysics sought to measure the mental data and to establish their correlation with related physical data. The opponents of this point of view raised the *quantity objection*, arguing that mind is not possessed of magnitude and is therefore not measurable. Most of these objectors were attacking only the quantitative status of psychology and seeking to establish it as an essentially qualitative, but mental, science. Other objectors preferred, however, to keep psychology quantitative by conceiving of it as physical, as the psychology of the *capacity* of the organism for response to stimulus. The older psychology met the quantity objection by showing that the nonexistence of mental magnitude does not preclude mental measurement, and then sought to protect itself against incursions of the physical observational attitude of the psychology of capacity by styling that attitude the *stimulus-error*. The implication would be that a psychology of capacity does not need to avoid the stimulus-error, but rather should cultivate it. The thesis of this paper is, however, that recent researches have shown that the observational attitude which is directed upon the stimulus — the attitude of the stimulus-error — may sometimes lead to equivocal correlations of stimulus and response which, because equivocal, are unscientific. In the case of the limen of dual impression upon the skin, for example, a psychology of capacity must make use of introspective data if it is to attain its own ideals.

B. Sensory Scaling

Psychophysical scaling developed from Fechner's desire to specify the functional relation between sensation and stimulus. He expected that the logarithmic relation between the physical intensity of the stimulus and the magnitude of sensation would apply wih great generality throughout the sensory realm. Since his logarithmic law was based directly upon Weber's law, the two could be expected to apply with equivalent generality. We saw in Section 3 that although Weber's law has limited validity for any particular sensory continuum it is approximately verified on many continua. Fechner's law therefore appeared to have approximately the generality he had hoped. (See R. D. Luce and W. Edwards, "The Derivation of Subjective Scales from Just Noticeable Differences" for a discussion of Fechner's mathematics.)

Those who did not believe that the magnitude of sensation was measurable could not, of course, accept the validity of Fechner's law. Nevertheless, some who would not accept the assumption that the just noticeable difference could be used as a unit of sensation magnitude could accept the assumption that the just noticeable difference corresponded to a unit of sense-distance. Therefore, just as Fechner used the results of discrimination experiments to construct scales of sensation magnitude, others could use the same results to construct scales of sense-distance. Not surprisingly, Fechner's general rule that equal ratios of stimulus magnitude produce equal differences in sensation magnitude appeared to hold also when the dependent variable was expressed as sense-distance. The logarithmic law therefore prevailed in psychophysics.

James McKeen Cattell, who viewed measures of differential discrimination as measures of combined biological and physical variability, tried to replace the term "just noticeable difference" with the term "error of observation." His statistical approach to discrimination received only minor attention until 1927, when L. L. Thurstone in "A Law of Comparative Judgment" applied a statistical model of discrimination to the construction of psychophysical scales. The Thurstonian and Fechnerian approaches to the construction of scales were quite similar in the sense that both derived a scale unit from the number of times that the observer confused one impression with another. Fechner believed his unit corresponded to a determinate psychophysical process, whereas Thurstone defined as his unit a simple measure of variability; Thurstone's approach was really a refinement of Fechner's. Moreover, the law of comparative judgment carried the additional advantage that its application did not depend upon measurement of the appropriate physical dimensions of the stimulus. It was used therefore to scale such attributes as the beauty of paintings and the quality of handwriting.

A question arises: how well do scales based on discrimination agree with direct experience and with scales based on direct judgments of sensory magnitude or sense-distance? James asserted that Fechner's assumption that equally perceptible increments in stimulus magnitude appear equally large was incorrect: "The many pounds which form the just perceptible addition to a hundredweight feel bigger when added than the few ounces which form the just perceptible addition to a pound. Fechner ignored this fact." In effect, James appealed to direct experience to refute Fechner. On the other hand, Titchener implied that scales of sense-distance based on discrimination agreed with those obtained when observers were asked to bisect the interval between sensations. It has still not been established with certainty whether discriminability scales agree with scales based on direct judgments of sense-distance. But it has been well established that scales based upon judgments of the ratio relations among sensations do not agree with those based upon discrimination procedures or judgments of intervals.

By what criteria do we decide what kind of psychophysical judgment is most valid? The discriminability scaling procedures are sometimes said to recommend themselves on the basis of the stability of results obtained from one observer to another. Criticism of these procedures is directed at the need for the assumption that confusion among stimuli (or sensations) can be used to measure sensory magnitude or sense-distance. W. R. Garner defended the use of discriminability procedures in his paper "Advantages of the Discriminability Criterion for a Loudness Scale." He argued that, in the case of loudness, ratio scaling procedures could not be accepted simply on the basis of their face validity because of findings that they were unreliable, sensitive to small variations in experimental procedure, unable to survive challenges of stimulus context, and that they generally produced results that did not agree with those obtained by any other procedures.

Interest in ratio scaling methods has been vigorous since the 1950's. It was then that S. S. Stevens first asked observers to match numbers directly to their sensations in such a way as to reflect the ratio relations among the sensations. This method, called "magnitude estimation," was simply an extension of previous ratio scaling methods, such as fractionation, where the observer was instructed to adjust one stimulus to have one-half the apparent intensity of another. An appealing feature of magnitude estimation was that it was easy to execute; it did not demand, for example, that the observer be given control over the intensity of the stimulus.

Just prior to the application of magnitude estimation to loudness scaling, Stevens had suggested that the psychophysical function for loudness (obtained from other direct ratio scaling procedures) was a power function. The equation for this function was $\psi = k\phi^{0.3}$ where ϕ refers to density of energy flux and ψ refers to loudness. Results obtained with magnitude estimation confirmed this result. Subsequent application of the method of magnitude estimation and companion methods to visual brightness and numerous other sensory continua revealed that the power relation between stimulus magnitude and sensation magnitude had great generality. The exponent of the function varied from one sensory continuum to another, but the form of the function did not. Stevens therefore proposed that a new psychophysical law, the power law, be substituted for the logarithmic law. In "The Surprising Simplicity of Sensory Metrics" S. S. Stevens outlined the development and application of what has come to be called the "new psychophysics."

Ratio scaling procedures have been used extensively in recent years. The arguments and counter-arguments about reliability and sensitivity to changes in experimental procedure or stimulus context remain with us. Ratio scaling procedures have been applied with apparent success to widely varied sensory problems, such as adaptation, inhibition, and spatial and temporal summation. Opinion varies, however, on the validity of any procedure. Luce and Edwards said about proponents of discrimination scaling and direct scaling procedures that "Each group asserts that its preferred scales are more nearly consistent with the bulk of psychophysical data than the other kind of scales; each group can produce impressive arguments to buttress its claim." Luce and Edwards raised the possibility that the two different procedures may tap different sensory processes. Another interesting suggestion for resolving the discrepancy between discriminability and direct ratio scaling procedures was offered by G. Ekman in a short note entitled "Is the Power Law a Special Case of Fechner's Law?"

One common technique of interval scaling divides the observer's judgment continuum into three or more categories. The observer is instructed to sort stimuli into these categories on the basis of their relative perceived magnitudes. This technique, called "category scaling" or "absolute scaling," sometimes yields a logarithmic function when the average category assigned to each stimulus is plotted against stimulus intensity. It does not always do so, however, as L. E. Marks showed in "Stimulus-Range, Number of Categories, and Form of the Category-Scale." Marks found that, with the help of an additive constant whose value was estimated from the data, category scales obtained from a large number of experiments could be described well by a power function. The application of this uniform mathematical description to a large number of scales carries several advantages. One is that the exponent of the power function can be used to describe how the form of the category scale depends on the range of stimulation and on the number of categories. Another is that category scales described by a power function can be compared readily with the scales obtained by ratio scaling procedures applied to the same stimuli.

In most investigations of sensory discrimination or psycho-

physical scaling the stimuli have been varied along one dimension at a time. There are some situations, however, in which it is necessary or desirable to vary the stimuli along more than one physical dimension, or in which variation in a single physical dimension causes concomitant variation in more than one psychological dimension. The latter occurs where a change in the wavelengths of visible light causes a change in the intensity (brightness) and in the quality (hue) of the visual sensation. The former may be seen where an experimenter desires to find how the perceived shape of irregular geometric objects varies as a function of the physical dimensions of the objects. "Shape" is a complex variable and its relevant stimulus correlates are rather difficult to specify. Nevertheless, observers find it quite easy to judge how similar the shape of one object is to that of another. When judgments of the similarity of a number of stimulus objects have been obtained, they can be analyzed by techniques such as factor analysis, which can help to reveal the underlying psychological dimensions of this complex variable.

Judgments of similarity can be obtained by direct or indirect procedures. One indirect procedure requires the observer to judge, for all the possible triads of stimuli, which two of the three stimuli are most similar and which two are least similar. A direct method, called "similarity estimation," is shown in "A Quantitative Principle of Qualitative Similarity" by G. Ekman, T. Engen, T. Künnapas, and R. Lindman. This technique requires the observers to judge similarity on a percentage scale, where zero represents "no similarity" and 100 represents "identity." In this paper, Ekman and his colleagues showed how a simple model could be used to describe the judgmental basis of estimated similarity. This model has application both to cases where similarity varies along a single dimension and where it varies along more than one dimension.

A LAW OF COMPARATIVE JUDGMENT

L. L. Thurstone

The object of this paper is to describe a new psychophysical law which may be called the *law of comparative judgment* and to show some of its special applications in the measurement of psychological values. The law of comparative judgment is implied in Weber's law and in Fechner's law. The law of comparative judgment is applicable not only to the comparison of physical stimulus intensities but also to qualitative comparative judgments such as those of excellence of specimens in an educational scale and it has been applied in the measurement of such psychological values as a series of opinions on disputed public issues. The latter application of the law will be illustrated in a forthcoming study. It should be possible also to verify it on comparative judgments which involve simultaneous and successive contrast.

The law has been derived in a previous article and the present study is mainly a description of some of its applications. Since several new concepts are involved in the formulation of the law it has been necessary to invent several terms to describe them, and these will be repeated here.

Let us suppose that we are confronted with a series of stimuli or specimens such as a series of gray values, cylindrical weights, handwriting specimens, children's drawings, or any other series of stimuli that are subject to comparison. The first requirement is of course a specification as to what it is that we are to judge or compare. It may be gray values, or weights, or excellence, or any other quantitative or qualitative attribute about which we can think "more" or "less" for each specimen. This attribute which may be assigned, as it were, in differing amounts to each specimen defines what we shall call the *psychological continuum* for that particular project in measurement.

As we inspect two or more specimens for the task of comparison there must be some kind of process in us by which we react differently to the several specimens, by which we identify the several degrees of excellence or weight or gray value in the specimens. You may suit your

From *Psychological Review*, 1927, 34, 273–286. Reprinted with permission of the American Psychological Association.

This is one of a series of articles by members of the Behavior Research Staff of the Illinois Institute for Juvenile Research, Chicago, Herman M. Adler, Director. Series B, No. 107.

own predilections in calling this process psychical, neural, chemical, or electrical but it will be called here in a non-committal way *the discriminal process* because its ultimate nature does not concern the formulation of the law of comparative judgment. If then, one handwriting specimen *seems* to be more excellent than a second specimen, then the two discriminal processes of the observer are different, at least on this occasion.

The so-called "just noticeable difference" is contingent on the fact that an observer is not consistent in his comparative judgments from one occasion to the next. He gives different comparative judgments on successive occasions about the same pair of stimuli. Hence we conclude that the discriminal process corresponding to a given stimulus is not fixed. It fluctuates. For any handwriting specimen, for example, there is one discriminal process that is experienced more often with that specimen than other processes which correspond to higher or lower degrees of excellence. This most common process is called here *the modal discriminal process for the given stimulus.*

The psychological continuum or scale is so constructed or defined that the frequencies of the respective discriminal processes for any given stimulus form a normal distribution on the psychological scale. This involves no assumption of a normal distribution or of anything else. The psychological scale is at best an artificial construct. If it has any physical reality we certainly have not the remotest idea what it may be like. We do not assume, therefore, that the distribution of discriminal processes is normal on the scale because that would imply that the scale is there already. We *define* the scale in terms of the frequencies of the discriminal processes for any stimulus. This artificial construct, the psychological scale, is so spaced off that the frequencies of the discriminal processes for any given stimulus form a normal distribution on the scale. The separation on the scale between the discriminal process for a given stimulus on any particular occasion and the modal discriminal process for that stimulus we shall call *the discriminal deviation* on that occasion. If on a particular occasion the observer perceives more than the usual degree of excellence or weight in the specimen in question, the discriminal deviation is at that instant positive. In a similar manner the discriminal deviation at another moment will be negative.

The standard deviation of the distribution of discriminal processes on the scale for a particular specimen will be called its *discriminal dispersion.*

This is the central concept in the present analysis. An ambiguous stimulus which is observed at widely different degrees of excellence or weight or gray value on different occasions will have of course a large discriminal dispersion. Some other stimulus or specimen which is provocative of relatively slight fluctuations in discriminal processes will have, similarly, a small discriminal dispersion.

The scale difference between the discriminal processes of two specimens which are involved in the same judgment will be called *the discriminal difference* on that occasion. If the two stimuli be denoted A and B and if the discriminal processes corresponding to them be denoted a and b on any one occasion, then the discriminal difference will be the scale distance $(a - b)$ which varies of course on different occasions. If, in one of the comparative judgments, A seems to be better than B, then, on that occasion, the discriminal difference $(a - b)$ is positive. If, on another occasion, the stimulus B seems to be the better, then on that occasion the discriminal difference $(a - b)$ is negative.

Finally, the scale distance between the modal discriminal processes for any two specimens is the separation which is assigned to the two specimens on the psychological scale. The two specimens are so allocated on the scale that their separation is equal to the separation between their respective modal discriminal processes.

We can now state the law of comparative judgment as follows:

$$S_1 - S_2 = x_{12} \cdot \sqrt{\sigma_1{}^2 + \sigma_2{}^2 - 2r\sigma_1\sigma_2,} \tag{1}$$

in which

S_1 and S_2 are the psychological scale values of the two compared stimuli.

x_{12} = the sigma value corresponding to the proportion of judgments $p_{1>2}$. When $p_{1>2}$ is greater than .50 the numerical value of x_{12} is positive. When $p_{1>2}$ is less than .50 the numerical value of x_{12} is negative.

σ_1 = discriminal dispersion of stimulus R_1.

σ_2 = discriminal dispersion of stimulus R_2.

r = correlation between the discriminal deviations of R_1 and R_2 in the same judgment.

This law of comparative judgment is basic for all experimental work on Weber's law, Fechner's law, and for all educational and psychological scales in which comparative judgments are involved. Its derivation will not be repeated here because it has been described in a previous article.[1] It applies fundamentally to the judgments of *a single observer* who compares a series of stimuli by the method of paired comparison when no "equal" judgments are allowed. It is a rational equation for the method of constant stimuli. It is assumed that the single observer compares each pair of stimuli a sufficient number of times so that a proportion, $p_{a>b}$, may be determined for each pair of stimuli.

For the practical application of the law of comparative judgment we shall consider five cases which differ in assumptions, approximations, and degree of simplification. The more assumptions we care to make, the simpler will be the observation equations. These five cases are as follows:

CASE I. The equation can be used in its complete form for paired comparison data obtained from a single subject when only two judgments are allowed for each observation such as "heavier" or "lighter," "better" or "worse," etc. There will be one observation equation for every observed proportion of judgments. It would be written, in its complete form, thus:

$$S_1 - S_2 - x_{12} \cdot \sqrt{\sigma_1{}^2 + \sigma_2{}^2 - 2r\sigma_1\sigma_2} = 0. \tag{1}$$

According to this equation every pair of stimuli presents the possibility of a different correlation between the discriminal deviations. If this degree of freedom is allowed, the problem of psychological scaling would be insoluble because every observation equation would introduce a new unknown and the number of unknowns would then always be greater than the number of observation equations. In order to make the problem soluble, it is necessary to make at least one assumption, namely that the correlation between discriminal deviations is practically constant throughout the stimulus series and for the single observer. Then, if we have n stimuli or specimens in the scale, we shall have $\frac{1}{2} \cdot n(n - 1)$ observation equations when each specimen is compared with every other specimen. Each specimen has a scale value, S_1, and a discriminal dispersion, σ_1, to be determined. There are therefore $2n$ unknowns. The scale value of one of the specimens is chosen as an origin and its discriminal dispersion as a unit of measurement, while r is an unknown which is assumed to be constant for the whole series.

[1] Thurstone, L. L., "Psychophysical Analysis," *Amer. J. Psychol.*, July, 1927.

Hence, for a scale of n specimens there will be $(2n - 1)$ unknowns. The smallest number of specimens for which the problem is soluble is five. For such a scale there will be nine unknowns, four scale values, four discriminal dispersions, and r. For a scale of five specimens there will be ten observation equations.

The statement of the law of comparative judgment in the form of equation (1) involves one theoretical assumption which is probably of minor importance. It assumes that all positive discriminal differences $(a - b)$ are judged $A > B$, and that all negative discriminal differences $(a - b)$ are judged $A < B$. This is probably not absolutely correct when the discriminal differences of either sign are very small. The assumption would not affect the experimentally observed proportion $p_{A>B}$ if the small positive discriminal difference occurred as often as the small negative ones. As a matter of fact, when $p_{A>B}$ is greater than .50 the small positive discriminal differences $(a - b)$ are slightly more frequent than the negative perceived differences $(a - b)$. It is probable that rather refined experimental procedures are necessary to isolate this effect. The effect is ignored in our present analysis.

CASE II. The law of comparative judgment as described under Case I refers fundamentally to a series of judgments *of a single observer.* It does not constitute an assumption to say that the discriminal processes for a single observer give a normal frequency distribution on the psychological continuum. That is a part of the definition of the psychological scale. But it does constitute an assumption to take for granted that the various degrees of an attribute of a specimen perceived in it by *a group* of subjects is a normal distribution. For example, if a weight-cylinder is lifted by an observer several hundred times in comparison with other cylinders, it is possible to define or construct the psychological scale so that the distribution of the apparent weights of the cylinder for the single observer is normal. It is probably safe to assume that the distribution of apparent weights for *a group* of subjects, each subject perceiving the weight only once, is also normal on the same scale. To transfer the reasoning in the same way from a single observer to a group of observers for specimens such as handwriting or English Composition is not so certain. For practical purposes it may be assumed that when *a group* of observers perceives a specimen of handwriting, the distribution of excellence that they read into the specimen is normal on the psychological continuum of perceived excellence. At least this is a safe assumption if the group is not split in some curious way with prejudices for or against particular elements of the specimen.

With the assumption just described, the law of comparative judgment, derived for the method of constant stimuli with two responses, can be extended to data collected from a group of judges in which each judge compares each stimulus with every other stimulus only once. The other assumptions of Case I apply also to Case II.

CASE III. Equation (1) is awkward to handle as an observation equation for a scale with a large number of specimens. In fact the arithmetical labor of constructing an educational or psychological scale with it is almost prohibitive. The equation can be simplified if the correlation r can be assumed to be either zero or unity. It is a safe assumption that when the stimulus series is very homogeneous with no distracting attributes, the correlation between discriminal deviations is low and possibly even zero unless we encounter the effect of simultaneous or successive contrast. If we accept the correlation as zero, we are really assuming that the degree of excellence which an observer perceives in one of the specimens has no influence on the degree of excellence that he perceives in the comparison specimen. There are two effects that may be operative here and which are antagonistic to each other.

1. If you look at two handwriting specimens in a mood slightly more generous and tolerant than ordinarily, you may perceive a degree of excellence in specimen A a little higher than its mean excellence. But at the same moment specimen B is also judged a little higher than its average or mean excellence for the same reason. To the extent that such a factor is at work the discriminal deviations will tend to vary together and the correlation r will be high and positive.

2. The opposite effect is seen in *simultaneous contrast*. When the correlation between the discriminal deviations is negative the law of comparative judgment gives an exaggerated psychological difference $(S_1 - S_2)$ which we know as simultaneous or successive contrast. In this type of comparative judgment the discriminal deviations are negatively associated. It is probable that this effect tends to be a minimum when the specimens have other perceivable attributes, and that it is a maximum when other distracting stimulus differences are removed. If this statement should be experimentally verified, it would constitute an interesting generalization in perception.

If our last generalization is correct, it should be a safe assumption to write $r = 0$ for those scales in which the specimens are rather complex such as handwriting specimens and children's drawings. If we look at two handwriting specimens and perceive one of them as unusually fine, it probably tends to depress somewhat the degree of excellence we would ordinarily perceive in the comparison specimen, but this effect is slight compared with the simultaneous contrast perceived in lifted weights and in gray values. Furthermore, the simultaneous contrast is slight with small stimulus differences and it must be recalled that psychological scales are based on comparisons in the subliminal or barely supraliminal range.

The correlation between discriminal deviations is probably high when the two stimuli give simultaneous contrast and are quite far apart on the scale. When the range for the correlation is reduced to a scale distance comparable with the difference limen, the correlation probably is reduced nearly to zero. At any rate, in order to simplify equation (1) we shall assume that it is zero. This represents the comparative judgment in which the evaluation of one of the specimens has no influence on the evaluation of the other specimen in the paired judgment. The law then takes the following form.

$$S_1 - S_2 = x_{12} \cdot \sqrt{\sigma_1^2 + \sigma_2^2}. \tag{2}$$

CASE IV. If we can make the additional assumption that the discriminal dispersions are not subject to gross variation, we can considerably simplify the equation so that it becomes linear and therefore much easier to handle. In equation (2) we let

$$\sigma_2 = \sigma_1 + d,$$

in which d is assumed to be at least smaller than σ_1 and preferably a fraction of σ_1 such as .1 to .5. Then equation (2) becomes

$$\begin{aligned} S_1 - S_2 &= x_{12} \cdot \sqrt{\sigma_1^2 + \sigma_2^2} \\ &= x_{12} \cdot \sqrt{\sigma_1^2 + (\sigma_1 + d)^2} \\ &= x_{12} \cdot \sqrt{\sigma_1^2 + \sigma_1^2 + 2\sigma_1 d + d^2}. \end{aligned}$$

If d is small, the term d^2 may be dropped. Hence

$$\begin{aligned} S_1 - S_2 &= x_{12} \cdot \sqrt{2\sigma_1^2 + 2\sigma_1 d} \\ &= x_{12} \cdot \sqrt{2\sigma_1}(\sigma_1 + d)^{1/2}. \end{aligned}$$

Expanding $(\sigma_1 + d)^{1/2}$ we have

$$\begin{aligned} (\sigma_1 + d)^{1/2} &= \sigma_1^{1/2} + \tfrac{1}{2}\sigma_1^{-(1/2)}d - \tfrac{1}{4}\sigma_1^{-(3/2)}d^2 \\ &= \sqrt{\sigma_1} + \frac{d}{2\sqrt{\sigma_1}} - \frac{d^2}{4\sqrt{\sigma_1^3}}. \end{aligned}$$

The third term may be dropped when d^2 is small. Hence

$$(\sigma_1 + d)^{1/2} = \sqrt{\sigma_1} + \frac{d}{2\sqrt{\sigma_1}}.$$

Substituting,

$$S_1 - S_2 = x_{12} \cdot \sqrt{2\sigma_1} \left[\sqrt{\sigma_1} + \frac{d}{2\sqrt{\sigma_1}} \right]$$

$$= x_{12} \left[\sigma_1\sqrt{2} + \frac{d}{\sqrt{2}} \right].$$

But $d = \sigma_2 - \sigma_1$;

$$\therefore S_1 - S_2 = x_{12} \frac{\sigma_2}{\sqrt{2}} + x_{12} \frac{\sigma_1}{\sqrt{2}}$$

or

$$S_1 - S_2 = .707x_{12}\sigma_2 + .707x_{12}\sigma_1. \tag{3}$$

Equation (3) is linear and very easily handled. If $\sigma_2 - \sigma_1$ is small compared with σ_1, equation (3) gives a close approximation to the true values of S and σ for each specimen.

If there are n stimuli in the scale there will be $(2n - 2)$ unknowns, namely a scale value S and a discriminal dispersion σ for each specimen. The scale value for one of the specimens may be chosen as the origin or zero since the origin of the psychological scale is arbitrary. The discriminal dispersion of the same specimen may be chosen as a unit of measurement for the scale. With n specimens in the series there will be $\frac{1}{2}n(n - 1)$ observation equations. The minimum number of specimens for which the scaling problem can be solved is then four, at which number we have six observation equations and six unknowns.

CASE V. The simplest case involves the assumption that all the discriminal dispersions are equal. This may be legitimate for rough measurement such as Thorndike's handwriting scale or the Hillegas Scale of English Composition. Equation (2) then becomes

$$S_1 - S_2 = x_{12} \cdot \sqrt{2\sigma^2}$$

$$= x_{12}\sigma \cdot \sqrt{2}.$$

But since the assumed constant discriminal dispersion is the unit of measurement we have

$$S_1 - S_2 = 1.4142x_{12}. \tag{4}$$

This is a simple observation equation which may be used for rather coarse scaling. It measures the scale distance between two specimens as directly proportional to the sigma value of the observed proportion of judgments $p_{1>2}$. This is the equation that is basic for Thorndike's procedure in scaling handwriting and children's drawings, although he has not shown the theory underlying his scaling procedure. His unit of measurement was the standard deviation of the discriminal differences, which is $.707\sigma$ when the discriminal dispersions are constant. In future scaling problems equation (3) will probably be found to be the most useful.

WEIGHTING THE OBSERVATION EQUATIONS

The observation equations obtained under any of the five cases are not of the same reliability and hence they should not all be equally weighted. Two observed proportions of judgments such as $p_{1>2} = .99$ and $p_{1>3} = .55$ are not equally reliable. The proportion of judgments $p_{1>2}$ is one of the observations that determine the scale separation between S_1 and S_2. It measures the scale distance $(S_1 - S_2)$ in terms of the standard deviation, σ_{1-2}, of the distribution of discriminal differences for the two stimuli R_1 and R_2. This distribution is necessarily normal by the definition of the psychological scale.

The standard error of a proportion of a normal frequency distribution is

$$\sigma_p = \frac{\sigma}{Z} \cdot \sqrt{\frac{pq}{N}}.^2$$

in which σ is the standard deviation of the distribution, Z is the ordinate corresponding to p, and $q = 1 - p$ while N is the number of cases on which the proportion is ascertained. The term σ in the present case is the standard deviation σ_{1-2} of the distribution of discriminal differences. Hence the standard error of $p_{1>2}$ is

$$\sigma_{p1>2} = \frac{\sigma_{1-2}}{Z} \cdot \sqrt{\frac{pq}{N}}. \tag{5}$$

But since, by equation (2)

$$\sigma_{1-2} = \sqrt{\sigma_1{}^2 + \sigma_2{}^2} \tag{6}$$

---

[2] See Kelley, T. L., *Statistical Method*, p. 90, equation 43.

and since this may be written approximately, by equation (3), as

$$\sigma_{1-2} = .707(\sigma_1 + \sigma_2) \tag{7}$$

we have

$$\sigma_{p1>2} = \frac{.707(\sigma_1 + \sigma_2)}{Z} \cdot \sqrt{\frac{pq}{N}}. \tag{8}$$

The weight, w_{1-2}, that should be assigned to observation equation (2) is the reciprocal of the square of its standard error. Hence

$$w_{1-2} = \frac{1}{\sigma_{p1>2}{}^2} = \frac{Z^2 N}{.5(\sigma_1 + \sigma_2)^2 p \cdot q}. \tag{9}$$

It will not repay the trouble to attempt to carry the factor $(\sigma_1 + \sigma_2)^2$ in the formula because this factor contains two of the unknowns, and because it destroys the linearity of the observation equation (3), while the only advantage gained would be a refinement in the weighting of the observation equations. Since only the weighting is here at stake, it may be approximated by eliminating this factor. The factor .5 is a constant. It has no effect, and the weighting then becomes

$$w_{1-2} = \frac{Z^2 N}{pq}. \tag{10}$$

By arranging the experiments in such a way that all the observed proportions are based on the same number of judgments the factor N becomes a constant and therefore has no effect on the weighting. Hence

$$w_{1-2} = \frac{Z^2}{pq}. \tag{11}$$

This weighting factor is entirely determined by the proportion, $p_{1>2}$ of judgments "1 is better than 2" and it can therefore be readily ascertained by the Kelley-Wood tables. The weighted form of observation equation (3) therefore becomes

$$wS_1 - wS_2 - .707wx_{12}\sigma_2 - .707wx_{12}\sigma_1 = 0. \tag{12}$$

This equation is linear and can therefore be easily handled. The coefficient $.707wx_{12}$ is entirely determined by the observed value of p for each equation and therefore a facilitating table can be prepared to reduce the labor of setting up the normal equations. The same weighting would be used for any of the observation equations in the five cases since the weight is solely a function of p when the factor σ_{1-2} is ignored for the weighting formula.

SUMMARY

A law of comparative judgment has been formulated which is expressed in its complete form as equation (1). This law defines the psychological scale or continuum. It allocates the compared stimuli on the continuum. It expresses the experimentally observed proportion, $p_{1>2}$ of judgments "1 is stronger (better, lighter, more excellent) than 2" as a function of the scale values of the stimuli, their respective discriminal dispersions, and the correlation between the paired discriminal deviations.

The formulation of the law of comparative judgment involves the use of a new psychophysical concept, namely, the *discriminal dispersion*. Closely related to this concept are those of the *discriminal process*, the *modal discriminal process*, the *discriminal deviation*, the *discriminal difference*. All of these psychophysical concepts concern the ambiguity or qualitative variation with which one stimulus is perceived by the same observer on different occasions.

The psychological scale has been defined as the particular linear spacing of the confused stimuli which yields a normal distribution of the discriminal processes for any one of the stimuli. The validity of this definition of the psychological continuum can be experimentally and objectively tested. If the stimuli are so spaced out on the scale that the distribution of discriminal processes for one of the stimuli is normal, then these scale allocations should remain the same when they are defined by the distribution of discriminal processes of any other stimulus within the confusing range. It is physically impossible for this condition to obtain for several psychological scales defined by different types of distribution of the discriminal processes. Consistency can be found only for one form of distribution of discriminal processes as a basis for defining the scale. If, for example, the scale is defined on the basis of a rectangular distribution of the discriminal processes, it is easily shown by experimental data that there will be gross discrepancies between experimental and theoretical proportions, $p_{1>2}$. The residuals should be investigated to ascertain whether they are a minimum when the normal or Gaussian distribution of discriminal processes is used as a basis for defining the psychological scale. Triangular and other forms of distribution might be tried. Such an experimental demonstration would constitute perhaps the most fundamental discovery that has been made in the field of psychological measurement. Lacking such proof and since the Gaussian distribution of discriminal processes yields scale values that agree very closely with the experimental data, I have defined the psychological continuum that is implied in Weber's Law, in Fechner's Law, and in educational quality scales as that particular linear spacing of the stimuli which gives a Gaussian distribution of discriminal processes.

The law of comparative judgment has been considered in this paper under five cases which involve different assumptions and degrees of simplification for practical use. These may be summarized as follows.

CASE I. The law is stated in complete form by equation (1). It is a rational equation for the method of paired comparison. It is applicable to all problems involving the method of constant stimuli for the measurement of both quantitative and qualitative stimulus differences. It concerns the repeated judgments of a single observer.

CASE II. The same equation (1) is here used for a *group* of observers, each observer making only one judgment for each pair of stimuli, or one serial ranking of all the stimuli. It assumes that the distribution of the perceived relative values of each stimulus is normal for the group of observers.

CASE III. The assumptions of Cases I. and II. are involved here also and in addition it is assumed that the correlation between the discriminal deviations of the same judgment are uncorrelated. This leads to the simpler form of the law in equation (2).

CASE IV. Besides the preceding assumptions the still simpler form of the law in equation (3) assumes that the discriminal deviations are not grossly different so that in general one may write

$$\sigma_2 - \sigma_1 < \sigma_1$$

and that preferably

$$\sigma_2 - \sigma_1 = d$$

in which d is a small fraction of σ_1.

CASE V. This is the simplest formulation of the law and it involves, in addition to previous assumptions, the assumption that all the discriminal dispersions are equal. This assumption should not be made without experimental test. Case V. is identical with Thorndike's method of constructing quality scales for handwriting and for children's drawings. His unit of measurement is the standard deviation of the distribution of discriminal differences when the discriminal dispersions are assumed to be equal.

Since the standard error of the observed proportion of judgments, $p_{1>2}$, is not uniform, it is advisable to weight each of the observation equations by a factor shown in equation (11) which is applicable to the observation equations in any of the five cases considered. Its application to equation (3) leads to the weighted observation equation (12).

ADVANTAGES OF THE DISCRIMINABILITY CRITERION FOR A LOUDNESS SCALE

W. R. Garner

During the past several years there has been a resurgence of interest in the nature and function of loudness scales. To some extent this renewed interest is due to the opportunity provided by the American Standards Association for a re-examination of the validity of the present loudness standard. And to some extent the interest has been due to experiments which have raised some doubt about the validity of the present loudness scale.

While it is probably a mistake to try to dichotomize anything, it seems fair to state that there are two basic classes of experimental technique which have been used to establish loudness scales — those which assume the validity of a direct numerical response on the part of an observer, and those which use some measure of discriminability to establish loudness units. The first of these methodological classes requires the assumption that human listeners experience auditory intensity as a magnitude of loudness and that they can describe this

From *Journal of the Acoustical Society of America*, 1958, 30, 1005–1012. Reprinted with permission of the author and the American Institute of Physics.

This report was prepared under Contract N5-ori-166, Task Order 1, between the Office of Naval Research and The Johns Hopkins University. This is Report No. 166-I-216, Project Designation No. NR 145-089, under that contract. Much of the material contained in this report was presented at the Fifteenth International Congress of Psychology, Brussels, 1957.

magnitude with a number system of some kind. The techniques which are based on these assumptions we can call the *direct response* methods, since in all of them some form of direct numerical reporting of loudness is required of the observer, and these numerical values are used in the actual construction of the loudness scales.

The other basic class of techniques used in loudness scaling are those which require some measure of *discriminability* for the loudness unit. The discriminability techniques assume that units of discriminability can be equated with units of loudness. The use of discriminability is on the surface an indirect technique compared to the use of the direct responses, but it is an indirect approach which has proved to be very valuable in many areas of psychological measurement. For example, the measurement of intelligence with the IQ scale has been eminently successful, and yet measurement of intelligence is essentially an indirect approach. And modern developments in opinion and attitude measurement have used the indirect approach with very great success. It may be that even for the measurement of loudness the long way around is the shortest way home.

Historically, of course, the discriminability approach to the problem of loudness scaling takes precedence. Fechner, in integrating the Weber fraction, assumed that the just-noticeable difference (jnd) is a legitimate unit of sensory magnitude, and provided the start of a long and continuing argument about the validity of his assumption. In recent years some psychologists, as well as other acoustical scientists, have argued strongly against the legitimacy of the Fechnerian assumption. Stevens [1] in particular has been a vociferous and prolific proponent of the validity of the direct-response scaling methods, and has challenged the validity of the Fechnerian assumption for loudness scaling on the grounds that discriminability scales do not agree with some of the direct response scales. This lack of agreement, however, can equally well be used to challenge the validity of the direct response methods.

The purpose of the present paper is to summarize some of the pertinent evidence concerning this issue and to make an argument for the use of the discriminability criterion in loudness scaling. Simply stated, my argument is that those psychological scaling methods which make use of the discriminability criterion are more legitimate, valid, and

[1] S. S. Stevens, *Psychol. Rev.* 64, 153–181 (1957).

meaningful for the scaling of loudness than are those methods which make use of various types of direct response on the part of the observer.

DIRECT RESPONSE METHODS

There are many different forms of the direct response methods, and the methods are so varied that at times it seems impossible to group them into a single meaningful category. They all have, however, one essential characteristic in common, namely, that an observer is expected to understand and to use some type of numerical scale in carrying out his experimentally assigned task, and the experimenter must assume that the properties of the number scale have been correctly used by the observer in order to construct a loudness scale from the data.

One subclass of the direct response techniques is that involving ratio scaling. Stevens [1] has described several varieties of this subclass. In all of them, two different stimulus intensities are used for a single judgment, and the observer is required either to assign a single ratio value, to produce a loudness ratio of a stated value, to assign two numerical values, or to produce stimuli by adjustment of intensity until they match two stated numerical values.

Another subclass of the direct response methods is that involving only an understanding of interval properties on the part of the observer. The observer may be required to produce a tone with a loudness bisecting the loudnesses of two other tones (method of bisection), or, more generally, he may be required to adjust a series of tones to produce a set of equally distant loudnesses (method of equisection).

Still a third subclass of direct response methods is that in which the observer makes a single numerical response (usually from a prescribed set of numbers) to each of a series of stimuli presented in order. This general method has been called absolute judgment by Garner and Hake,[2] and category scaling by Stevens and Galanter.[3] The latter authors have used the term category scaling to suggest their lack of confidence that observers using this procedure in fact use the ratio and interval properties of the number scale. In terms of a logical analysis of the method, however, it does belong with the direct response pro-

[2] W. R. Garner and H. W. Hake, *Psychol. Rev.* 58, 446–459 (1951).
[3] S. S. Stevens and E. H. Galanter, *J. Exptl. Psychol.* 54, 377–411 (1957).

cedures, since observers are required to use numbers and the numerical responses are used to construct loudness scales.

RATIO SCALING

While, logically, all of the direct response procedures should be discussed as a group, the present discussion will be concerned primarily with the ratio scaling procedures, particularly the variety called fractionation, in which the observer either adjusts one of two tonal intensities to produce a stated fraction of loudness or numerically describes the loudness ratio produced by two different tones. These techniques are the most commonly used; the present *sone* scale of loudness is based primarily on them; and Stevens, in his various writings, clearly assumes this procedure to give the most valid results. This assumption is so strong for Stevens that he uses results from the fractionation procedure to determine the validity of all other procedures. As we shall see, this approach would exclude the majority of scaling techniques as invalid.

As a starting point, we can note that the validity of a loudness scale based on the ratio scaling procedures rests entirely on its face validity — i.e., we must assume that observers are in fact capable of describing their experience of loudness with the kind of arithmetic implied by the fractionation procedure. Since observers actually use ratio numbers for their responses, or actually make an adjustment of the intensities of tones to produce a stated fraction or ratio without violent objection, we assume that the responses truly reflect ratio properties of the loudness scale. We cannot, however, accept simple face validity of the observers' proper use of ratios any more than we would feel free to accept the validity of the observers' proper use of exponents to describe their loudnesses.

The fact is that the face validity of these procedures is extremely questionable. Certainly one of the first requirements for accepting the validity of this type of judgment is that other procedures which logically imply the same kind (or a simpler kind) of arithmetic understanding on the part of an observer should give results which are in agreement. If a loudness scale is unique for the fractionation procedure, rather than being general for all direct response methods, we are on very shaky ground.

The equisection method, or its special case, the bisection method, is certainly a technique which should give equivalent results. Rarely, however, have the same results been found when this technique has been used.[4] When I tried this procedure a few years ago,[5] I found that individual observers using both the equisection and the fractionation procedures did not agree with themselves on the shape of the loudness function. Furthermore, scales based on average results with these two methods gave quite different loudness scales, as shown in Fig. 1. The curves shown there were obtained from 18 observers, each of whom was required to adjust the intensity of one tone of a pair to produce a ratio of half, and also to produce five- and seven-tone equisections. The two curves have considerably different curvatures, with the equisection curve being more linearly related to loudness level (intensity level of 1000-cps tone). The data of Newman, Volkmann, and Stevens,[4] and of Wolff[4] are even more linearly related to log intensity. It is quite clear that there is little agreement between loudness scales based on fractionation data and scales based on equisection data.

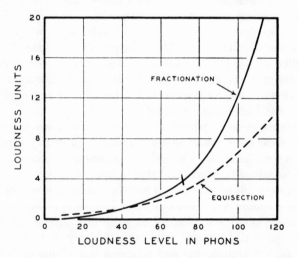

FIGURE 1   *Loudness scales based on equisection and on fractionation data. Each scale is based on data from the same 18 observers. These data are from Garner.*[5]

The absolute judgment procedures logically should also, of course, produce loudness scales in agreement with those obtained with the

[4] Newman, Volkmann, and Stevens, *Am. J. Psychol.* 49, 134–137 (1937); W. Wolff, *Z. Psychol.* 136, 325–340 (1935).

[5] W. R. Garner, *J. Acoust. Soc. Am.* 26, 73–88 (1954).

fractionation procedure. Stevens and Galanter [3] have summarized data from many experiments of this type, including some of my own, and no elaboration is required here. It is sufficient to point out that there is little agreement between loudness scales based on this method and those based on the fractionation procedure. More reference will be made to this point later.

Another disadvantage of the fractionation technique is that interobserver differences are so great that while measures of central tendency can be computed, they have little value in predicting what any single observer will do in an experiment. In one experiment of mine on half-loudness adjustments,[6] interobserver differences provided the largest single source of variability in the data; at high intensities the standard deviation of the fractional intensities was 6 db, and in some cases observers differed from each other by as much as 16 db. Such differences in attenuations required for half-loudness, of course, make tremendous differences in the resultant loudness scales. It is interesting to note in this connection that in the experiment in which the same observers made both fractionation and equisection judgments, interobserver differences in the loudness scales were considerably smaller with the equisection procedure than with the fractionation procedure. Thus, by this criterion, the equisection method should be accepted as more valid than the fractionation method.

Still another question which can be raised is whether the fractionation procedure gives results that are relatively invariant from experimenter to experimenter, where slight procedural differences can be assumed to exist. The fractionation procedure has been notorious for producing large differences with minor variations in experimental procedure. In a summary of results by many investigators, Stevens [7] shows that at high intensities different experimenters report attenuations necessary for half-loudness from approximately 5 to over 20 db. Stevens, Rogers and Herrnstein [8] repeated one of the earlier experiments which had shown large required attenuations for half-loudness, and essentially duplicated the results when the procedure was duplicated as nearly as possible. These authors concluded that that particular procedure should not be used. An alternative conclusion is that the basic method is at best unreliable, and at worst invalid.

[6] W. R. Garner, *J. Acoust. Soc. Am.* 24, 153–157 (1952).

[7] S. S. Stevens, *J. Acoust. Soc. Am.* 27, 815–829 (1955).

[8] Stevens, Rogers, and Herrnstein, *J. Acoust. Soc. Am.* 27, 326–328 (1955).

Geiger and Firestone [9] had shown much earlier that the use of different stated ratios gave different loudness scales. And more recently Stevens and Poulton [10] showed that observers required to adjust to a half-loudness value differed on the average by more than 6 db when they used a standard decibel attenuator rather than a specially constructed attenuator which varied according to the *sone* scale of loudness. Once again Stevens (with Poulton) concluded that one of the procedures is right and the other wrong. An alternative conclusion is that the basic procedure is invalid.

Another problem which raises considerable doubt about the validity of ratio scaling procedures is that of the stability of a single observer's judgments in the course of a single experiment. I am referring here to what has been called the context effect, in which the judgments and responses of an observer seem to be more influenced by the context of stimuli provided him than they are by any loudness scale in his sensorium. In one experiment of mine,[11] for example, three different groups of ten observers each were required to state whether the second (comparison) of a pair of tones was more or less than half as loud as the first (standard) of the pair. All groups had standard tones of 90 db SPL, but each group had a different range of intensities for the comparison tones. One group had comparison tones from 55 to 65 db, another from 65 to 75 db, and the third from 75 to 85 db. After a total of 600 judgments was made by each observer, his median value was determined and then the mean half-loudness value for each group. These mean values for each group were not significantly different from the mid-points of the ranges of comparison stimuli, indicating that the half-loudness values had been completely determined by the stimulus context, and not at all by any "true" half-loudness value on which the observers could base their judgments. Such a result suggests that there is little meaning to fractionation judgments.

One implication from these results is that we ought to obtain data from an experiment in which there is no stimulus context, with the assumption that then only the "true" loudness scale could influence the results. In another experiment, I came as close as possible to doing just that.[12] A total of 135 observers was used and the very first judg-

[9] P. H. Geiger and F. A. Firestone, *J. Acoust. Soc. Am.* 5, 25–30 (1933).

[10] S. S. Stevens and E. C. Poulton, *J. Exptl. Psychol.* 51, 71–78 (1956).

[11] W. R. Garner, *J. Exptl. Psychol.* 48, 218–234 (1954).

[12] W. R. Garner, *J. Exptl. Psychol.* 55, 482–485 (1958).

ment of each observer was recorded — a judgment made before any specific stimulus context could operate. The results of these judgments are shown in Fig. 2, where the percentage of judgments of "more than half as loud" are plotted as a function of the intensity of the comparison tone. For these data, the computed half-loudness value is 12.5 db below the level of the standard. However, even here the picture is not entirely clear. These data are probably biased due to the difficulty observers had in clearly understanding that they were to make judgments with respect to half-loudness rather than to equal loudness (no demonstration trials were possible). Since the second tone was always less loud than the first, this factor would give a biased estimate of any true half-loudness value. Several observers reported afterwards that they had judged with respect to equal loudness, and their data were discarded. How many others may have done the same thing and not admitted it, is impossible to tell.

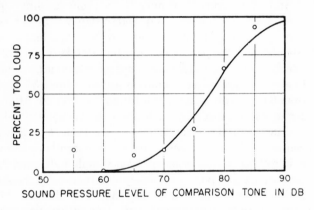

FIGURE 2   *Half-loudness judgments without prior stimulus context. A standard tone of 90 db SPL was presented first, followed, one second later, with a comparison tone of intensity indicated on the abscissa. The ordinate shows percent of observers judging the second tone more than half as loud as the first. Each point represents the first judgments of 15 different observers, except those at 65 and at 75 db, where 30 observers were used. These data are from Garner.*[12]

But even allowing the possibility that there is a true half-loudness value which can be determined from such experiments, there are other questions. It is clear that the confidence level of observers making such judgments is extremely low, since the context effect operates so rapidly after the first presentation of the stimulus. Figure 3, for example, shows

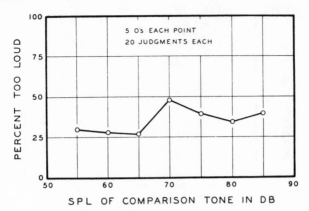

FIGURE 3   *Half-loudness judgments showing rapid effect of stimulus context. Each of 5 observers made 20 successive judgments whether the second tone of a pair was more than half as loud as the first tone, which had an intensity of 90 db SPL. For each observer the second tone was in a range of 4 db around the mid-value indicated on the abscissa. Since data for each point were obtained from different observers, no over-all context effect is operating.*

the results of this same experiment after 20 successive judgments had been made. Each observer was given stimulus intensities in a range of 4 db around the intensity of the first comparison tone he heard (the value plotted on the abscissa of Fig. 3). These data show no significant differences between the various intensities, i.e., we have no evidence that there is any single value which can properly be called a half-loudness value. It should be remembered here that data for each point were obtained from different observers so that no context effect is operating for the entire range of stimulus values.

Within a single group of observers, of course, the context effect is operating. This context effect produces the same total number of "too loud" judgments regardless of the actual intensities presented to the observer. The same effect produces discrimination between comparison stimuli heard by a single observer, and this discrimination occurs just as rapidly as does over-all neutralization of judgment. Figure 4 shows the results for the various comparison stimuli heard by one group of observers — the group plotted at 85 db in Fig. 3. The total of 20 judgments made by each observer in this group was actually composed of four judgments of each of five different comparison intensities. Notice that while on the average somewhat less than half the

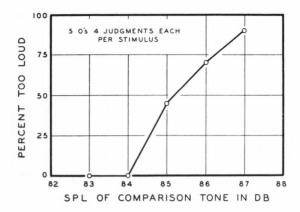

FIGURE 4   *Half-loudness judgments showing the effect of stimulus context within a single group of observers. This graph shows the detailed judgments of the five observers used for the 85 db condition shown in Fig. 3. Each observer made four judgments at each of the five different intensities indicated on the abscissa.*

judgments were "more than half as loud," there is considerable discrimination between stimuli spaced just 1 db apart. Not once was either 83 or 84 db called "too loud," and there were altogether 40 opportunities for one of them to be so judged. The actual sequence in which the first seven comparison stimuli were presented is 85, 85, 83, 87, 86, 84, 84 db. Thus an 83, which when presented first would nearly always be called "too loud" is always called "too soft" when the observer has heard just two preceding comparison stimuli, both of them just 2 db more intense. Likewise an 84-db stimulus is always called "too soft" after the observer has heard just 5 preceding stimuli, not all of them louder than this one. It is difficult to conceive of a context effect which operates more rapidly and with such a compelling effect. In fact, these data strongly suggest that observers have no confidence in their judgments of half-loudness.

These results make it clear that the context effect operates almost immediately, so that meaningless results are obtained from experiments of this sort if only a few trials are used for each observer. Or, to put this another way, any amount of prior stimulus experience in the judgmental situation, no matter how seemingly trivial, will affect the nature of the judgments made. When a method of adjustment is used, for example, the comparison stimulus must be preset to some intensity which the observer hears when he starts to make his adjustments, but this preset value will affect his final adjustment. In other words, as soon as the observer has heard the standard and comparison stimuli, he is no longer an unbiased observer, and his results have, at best, limited validity.

DISCRIMINABILITY PROCEDURES

Just as there are many forms of direct response methods, so also are there many forms of discriminability scaling methods. The original Fechner law requires the integration of jnd's, without specifying the method by which the jnd is to be obtained. Nevertheless, certainly the simple addition of jnd's is one basic method of obtaining a loudness scale based on discriminability.

In recent years techniques based on Thurstone's classic work have become more popular. The paired-comparison technique requires that all stimuli in a set be paired with each other in all possible combinations for a comparative judgment, and then a scale is constructed based on the assumption that equal units of discriminability are equal units of magnitude, in this case loudness. The paired-comparison technique is not particularly appropriate for loudness scaling, and, to my knowledge, has never been used for this purpose.

There is also a group of techniques based on the Thurstone procedures which have been used for loudness scaling more recently. These techniques all make use of direct ratings (absolute judgments) as the experimental technique, but the loudness scale values are based on the dispersions and overlaps of the distributions of responses. Garner and Hake [2] describe one such scaling procedure which results in an "equal discriminability" scale based on data obtained from the absolute judgment procedure.

The one factor which all of these techniques have in common is that they do not depend on the assumed validity of the direct response of the observer, but rather make use of the statistical characteristics of entire distributions of responses. Normally some measure of dispersion is used as the unit of scale value.

As a starting point, we are in exactly the same situation with these procedures as we are with the direct response procedures. We start with an arbitrary assumption (taking face validity again) that measures of discriminability or judgmental dispersion are legitimate measures of sensory magnitude. There is no problem here of whether Fechner's original assumption has been proved invalid by comparison with direct response methods, since we have no more than face validity for these methods either.

However, loudness scales based on the discriminability criterion show much less variability between observers than do scales based on fractionation procedures, as was true also for scales based on the equisection procedure. In addition, and more importantly, loudness scales based on the discriminability criterion show much less effect of specific experimental procedures and different experimental conditions than do the direct response scales. For example, Garner [13] showed that an equal discriminability scale based on dispersions of absolute judgments has essentially the same shape as a scale based on the integration of jnd's, when Riesz' data [14] were used for the jnd's. And, of course, there is a vast literature on jnd's for auditory intensity showing that only to a slight extent is the relation between auditory sensitivity and intensity a function of the particular experimental method. These various techniques all give loudness functions which are roughly linear with log intensity, although showing some positive acceleration. The equal discriminability scale shows, in addition, a greater slope at the two ends of the continuum presented to the observer for judgment — an effect which seems to be due to subjective anchoring. At any rate, with the relative stability of the loudness function shown with these various techniques, we can feel a bit more certain that we do not have loudness scales unique to a highly specific procedure.

One of the most compelling arguments in favor of the discriminability procedures, however, is the relative imperviousness of these techniques to the context effect. In one experiment of mine,[13] for example, judgments on a 21-point scale were obtained over a wide range of intensities with two quite different distributions of stimuli. In one distribution, the stimuli were spaced every 5 db. In the other distribution, the stimuli covered the same range of intensities, but the distribution of them was severely skewed, with stimuli crowded into the upper half of the intensity range. This set of stimuli was actually distributed to provide equal spacing on a loudness function based on the observer's own fractionation judgments, i.e., the stimuli were deliberately distributed to correspond to direct responses of the fractionation type. The discriminability scales based on these two distributions of stimuli are shown in Fig. 5, with the open circles representing stimuli spaced

[13] W. R. Garner, *J. Exptl. Psychol.* 43, 232–238 (1952).

[14] R. R. Riesz, *Phys. Rev.* 31, 867–875 (1928).

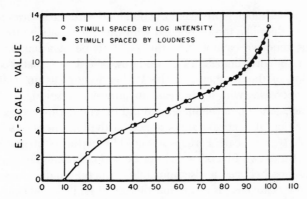

FIGURE 5   *A scale of equal discriminability based on two different distributions of stimuli. For the open circles, the stimuli used were spaced every 5 db; for the closed circles, the stimuli were spaced equally according to a loudness scale constructed from the observers' own half-loudness judgments. The same six observers were used for each set of judgments. These data are from Garner.*[13]

by log intensity, and the closed circles representing stimuli spaced by the fractionation loudness function. Clearly the two sets of points fall on the same function with remarkable closeness. And equally clearly we are dealing with a relatively invariant and stable property of the human perceptual system when we use a discriminability function.

There are, of course, individual differences with these methods, and differences due to experimental method and procedure. But these differences are slight compared to those found with the direct response methods. Certainly by contrast we can feel that the discriminability procedures are measuring some aspect of the perceptual system which is a limiting property — a property little affected by factors which easily affect the ratio scaling procedures.

OTHER DIRECT RESPONSE PROCEDURES

Earlier I set up a dichotomy between the direct response techniques and the discriminability techniques, but discussed primarily the fractionation or ratio scaling procedures. And, as pointed out above, one of the reasons for this schema is that the various direct response methods do not give the same kinds of loudness scales, even though logically they should. The equisection method, as mentioned, does not give a loudness scale which agrees with that obtained with the fractionation method. In actual fact, most of the direct response methods result in loudness scales much more like those obtained with the discriminability procedures than like those obtained with the fractionation procedures.

At this time we cannot state the exact shape of a loudness scale based on the discriminability procedures. We know that Fechner's assumption of the constancy of the Weber fraction is not valid; this fraction decreases with an increase in intensity, resulting in a slight positive acceleration to the integrated jnd function. However, as a first approximation, it is not far amiss to accept the log intensity scale as a reasonable type of scale. Perhaps it would be better to integrate Riesz' jnd's but these two functions will not be seriously different. Certainly the difference between a discriminability function and the *sone* scale suggested by Stevens [7] is clear, and there will be little difficulty in determining whether another function is more like the fractionation function or the discriminability function.

Callaway [15] had observers rate the loudnesses of a series of recorded truck noises on a six-point scale, and he found that these ratings were more linearly related to log intensity than to loudness measured in *sones*. A similar result was found by Beranek [16] for ratings of office noises. The results of these two experiments make it clear that a natural direct response is much more clearly related to a discriminability function than to a fractionation function, and that to a normal observer there is no real discrepancy between loudness and discriminability.

In an earlier section I mentioned an experiment of mine in which direct ratings were obtained with two different distributions of stimulus intensities, and it was pointed out that the equal discriminability scales were unaffected by the difference in stimulus context. We can also plot the mean responses obtained in that experiment, as has been done in Fig. 6. For these data the observers had been instructed to use their numerical ratings according to a loudness criterion. The two functions do not agree quite as closely as do the discriminability functions, but the agreement is still very good. What is even more interesting is the obvious fact that the direct rating function is very similar to the equal discriminability function, and very dissimilar to a loudness function based on fractionation judgments.

This would not be very surprising if we were considering only the distribution of stimuli based equally in decibels, since with such a distribution any tendency on the part of the observers to use numbers

[15] D. B. Callaway, *Trans. Soc. Automotive Engrs.* 62, 151–162 (1954).
[16] L. L. Beranek, *J. Acoust. Soc. Am.* 28, 833–852 (1956).

equally often will result in a function approximately linear with respect to log intensity, as Stevens[17] has pointed out. However, the same function occurs when the stimuli are distributed according to the observers' own fractionation responses. In order for this to occur, the observers had actually to use an unequal distribution of responses to produce the function shown in Fig. 6, i.e., to work against this normal tendency. With instructions to respond according to a loudness criterion, and with a distribution of stimuli spaced according to the fractionation judgments, the experiment was in effect loaded for the observers to reproduce the loudness function based on the fractionation judgments. If the observers had done this, there should have resulted a linear relation between the ordinal position of the stimulus and the mean response. Figure 7 shows how far off the observers were from doing this.

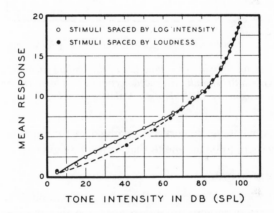

FIGURE 6   *Loudness scales based on the mean numerical response to a series of stimuli. These data correspond with those of Fig. 5, except that the actual numerical response is plotted, rather than the derived discriminability measure. The observers were allowed to use numbers from "0" through "20."*

This last experiment makes it clear that observers will make direct ratings with a discriminability criterion even when it is made very easy for them to use the same criterion as that used with fractionation judgments. Observers are in fact either unable or at least unwilling to make direct ratings according to anything but a discriminability cri-

[17] S. S. Stevens, *Am. J. Psychol.* 69, 1–25 (1936).

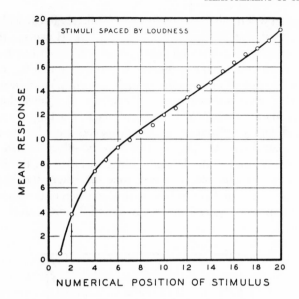

FIGURE 7 *Mean response as a function of the ordinal numerical position of the stimulus when the stimuli are spaced according to a loudness scale based on half-loudness judgments. These data are replotted from Fig. 6.*

terion. Thus, whatever factors are involved in the fractionation judgments, they seem to be unique to that form of judgment.

CONCLUSIONS

What can we conclude from all these facts? Certainly it is clear that we are on very dangerous ground in assuming that the loudness scale proposed by Stevens has any real meaning in the experience of normal observers. The various ratio scaling procedures are extremely unreliable, and slight differences in experimental procedure produce large differences in the loudness scales. In view of this, we can no longer insist that some of these procedures should be ruled out because they give results inconsistent with others, without realizing that this very inconsistency raises a serious doubt about the validity of the entire class of procedures.

If there exists any generality to the concept of a loudness function, this generality seems bound to come from functions based on a discriminability criterion. It is the criterion which is directly meaningful to normal observers, the one which they will use in almost all judgment situations with the exception of a few of the ratio scaling procedures. We can no longer accept the face validity of the fractionation procedures and judge the validity of other procedures by the criterion of agreement with results of the fractionation procedures. We cannot continue to say that all of the other procedures are out of step with the fractionation procedures, but must finally admit that the fractionation procedures are out of step with reality.

It is, of course, possible that a function similar to the present *sone* scale has some utility in various calculations, such as was true for Fletcher and Munson.[18] It seems highly likely that other functions could serve the purpose quite as well, as I pointed out earlier.[5] But when it is proposed that a standard loudness function be established, we are not concerned with a function whose value is to make certain calculations possible by serving as an intervening variable; rather we are concerned about obtaining a function which is meaningful to people in describing how they experience loudness. A discriminability function is clearly more meaningful in this respect.

If, therefore, it is necessary or desirable to have a standardized loudness scale, it should be based on some discriminability criterion, not on data obtained with the fractionation technique. Even as a first approximation, the decibel scale, or the loudness-level scale, would more correctly reflect the nature of the loudness experience than would the present *sone* scale. There is much to be said for simply using the loudness-level scale. It is a scale whose meaning is quite unambiguous. The operations for determining loudness level are fairly simple, and they can be applied experimentally with not too much difficulty if the loudness level cannot accurately be calculated. Finally, the loudness-level scale is not too discrepant from any of the possible discriminability scales, and thus would come much closer to providing numbers with direct meaning to observers than the *sone* scale. These advantages of the loudness-level scale may more than offset the fact that a discriminability function is not exactly the same as the loudness-level scale. However, for real meaning, some discriminability function should be used.

[18] H. Fletcher and W. A. Munson, *J. Acoust. Soc. Am.* 5, 82–108 (1933).

THE SURPRISING SIMPLICITY
OF SENSORY METRICS

S. S. Stevens

If you shine a faint light in your eye, you have a sensation of brightness — a weak sensation, to be sure. If you turn on a stronger light,
the sensation becomes greater. Clearly, then, there is a relation between perceived brightness and the amount of light you put in the
eye. The visual sense organ behaves as a transducer with an operating
characteristic of some kind — an input-output function. But how, precisely, does the output of the system (sensation) vary with the input
(stimulus)? Suppose you double the stimulus, does it then look twice
as bright?

The answer to that question happens to be no. It takes about nine
times as much light to double the apparent brightness, but this specific
question, interesting as it may be, is only one instance of a wider problem: what are the input-output characteristics of sensory systems in
general? Is there a single, simple, pervasive psychophysical law?

Unlikely as it may seem, there appears to be such a law. Its form
is a power function, and not the logarithmic relation that is almost
universally cited in textbooks. The power law, although not yet widely
known, is becoming so well fortified with evidence that it may some-
day replace the older law in all discussions of sensory dynamics. The
wonder is, in fact, how we could have missed finding the power law
for so long, especially since it is so surprisingly simple to demonstrate.

I pause at this point to pay respect, as is the custom, to the engross-
ing pursuit we call science — that relentless intellectual scrimmage
which means such diverse things to its many devotees. Some regard
it as a quest, a nomological quest, wherein the quarry reveals itself
from time to time in the form of simplicities and uniformities in the
complex of nature. Others regard the canons of impersonal, nomothetic
endeavor as oppressive strictures against the free-wheeling development of an ideographic, personal science. These two polar points of
view have always been with us — the tough- and tender-minded, as

From *American Psychologist*, 1962, 17, 29–39. Reprinted with permission of the author
and the American Psychological Association.

William James called them; the hircine and the ovine, as E. G. Boring suggests they be named — and the clash of their differing value systems will no doubt resound until the final éclat. My own guess is that even a phenomenological existentialist would cherish a natural law if he found one. Perhaps the psychologists' questing for nomological principles ought to get extinguished for lack of frequent reinforcement, but obviously it does not. Maybe it comes with the organism, like native curiosity, wired in from the start. Whatever it is that motivates inquiry, we can be sure that psychologists will not renounce the experimental search for simple and powerful principles of behavior.

The discovery of a law does not put an end to the nomological pursuit. At least it never has. There seems in fact to exist a meta-nomological principle, a kind of higher law, which says: the announcement of a presumed law in science will trigger prompt and vigorous attempts at its refutation. This higher law holds in all the sciences, but it sometimes appears to enjoy its freshest expression in psychology, where, by precept and performance, we often set criticism above creation.

As regards the psychophysical power law, criticism must be left to others. My task is to explain why I think it is a law. A pleasant enough task, to be sure, but one that gives rise to a curious sense of embarrassment. Why, if the power law is so simple, obvious, and easy to confirm, did we fumble around for so long without noting its existence?

It is difficult to account for acts of unobservant oversight, for they are essentially empty and neutral. What can you say about what you did not see? One can only try to lessen the embarrassment by describing those matters that diverted attention from the proper object, or that led from seemingly sound premises to wrong conclusions.

In a larger sense, psychophysical metrics got sidetracked for a hundred years, mainly by Fechner's diligence in behalf of his famous logarithmic law. I will not dwell on that diversion, for it has been dealt with at length in another place (Stevens, 1961). To many of us who worked in audition in the 1930s there was no question that Fechner's law was awry, for did not the sone scale of loudness issue from experiments that had been undertaken simply because it was so obvious to the acoustical engineers that loudness is not proportional to decibels, as Fechner's law would make it? Yes, a quarter of a century ago we knew better than to rely on Fechner's law, but, for reasons that I will try to explain, we did not know what to put in its place. All that has now changed.

EVIDENCE FOR THE POWER LAW

Within a first-order approximation, there appears to be no exception to the principle that equal stimulus *ratios* correspond to equal sensation *ratios*. (Fechner proposed, 101 years ago, that equal stimulus *ratios* correspond to equal sensation *differences*, and it is this hypothesis that the ratio rule denies and that the evidence refutes.)

The psychophysical power law relating the psychological magnitude ψ to the physical stimulus φ can be written

$$\psi = k(\varphi - \varphi_0)^n$$

where k is a constant determined by the choice of units. The exponent n varies with the modality, and also with such parameters as adaptation and contrast. Generally speaking, each modality has its characteristic exponent, ranging from about 0.33 for brightness to about 3.5 for electric shock. The value of φ_0 is determined by the effective "threshold" that obtains under the circumstances of the experiment. It is the point on the physical scale from which we must start if we want to measure the effective stimulus.

The power function has the happy virtue of describing a straight line in a log-log plot — a line whose slope is determined by the exponent. How this works for three different continua is shown in Figure 1, where we see how different the slopes (exponents) can be. In linear-linear coordinates these same three functions take the forms shown in Figure 2. Slope in the log-log plot becomes curvature in the linear-linear plot.

By much trial and error — *after* it had become plain that a power function governs the growth of sensation — we learned how to get reasonably clean data from observers by asking them to estimate numerically the subjective magnitudes of a succession of stimuli. This procedure, called the method of magnitude estimation, is only one of four numerical procedures that have been elaborated, but it is perhaps the simplest to execute. In this business, simplicity and validity seem not unrelated, but it has been hard for us psychophysicists to forsake the complex, indirect procedures in favor of a plain, straightforward, direct approach.

Consider, for example, the results in Figure 3. In an effort to see how far one could go in removing all biasing constraints from the task set for the listener, I gave each listener an irregular series of loudnesses and asked only one thing: to each loudness assign the number that

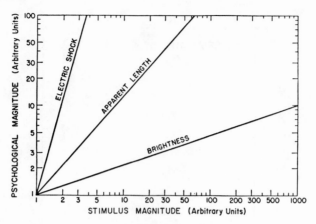

FIGURE 1   *In log-log coordinates the power function plots as a straight line. The exponent determines the slope. These exponents are: electric current through the fingers, 3.5; apparent length of short lines, 1.1; brightness of luminous spot, 0.33.*

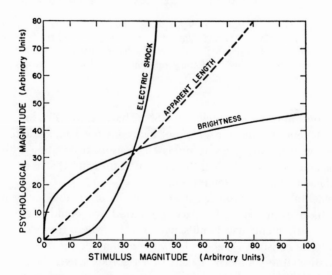

FIGURE 2   *The straight lines in Figure 1 become curved in linear-linear coordinates. The curvature is upward or downward, depending on whether the exponent is greater or less than one.*

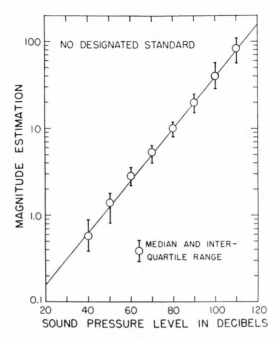

FIGURE 3   *Loudness function for 1,000 cycle tone. The points are the median magnitude estimations obtained when the tone was presented twice at each of eight levels in irregular order to 26 listeners. The listener assigned to the first loudness he heard any number he deemed appropriate and tried to assign proportional numbers to the succeeding loudnesses.*

seems most appropriate (Stevens, 1956). That was in 1954, long before J. C. Stevens (no relation of mine) had convinced me that the geometric mean usually gives an unbiased measure of location with data of this kind. I was still using the median, a measure that is somewhat less efficient than the geometric mean.

Incidentally, the arithmetic mean is wholly unsuitable for averaging magnitude estimations. If space permitted we could examine the plausible argument that, in all scientific work where the *relative* error tends to be constant (Weber's law), the arithmetic mean is not as appropriate as the geometric mean. In a rigorous sense, the arithmetic mean has little legitimate use in science, for its proper domain is limited to metathetic continua and the like.

The International Standards Organization has recently fixed on a function of the form shown in Figure 3 as the relation between loudness and sound pressure to be used for engineering calculations. Thus the psychophysical law is coming to have practical uses in the market place.

Meanwhile other modalities have been explored with equally good results. Figure 4 shows three different functions determined for brightness by J. C. Stevens. Each curve was determined with a different version of the method of magnitude estimation. The observers (previously dark adapted) viewed a luminous disk of light in a dark field and made judgments of its apparent brightness. We call this the standard viewing condition (S. S. Stevens and J. C. Stevens, 1960).

Interestingly enough, the power function is little affected when the

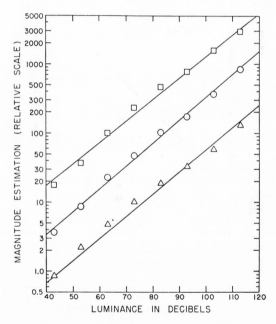

FIGURE 4 *Brightness functions for white light, based on geometric means of magnitude estimates made in three different experiments.* Squares: *as in Figure 3, there was no designated standard; each of the 18 observers used numbers of his own choosing.* Circles: *a standard called 10 was presented once at the beginning of each run.* Triangles: *the standard called 10 was repeated 10 seconds before each stimulus to be judged. These procedural variations made little difference to the outcome. Except where otherwise stated, the reference value for decibels of luminance is 10⁻¹⁰ lambert.*

area of the target is made to fill the entire field of view. The results of three experiments by Gordon Bermant with wide-angle fields are shown in Figure 5. At the other extreme, when the target is reduced to a point source, the power function still holds, but the value of the exponent increases from about ⅓ to about ½. The squares in Figure 6 show how the line in the log-log plot grows steeper when the observer estimates the brightness of a very small target. The circles, giving an intermediate slope, are from an early experiment by E. G. Heinemann, who used a target of an intermediate size (28 minutes).

There exist dozens of functions like these, compiled by several dif-

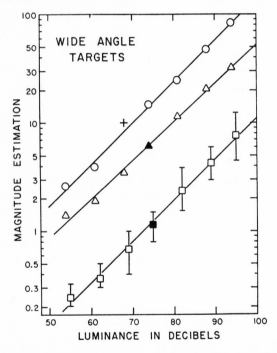

FIGURE 5 *Brightness functions for targets subtending large visual angles. The* circles *and* triangles *are for experiments in which the observer sat close to a large illuminated screen. The squares show the data obtained with a more nearly ideal Ganzfeld. Pieces of milk glass held close to the eyes were illuminated from in front of the observer. The standard, called 10, was the stimulus shown by the filled symbols and the cross. Each point is the geometric mean of 20 judgments (10 observers), except that the cross was not actually presented for judgment after it had served to define the modulus 10.*

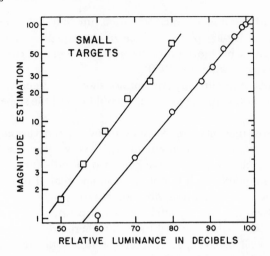

FIGURE 6 *Brightness functions for small targets subtending visual angles of 1.5 minutes of arc (squares) and 28 minutes (circles). The abscissa gives relative levels only. The highest level for the smaller target was about 110 db re 10^{-10} lambert. The larger target had a different highest value in each of four different experiments, all of which were averaged to obtain the circles.*

ferent experimenters, and covering such sense modalities as vision, hearing, taste, smell, vibration, kinesthesis, warmth, cold, and so forth (Stevens, 1960). Perhaps for some people this total array would constitute a convincing exhibit, but for others it is possible that no amount of this recording of verbal behavior — subjective numerical estimations — would carry conviction. Some of my esteemed colleagues make forthright objection to our treating the observer's utterances as measurements.

CROSS-MODALITY VALIDATIONS

There is nothing like a colleague's objection to send the scientist back to his apparatus. With hope that it might work, coupled with apprehension that it might fail, I decided to try to test the validity of the power functions, and their exponents, by methods that would eliminate the verbal behavior. There would be no subjective numerical estimates. Instead, the observer would be asked to adjust a loudness in his ear until it seemed as strong as a vibration applied to his finger tip, or vice versa. If the power law is correct, these cross-modality comparisons must result in an equal-sensation function that is also a power function. In a log-log plot the slope of the equal-sensation function should be given by the ratio of the exponents of the two modalities under comparison (Stevens, 1959).

The results of the first experiment are shown in Figure 7. The function is linear in the log-log plot as it should be, and the slope lies nicely where it belongs.

Other cross-modality comparisons followed, but the huge task of comparing each sensory continuum with every other continuum has not been completed. Thus far we have had to settle for a collection of interesting samples. Much to my surprise, and that of many observers, the matching of a sound to a vibration is satisfyingly easy — certainly no harder than the task of matching two disparate sounds in loudness, or two colored lights in brightness. Furthermore, the variability is reasonably well behaved, so that geometric averaging is clearly appropriate.

The largest number of cross-modality comparisons made thus far have been with handgrip. Instead of vocalizing, the observer merely squeeezes a precision dynamometer (Fig. 8) to indicate his judgment

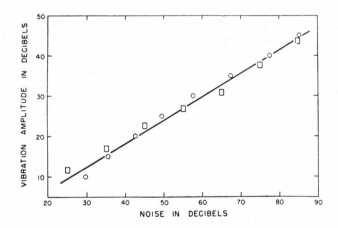

FIGURE 7   *Equal-sensation function produced by the cross-modality matching of loudness to vibration (60 cps on fingertip). Circles: the loudness was adjusted to match the vibration. Squares: the vibration was adjusted to match the loudness. Each procedure determines a slightly different slope, but the two experiments together define a power function whose exponent is equal to the ratio between the exponents for loudness and vibration.*

of the apparent strength of the sound, or the light, or the electric shock. First we must ask what happens when the experimenter names numbers in irregular order and the observer squeezes what he judges to be a proportional amount (method of magnitude production). Typical results, obtained by J. C. Stevens and J. D. Mack (1959) in two separate experiments, are shown in Figure 9. Each line is for a different observer. Presented in this manner, the data show that each observer follows a power function when he judges apparent force of handgrip. From this and other studies it appears that, for the median observer, the sensation of strain in the production of handgrip grows as the 1.7 power of the force exerted. When a person actually squeezes twice as hard, he judges it to be about three times as hard.

Equipped with this dynamometer and the measured exponent for force of handgrip, we have gauged the growth of sensation on nine other continua by asking observers to emit squeezes instead of numbers. The resulting equal-sensation functions are shown in Figure 10. When the exponents determined by the slopes of these functions are multiplied by the factor 1.7, the resulting values agree remarkably well with the exponents measured directly by magnitude estimation (Stevens, Mack, and Stevens, 1960).

The largest discrepancy between the exponent determined by verbal report and the exponent determined indirectly by squeezing turned out to be 0.07. We regard it as rather good that the greatest difference occurs only in the second decimal place.

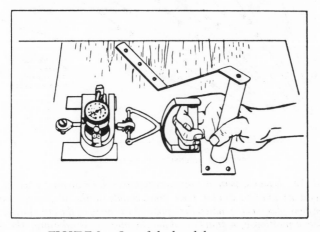

FIGURE 8   *One of the hand dynamometers.*

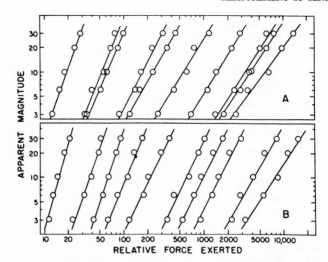

FIGURE 9 *Functions for apparent force of handgrip obtained by magnitude production. The experimenter designated certain numerical values (ordinate) in irregular order, and the observer produced proportionate squeezes (abscissa.) Each curve is for a single observer. Plots A and B are for two different kinds of dynamometer. Points are medians of 7 squeezes (A) and 10 squeezes (B).*

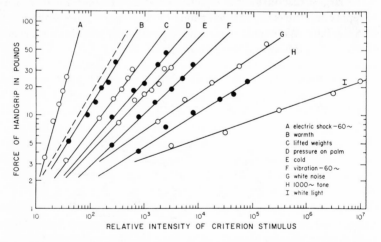

FIGURE 10 *Equal-sensation functions obtained by matching force of hand-grip to various criterion stimuli. Each point stands for the median force exerted by 10 or more observers to match the apparent intensity of the criterion stimulus. The relative position of a function along the abscissa is arbitrary. The dashed line shows a slope of 1.0 in these coordinates.*

Confronted with this richly interconnected evidence, some of us find it difficult to escape the belief that there exists a general principle of psychophysics — a principle that governs to a good approximation throughout all the prothetic perceptual domain. Psychophysics, we venture to suggest, has found itself a law.

DIFFICULTIES AND IMPEDIMENTS

If the growth of sensation is so easy to measure, and if a single equation relates all sensory magnitudes to the stimulus magnitudes that produce them, why then did it take so long for the nomological quest to corner its prize? The reproach inherent in this question engenders chagrin mainly because the power law seems now so obvious, and ample data supporting it have long been at hand. But many experimenters have produced data that accord with a power law, without seeming aware of it, so that I find my own chagrin well tempered with companionship. The psychophysical power function has had to rise up, as it were, and strike us full in the face for acknowledgment. Why was this so?

First I should hasten to note that nothing is ever without its antecedents, and like certain other functions the power function has had its occasional champion. It begins perhaps with a letter by Gabriel Cramer, cited by Daniel Bernoulli (1738), in which Cramer suggested that a power law (square root) might govern subjective value — a psychological variable that the economist calls *utility*. Bernoulli favored a logarithmic function, the same function advocated a century later by Fechner. Some time in the 1850s Plateau seems to have proposed a cube-root law for apparent brightness, or at least Delboeuf says he did, but Plateau later changed his mind about the power law. He defected, as it were, when he was confronted with some of Delboeuf's data. Then there were various theories regarding differential sensitivity, two of which, Brentano's and Guilford's, took forms that led, via different sets of questionable assumptions, to a power law. So we see that the power function was certainly not unheard of (Stevens, 1957). Indeed, it was like many other mathematical functions that are constantly being tried out here and there. For instance, the power function was one of three equations tried out in 1932 by Ham and Parkinson when they were looking for a formula to fit their results on loudness estimation.

Ham and Parkinson were on the right track, it now appears, but the *piste* promptly got itself obscured by an unfortunate experiment on loudness fractionation by Laird, Taylor, and Wille (1932) whose results have ever since eluded explanation and repetition. Stevens, Rogers, and Herrnstein (1955) even tried to repeat them with the aid of the same kind of antique audiometer. But other experimenters continued to worry about the rather obvious fact that loudness does not seem to grow proportional to decibels (as Fechner's logarithmic law says it should), and experiments continued to accumulate.

In 1938 Davis and I were able to publish the loudness function for the standard 1000 cycle tone in the form shown in Figure 11. There we see an empirical function based on considerable data, but plainly it is not a power function, for it does not lie straight in the log-log plot. It was the curvature in that 1000 cycle loudness function that led us

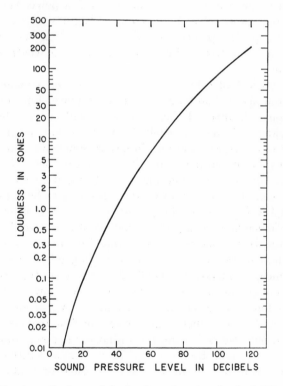

FIGURE 11   *An early form of the loudness function for the 1,000-cycle tone. The curvature may be ascribed to three factors, none of which was suspected in 1938.*

astray for more than a decade — indeed until work was begun on visual brightness in 1953. By the end of 1953 I was ready at last to advocate the power function (Stevens, 1954), but I would still have been hard pressed to convince a skeptic, for the evidence was not overwhelming. Not yet. But then began a long, ebullient period of proving and testing the law on a score of continua, and by every means we have been able to devise.

REASONS FOR CURVATURE
IN THE LOUDNESS FUNCTION

Why did we not obtain a clean power function when we plotted the loudness data in 1938? If the truth is so simple, how could we have missed? In retrospect there appear to be three causes. Three different sources of bias combined to hide the naked simplicity of the psychophysical law.

1. Fractionation, the setting of one loudness to half the value of a standard, has the built-in bias of an unbalanced experimental design. In those days it was a widely used method for scaling, but sometimes *halving* was not complemented by *doubling*. The underlying power function can be obscured by the resulting bias.

2. Much of the data available in 1938 was based on binaural vs. monaural loudness balances. This was because Fletcher and Munson, two important pioneers in loudness measurement, had made the assumption that a sound in two ears is twice as loud as the same sound heard in only one ear. Furthermore this simple and engaging rule seemed to be nicely confirmed by fractionation experiments. That, indeed, is the unfortunate aspect of it: the assumption of perfect binaural summation turns out to be *almost* correct. It is, in fact, so nearly correct that it required a many-pronged attack to prove that the rule is false (Reynolds and Stevens, 1960). Samples of some of this work are shown in Figures 12 and 13. These and many other observations have shown that binaural loudness grows with an exponent of 0.6, whereas monaural loudness grows with an exponent of 0.54. At one sound pressure level (90 db) the binaural loudness happens to be exactly double the monaural loudness, but at no other level does this simple ratio appear to hold. The false assumption that the 2-to-1 ratio holds throughout the scale was a factor that helped put curvature into the loudness function, which caused us to look for a complicated equation when a simple one would do.

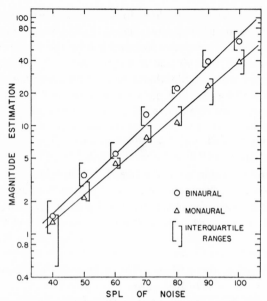

FIGURE 12   *Loudness functions for binaural and monaural listening. The signal was a band of noise 250 to 2,000 cps. Levels were presented at random to right, left, or both ears and the observer estimated the apparent loudness.*

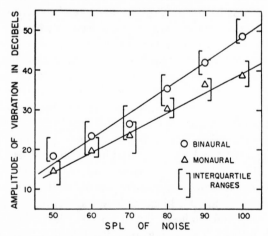

FIGURE 13   *Equal-sensation functions for loudness vs. vibration on the fingertip. The observer adjusted the vibration (60 cps) to match the apparent loudness of the band of noise (250 to 2,000 cps) presented to right, left, or both ears. Cross-modality matching confirms the evidence in Figure 12 that monaural loudness grows less rapidly than binaural loudness.*

3. Even when all biases in the procedures and all false assumptions regarding the binaural-monaural relation have been cleared away, there still remains some residual curvature near the lower end of the loudness function. That is the reason for the constant φ_0 in the equation above. In order to get a power function one must measure the stimulus beginning at threshold, not at the conventional zero of the physical scale. This need for a threshold correction was most dramatically evident in our work on the perception of warmth and cold, because absolute zero on the temperature scale is far removed from "physiological" zero (J. C. Stevens and S. S. Stevens, 1960). With the temperature senses it would seem silly to measure from absolute zero — and indeed it is.

With sufficient care one can also show the need for φ_0 in the loudness equation, even though its value is small. A careful exploration of the low end of the loudness function by B. Scharf and J. C. Stevens (1961) gave the data in Figure 14. The unfilled points that curve downward are the uncorrected values. The subtraction of a constant φ_0

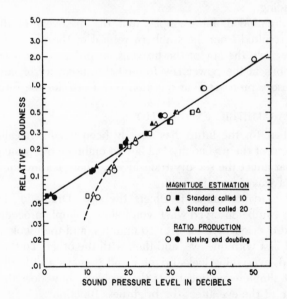

FIGURE 14 *Showing how the low end of the loudness function can be rectified if the stimulus is measured starting from threshold. The original data, obtained by various methods, follow the dashed curve (unfilled symbols). When a constant value, approximately equal to threshold, is subtracted from each experimental value, the filled points are obtained. The corrected points fall close to the sone function, represented by the straight line with a slope of 0.6.*

from each of the experimental points makes them all lie reasonably close to the same straight line and thereby restores the power function.

It was against the foregoing three sources of obfuscation that the power law had to fight its way into clarity. Curiously enough, it was only by working on other sense modalities that we found out what was wrong with the early form of the loudness function. If knocking your head against one wall produces no answers, it sometimes pays to knock against another wall.

PERTURBATIONS

I do not mean to imply by the foregoing remarks that loudness can now be shown to follow a perfect power function. It is probably not quite that simple — at least not for sounds of all spectra (Stevens, 1955). The scientific leverage that accrues from having an equation adequate to the first-order sensory transductions is simply this: once the first-order effect is reduced to a formula, the second-order departures from the basic law may conceivably lead to new and deeper understanding.

One is reminded, for example, that the discovery of the planet Neptune resulted from the stubborn refusal of the planet Uranus to follow precisely the law of the heavens, as ordained by Newton. Do perturbations in the power law foretell the discovery of new factors in the sensory process? That question sets a task for the future.

PARAMETRIC EXPLORATIONS

Another task for the future has already been begun. It calls for the enlargement of the psychophysical law to embrace the principal parameters that affect the sensory transducers. There is time for only one example of what I have in mind.

Consider adaptation as it affects the eye. Dramatic changes in brightness can be observed when you follow a simple procedure. Hold your hand over one eye for 5 to 10 minutes, and then look around at the world first with one eye, and then with the other. To the eye that was closed, everything looks brighter and perhaps a little different in hue. That simple experiment sets the problem: how does the state of adaptation of the eye affect the brightness function?

First I should mention that all the brightness functions described above were determined with the eyes "dark adapted," that is to say, adapted to a level well below the level of the stimulus presented. That procedure we take as the standard or reference condition. One has to start somewhere. In the dark-adapted state the visual system responds to luminous stimuli in accordance with a power law having an exponent of about 0.33. We define a *bril*, the unit of the brightness scale, as the brightness seen by the dark-adapted eye when it views a 5 degree target at a luminance that is 40 decibels above the reference level 10⁻¹⁰ lambert.

Our next concern is to measure the effect of changing the state of the eye by adapting it to a prescribed level of luminance. In order to measure these effects we take advantage of the fact that we have two eyes; we light adapt one eye and dark adapt the other. With the two eyes thus differently adapted, we can do two kinds of experiments. We can measure the brightness function for each eye separately by the method of magnitude estimation. We can also compare these two functions directly by *matching* the brightness seen by the dark-adapted eye to that seen by the light-adapted eye. This interocular matching procedure has been used by Hering and many other workers.

Results of both procedures, matching and magnitude estimation, are shown in Figure 15. Each curve is for a different level of adaptation. In each of the many experiments (carried out mainly by J. C. Stevens), the left eye was dark adapted and the right eye was light

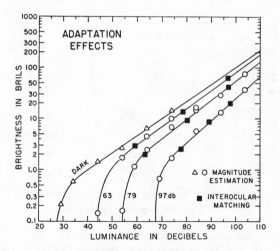

FIGURE 15   *Results of determining brightness functions under different states of adaptation. The upper curve is the "standard" bril function for the "dark-adapted" eye. Each of the other curves is for the eye adapted to a given luminance, indicated in decibels re 10⁻¹⁰ lambert.*

adapted. (The right eye stared at a large white cardboard illuminated at various levels.) When the eyes were fully and differently adapted, the test target, subtending about 5.7 degrees, was presented briefly to one eye or the other.

The experimental data in Figure 15 show two things. Under different levels of adaptation, the "operating characteristic" of the visual system continues to be a power function, but both the "operating point" and the "gain function" are affected by light adaptation. Stated in another language, light adaptation alters each of the parameters in the equation $\psi = k(\varphi - \varphi_0)^n$. For each level of adaptation the parameters k, φ_0, and n take on a characteristic value.

How the parameters of the brightness function depend upon the state of the eye can best be seen in Figure 16. As the level of the light adaptation increases, the following changes occur: the constant k grows smaller, the exponent n grows slightly larger, and the threshold (labeled B_0) grows very much larger. All these changes accord well with common, everyday observation. There is nothing very new or mysterious about it — except perhaps that what everyone knows in a vague and general way has here been reduced to quantitative order.

When the parameters depicted in Figure 16 are used to generate a

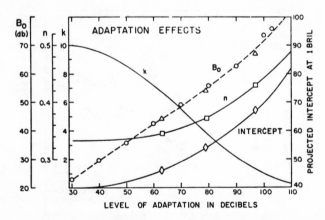

FIGURE 16   *Parameters of the brightness equation as a function of level of adaptation of the eye. The exponent values* (squares) *were read from Figure 15, as were the 1 bril intercepts* (diamonds). *The values of* k *were then calculated on the assumption that the luminance B is measured in millilamberts. The threshold values of B were estimated from Figure 15 and plotted as triangles. The* circles *show the threshold values directly measured by P. G. Nutting.*

complete family of brightness functions, like those shown in Figure 17, a basis is laid for a new and fuller understanding of the visual trans- ducer. These functions tell us how any given target, exposed for a second or two, will look to an eye in any of several states of adaptation (S. S. Stevens and J. C. Stevens, 1960).

The implications of these functions could be spelled out in a long chapter, but we have time for only one of the more interesting details. A series of circles appears in Figure 17 connected by a dashed line. These circles mark the locus of the equilibrium function — the bright- ness seen when the eye, adapted to a given level, is shown a stimulus at that same level. Another name we give the dashed curve is the "ter- minal brightness function," because it is the function that tells us how bright a target will look after the observer has stared at it for a long period of time — long enough to reach full adaptation. This terminal brightness function does *not* follow a power law.

We note another interesting feature: the dashed curve becomes horizontal at the upper end. If the viewer becomes fully adapted to the level of the stimulus, does he then see a maximal brightness regardless of the stimulus intensity? The answer is yes. This remarkable prediction accords with a result by K. J. W. Craik (1940), who pursued this ques- tion to the heroic level of 75,000 foot-lamberts (119 db re 10^{-10}

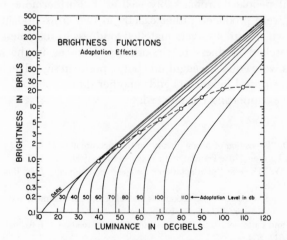

FIGURE 17 *Family of brightness functions for a wide range of adaptation levels. The dashed line is the terminal brightness locus—the level of sensation reached when the eye comes into full equilibrium with the luminance it is viewing.*

lambert). Levels like that are about ten times greater than the luminance of snow under the noonday sun. The equilibrium brightness function measured by Craik was still flat at the high level.

Much more could be said, and no doubt will be said, about the varied and exciting principles that regulate the input-output functions of the sensory transducers. Tortuous and delayed as may have been the discovery of the basic law — the psychophysical power function — the way is now clear, even for the potential usefulness of proven discrepancies, when such there are.

One final note. The power function has asserted itself not only on continua that involve well-known stimulus variables, but also on a continuum, tactual roughness, for which we had at first thought there would be no metric stimulus-correlate (Stevens & Harris). Our first guess proved delightfully in error, for we found that apparent roughness grows as the 1.5 power of the diameter of the abrasive particles on standard emery cloths. When the observers judged the apparent smoothness of the same emery cloths, the exponent turned out to be nearly equal in magnitude, but opposite in sign. We thereby demonstrate the observer's remarkable ability to judge a continuum in terms of its reciprocal function. Judging the inverse aspect is not as easy, it seems, but people do remarkably well at it. Furthermore, reciprocal functions were produced rather exactly in two cross-modality experiments in which ten observers matched loudness to roughness, and ten others matched loudness to smoothness. Here again the measured exponents were equal in magnitude but opposite in sign. The testimony of these reciprocal judgments adds another dimension to the network of evidence supporting the power law.

REFERENCES

Bernoulli, D. "Exposition of a new theory on the measurement of risk." Originally published in Latin in 1738. Translation in *Econometrica*, 1954, 22, 23–35.

Craik, K. J. W. "The effect of adaptation on subjective brightness." *Proc. Roy. Soc.*, 1940, B128, 232–247.

Fletcher, H. and Munson, W. A. "Loudness, its definition, measurement and calculation." *J. Acoust. Soc. Amer.*, 1933, 5, 82–108.

Ham, L. B. and Parkinson, J. S. "Loudness and intensity relations." *J. Acoust. Soc. Amer.*, 1932, 3, 511–534.

Laird, D. A., Taylor, E., and Wille, H. H., Jr. "The apparent reduction of loudness." *J. Acoust. Soc. Amer.*, 1932, 3, 393–401.

Reynolds, G. S. and Stevens, S. S. "The binaural summation of loudness." *J. Acoust. Soc. Amer.*, 1960, 32, 1337–1344.

Scharf, B. and Stevens, J. C. "The form of the loudness function near threshold." In *Proc. 3rd Int. Congr. Acoustics*. Amsterdam: Elsevier, 1961. Pp. 80–82.

Stevens, J. C. and Mack, J. D. "Scales of apparent force." *J. Exp. Psychol.*, 1959, 58, 405–413.

Stevens, J. C., Mack, J. D., and Stevens, S. S. Growth of sensation on seven continua as measured by force of handgrip. *J. Exp. Psychol.*, 1960, 59, 60–67.

Stevens, J. C. and Stevens, S. S. "Warmth and cold: dynamics of sensory intensity." *J. Exp. Psychol.*, 1960, 60, 183–192.

Stevens, S. S. "Biological transducers." *Convention Record, I.R.E.*, 1954, Part 9, 27–33.

Stevens, S. S. "The measurement of loudness." *J. Acoust. Soc. Amer.*, 1955, 27, 815–829.

Stevens, S. S. "The direct estimation of sensory magnitude — loudness." *Amer. J. Psychol.*, 1956, 69, 1–25.

Stevens, S. S. "On the psychophysical law." *Psychol. Rev.*, 1957, 64, 153–181.

Stevens, S. S. "Cross-modality validation of subjective scales for loudness, vibration, and electric shock." *J. Exp. Psychol.*, 1959, 57, 201–209.

Stevens, S. S. "Psychophysics of sensory function." *Amer. Sci.*, 1960, 48, 226–252; also in W. A. Rosenblith (Ed.), *Sensory Communication*, New York: M.I.T. Press and Wiley, 1961.

Stevens, S. S. "To honor Fechner and repeal his law." *Science*, 1961, 133, 80–86.

Stevens, S. S. and Davis, H. *Hearing.* New York: Wiley, 1938.

Stevens, S. S. and Harris, Judith R. "The scaling of tactual roughness and smoothness." *J. Exp. Psychol.*, 1962, 64, 489–494.

Stevens, S. S., Rogers, M. S., and Herrnstein, R. J. "The apparent reduction of loudness: a repeat experiment." *J. Acoust. Soc. Amer.*, 1955, 27, 326–328.

Stevens, S. S. and Stevens, J. C. "The dynamics of visual brightness." Psychophysical Lab. Rep., Harvard University, August 1960, PR-246.

IS THE POWER LAW A SPECIAL CASE
OF FECHNER'S LAW?

Gösta Ekman

Let us assume, for the purposes of the present discussion, that Fechner's law is generally valid, so that

$$R_S = a + b \log S, \qquad (1)$$

where R_S is a subjective magnitude corresponding to the stimulus

Reprinted with permission of author and publisher: Ekman, G., "Is the Power Law a Special Case of Fechner's Law?" *Perceptual and Motor Skills*, 1964, 19, 730.

magnitude S. Let us further assume that a subject reacts also to *number stimulation* according to Fechner's law. Then

$$R_N = c + d \log N, \tag{2}$$

where R_N is the subjective magnitude corresponding to the stimulus magnitude, i.e., the number N, to which the subject is exposed.

In a typical scaling experiment with a direct method, the subject is instructed to respond to a stimulus S with a number N chosen so that $R_N = R_S$. On this condition we obtain from Equations 1 and 2 the relation

$$\log N = \alpha + n \log S,$$

where $\alpha = (a - c)/d$ and $n = b/d$, or

$$N = \beta S^n, \tag{3}$$

where $\beta =$ antilog α. This is the well-known power law in its simplest form, which has now been derived from Fechner's law.

The essential feature of the response model presented here is the assumption that a subject reacts to number stimulation in the same way, i.e., according to Fechner's law, as he reacts to any stimulation. In this sense the derivation of the power function is based on a generalization of Fechner's law. According to the model, a direct scaling method is a procedure in which the subject *matches* two sets of *stimuli*.

The power law may be regarded *either* as describing the relation between a subjective variable and a stimulus variable, in which case it is the "true" psychophysical law, *or* as describing the relation between two stimulus variables, in which case it represents Fechner's law expressed in terms of stimulation. I do not think that the choice between these alternative interpretations can be based entirely on present knowledge.

THE DERIVATION OF SUBJECTIVE SCALES FROM JUST NOTICEABLE DIFFERENCES

R. Duncan Luce and Ward Edwards

The study of cumulated jnd scales began with Fechner; Fechner's law is such a scale. Psychophysicists have been deriving such scales and comparing them with scales derived in other ways, notably by fractionation, ever since, and a lot of controversy has resulted. The controversy is particularly hot at present because Stevens and Galanter (16) and Stevens (14) have assembled a lot of data which indicate that cumulated jnd scales do not agree with magnitude scales derived by other methods for intensity continua such as loudness, brightness, and pain.

Unfortunately, Fechner's procedure for cumulating jnds, which has been widely defended but not widely applied since his day, rests on an assumption which is inconsistent with one of his definitions. This means that cumulated jnd scales developed by his procedure are incorrect, and so comparisons between them and other kinds of scales are meaningless.

This paper begins by showing that Fechner's method contains internal contradictions for all but a few special cases, and that it cannot be rescued by minor changes. It goes on to derive a new and mathematically appropriate method for cumulating jnd's. This method turns out to be the simplest possible one: you can best cumulate jnd's simply by adding them on top of each other, like a stack of plates. Unfortunately, the detailed mathematical equivalent of this very

From *Psychological Review*, 1958, 65, 222–237. Reprinted with permission of the authors and the American Psychological Association.

Work on this paper began when Luce was a Fellow at the Center for Advanced Study in the Behavioral Sciences. Later work was supported by: the Office of Naval Research, through contracts with Columbia University; the Behavioral Models Project, Bureau of Applied Social Research, Columbia University; and the Air Force Personnel and Training and Research Center under Project 7737 Task 27107. Permission is granted for reproduction, translation, publication, use, and disposal in whole and in part by or for the United States government. This paper will be listed as Publication A-243 of the Bureau of Applied Social Research, Columbia University.

We are grateful to J. K. Adams, E. G. Boring, L. S. Christie, E. H. Galanter, A. Hastorf, C. K. Kluckhohn, W. J. McGill, F. Mosteller, and S. S. Stevens for advice and help at various stages in the preparation of the paper.

simple operation is often fairly complicated. A simple but sometimes tedious graphic procedure, however, is readily available — and indeed has customarily been used by most scientists when developing cumulated jnd scales. This paper ends by discussing practical applications of this method, the relation it bears to scaling methods based on the law of comparative judgment, and the current controversy about scaling methods in psychophysics.

THE MODEL OF A SENSATION SCALE

The psychophysical model of a sensation scale is a mathematical model; a sensation scale is an intervening variable. The rules by which sensation scales should be constructed are to some degree arbitrary, limited by logic, convenience, intuition, and best fit to data.

The model of a sensation scale goes as follows. Corresponding to many of the major subjective dimensions of change of sensory experience, there are primary physical dimensions of change (e.g., pitch and frequency, loudness and amplitude, etc.). Once parametric conditions for significant variables have been specified, we assume that a single-valued, monotonic, everywhere differentiable (smooth) function exists that relates the subjective dimension to its corresponding physical dimension. From here on, we shall use the words "dimension" and "continuum" interchangeably; we shall usually talk about a stimulus continuum and its corresponding sensory continuum.

That is the model, and it is very easy to state. The big difficulty comes when we try to decide how to fit data to it. All methods for doing this must introduce definitions and assumptions beyond those listed in the previous paragraph. These differ from one method to another.

The oldest sensory scaling method, Fechner's, is based upon a further condition that says that any jnd on a given sensory continuum is subjectively equivalent to any other jnd on that continuum. Whether this added condition is to be interpreted as merely a definition of the scale under consideration or as an assumption is a matter of opinion. Textbooks usually say Fechner "assumed" that all jnd's for a sensory dimension are equal to one another (1). It is not easy to know what he had in mind, but judging by his writings he probably did view it as an assumption having implications beyond scale construction. Since it is not directly observable and since its indirect consequences are highly debatable, others since Fechner have suggested that it might better be viewed as a definition. It is our view that this is the more sensible position; it certainly is the one for us to take in this paper since our point is a logical one, not a substantive one. If equality of jnd's is taken as a definition, then it cannot be proved or disproved by any kind of empirical evidence. An experiment, for instance, that showed that a tone 20 jnd's loud is not half as loud (according to fractionation judgments) as a tone 40 jnd's loud would not have any relevance to what we may call Fechner's definition; it would only show that the kind of sensation scale implied by his definition does not agree with the kind implied by the definitions used in fractionation experiments. The issue, then, becomes what are the different scales useful for, and what is their relationship one to another. The latter part of this paper touches briefly on this problem.

The main purpose of the paper is to explore the consequences of Fechner's definition. Therefore, we must be certain of its meaning. It clearly does not mean, for instance, that all jnd's for loudness contain the same number of physical units. It is only on the sensory continuum, not on the stimulus continuum, that jnd's are defined as equal to one another. Furthermore, this definition holds only if all stimulus properties except those on the primary stimulus continuum remain constant. So there is no reason, for instance, to expect that the subjective size of a loudness jnd at 1,000 cycles per second (cps) should be the same as that of a loudness jnd at 4,000 cps. Of course, it would be pleasant if they were equal in size, but the model does not require it.

From here on we will talk about two kinds of jnd's. A sensation jnd is the magnitude of a jnd as measured in the units of the appropriate sensation continuum. By definition, all sensation jnd's for a given sensation continuum are equal to one another, given unchanged values of all stimulus properties except those on the primary stimulus continuum. A stimulus jnd is the magnitude of the change on the primary stimulus continuum, measured in appropriate physical units, which is just sufficient to produce a change of one sensation jnd upward at that point. (A discussion of the essentially statistical nature of jnd's appears later in this paper.) In general, stimulus jnd's will have different sizes at different points on the primary stimulus continuum. The rest of this paper will not be intelligible unless you keep the distinction between these two kinds of jnd's in mind.

We have assumed that jnd's are measured upward on the stimulus continuum. They could also be measured downward, and the possibility exists that the two measurements might not agree. In fact, they are certain not to agree if the distance spanned is more than two jnd's, and if the size of the jnd at the end where measurement starts is used as the unit of measurement, since this means that the size of the measurement unit will be different depending on direction of measurement. However, such discrepancies might exist in the measurement of a single jnd; this, if it happened, would mean that jnd's are not suitable units of measurement unless direction is specified. We have therefore confined ourselves to upward jnd's.

Now we can say exactly what this paper is about. Given a function (obtained from experiment, theory, or both) relating stimulus to sensation jnd's for all points of the primary stimulus continuum, what may we infer about the sensory scale implied by that jnd function?

FECHNER'S DERIVATION
OF FECHNER'S LAW

On October 22, 1850, Fechner (2) thought up the first (incorrect) answer to the question which ended the previous paragraph. Let us call any function that gives the size of a stimulus jnd at each point of the stimulus continuum a *Weber function* (corresponding to "a function relating stimulus to sensation jnd's" of the previous section), and any one-to-one function based on cumulated jnd's which relates the stimulus continuum to a sensory scale a *Fechner function* (corresponding to "a sensation scale" of the previous section). These definitions do *not* restrict our attention to those two special functions which have come to be known in psychophysics as Weber's law and Fechner's law! Fechner believed that the Fechner function corresponding to any Weber function could be expressed as the solution (integral) of a first order linear differential equation involving that Weber function. He applied this procedure to Weber's law, which asserts that for a given stimulus continuum the size of the stimulus jnd, Δx, divided by the value of the stimulus at that point, x, is a constant $(\Delta x/x = k)$. Let us examine his argument.

If Weber's law is true, then, since all sensation jnd's are equal by definition, there is a constant A such that

$$\frac{\Delta u}{\Delta x} = \frac{A}{x} \tag{1}$$

where Δu denotes the size of the sensation jnd. The heart of Fechner's solution to his and our basic problem was to "rewrite" Equation (1) as the differential equation

$$\frac{du}{dx} = \frac{A}{x} \tag{2}$$

How did Fechner make this step from differences (deltas) to differentials? He used what he called a "mathematical auxiliary principle," the essence of which is that what is true for differences as small as jnd's ought also to be true for all smaller differences and so true in the limit as they approach zero (differentials). If this argument were acceptable (which it is not), the rest would be simple. Equation (2), when integrated, yields the familiar logarithmic relationship between sensation and stimulus which is known as Fechner's law.

Fechner thought that his general procedure ought to be applicable to any Weber function, not just to Weber's law. It is not. Except for a few special cases like Weber's law, the definition of sensation jnd's as equal and the "mathematical auxiliary principle" are mutually contradictory. For example, consider the Weber function $\Delta x/x^2 = k$. Then, following Fechner's procedure, we should write:

$$\frac{\Delta u}{\Delta x} = \frac{A}{x^2} \text{ and so } \frac{du}{dx} = \frac{A}{x^2}$$

Integrating, we get

$$u = B - \frac{A}{x}$$

Let us now check to see whether this new Fechner function satisfies the definition which says that sensation jnd's are equal to one another. If we are at point x on the stimulus continuum, a stimulus jnd, according to the Weber function used in this example, is kx^2. The sensation increment corresponding to this change, the sensation jnd at this point, is therefore given by:

$$u(x + kx^2) - u(x) = B - \frac{A}{(x + kx^2)} - B + \frac{A}{x}$$
$$= \frac{Ak}{1 + kx}$$

which is clearly not a constant for any value of the constant A except zero.

This, although only one example, is typical in the sense that almost any example you could think of would show the same discrepancy.

Only for a very few Weber functions — some pathological ones, Weber's law, and its generalization $\Delta x = kx + c$ — does the "mathematical auxiliary principle" yield a Fechner function with equal jnd's. We will not take space to prove this formally, but a formal proof is available.

THE FUNCTIONAL EQUATION SOLUTION

We have shown that Fechner's procedure involves a self-contradiction. We shall show later that it leads to wrong results in all important cases except Weber's law. Obviously the "mathematical auxiliary principle" is wrong and must go.

How, then, should we cumulate jnd's? The simplest, most obvious procedure (which has very often been used exactly because it is simplest and most obvious) is simply to add them up one at a time. If the first jnd on a primary stimulus continuum is 5 stimulus units, then two points on our cumulated jnd scale should be 0, 0 and 1, 5, where the first number is the scale value on the y axis and the second number is the corresponding stimulus value on the x axis. If we then find that the size of the stimulus jnd at 5 on the stimulus continuum is 8, then the third point is 2, 13. If we find that the size of the stimulus jnd at 13 is 10, then the fourth point is 3, 23, and so on.

Fechner and some of his more modern imitators went way out of their way to avoid this simple and sensible procedure; in retrospect it is hard to decide why they did so. At any rate, the next two sections of this paper will develop a formal mathematical solution to Fechner's mathematical problem — a solution which turns out to be the mathematical equivalent of the simple graphical or arithmetic technique discussed in the previous paragraph. The mathematical problem centers about how to fill in the curve between the discrete points arrived at by the graphical method.

What mathematical tools can we use to replace Fechner's "mathematical auxiliary principle"? Equation (1), and the corresponding ones based on other Weber functions, can be solved directly without any mathematical auxiliary principles or other further assumptions. They are examples of what mathematicians call functional equations. The papers on which most of our discussion is based (5, 6) were published in the 1880s, twenty years after Fechner first published his work.

The kind of functional equation implied by the definition of equality of sensation jnd's is soluble for a very wide class of Weber functions. Unfortunately, there is an infinity of inherently different solutions to each of these equations. However, further consideration of what we mean by a sensation scale will lead us to properties which we usually take for granted and which are enough to narrow the solutions down to just one interval scale, unique except for its zero point and unit of measurement. It is interesting that in the case of the linear generalization of Weber's law, and in that case only, the functional-equation solution is the same as that obtained by Fechner's auxiliary principle; for all other Weber functions the two solutions are different.

First, we will state the general mathematical problem and its solution. Let x, $x \geq 0$, denote a typical value of the stimulus continuum, and let u denote the (unknown) Fechner function. Let g be the (given) Weber function; i.e., a stimulus magnitude y, $y \geq x$, is detected as larger (in a statistical sense) than x if $y > x + g(x)$, whereas it is not discriminated as different from x if $x \leq y \leq x + g(x)$. We write $x + g(x) = f(x)$. By definition, a sensory jnd at the sensation $u(x)$ is given by the increment[1]

$$u[\,f(x)] - u(x)$$

(In the usual "delta" notation, $g(x) = \Delta x$ and $u[\,f(x)] - u(x) = \Delta u$.) The condition that sensation jnd's be equal simply means that all sensation jnd's are a constant, which we may take to be 1 for convenience, since an arbitrary change of unit does not matter. Thus, we have our major mathematical problem:

> Find those real-valued differentiable functions u, defined for all $x \geq 0$, such that $u[\,f(x)] - u(x) = 1$, for all $x \geq 0$.

Note that we have said *those* functions, not *that* function, for there may be more than one such function. This uniqueness question has not traditionally been raised, for so long as the problem was formulated in terms of linear differential equations, the uniqueness theorems of that branch of mathematics insured only one solution. In the realm of functional equations, we have no such assurances.

It is very lucky that the functional equation which has arisen in this

[1] Throughout this paper we shall have to use functions of functions. In general, if v and w are two real-valued functions of a real variable x, $v[w(x)]$ denotes the number obtained by calculating $y = w(x)$ and then finding $v(y)$. Clearly, the order of writing v and w is material, for $v[w(x)]$ does not generally equal $w[v(x)]$. Consider, for example, $v(x) = ax$, where $a \neq 1$, and $w(x) = x^2$. Then, $v[w(x)] = v(x^2) = ax^2$, whereas $w[v(x)] = w(ax) = a^2x^2$.

problem is one of the more famous in the literature; it is called Abel's equation.[2] The principal results we shall need concerning this equation were presented by Koenigs (5, 6) in 1884 and 1885.[3] First, we will present his uniqueness results, which illustrate the method of attack and lead up to the general solution. Suppose that $u_0(x)$ is a solution to Abel's equation, and suppose $p(x)$ is an arbitrary periodic function with period 1 — in other words, any function satisfying

$$p(x + 1) = p(x)$$

$K \sin 2\pi x$ is periodic with period 1, and so is an example of a function $p(x)$. It is easy to show that the function $u_p(x) = u_0(x) + p[u_0(x)]$ is also a solution to Abel's equation:

$$\begin{aligned} u_p[\,f(x)] &= u_0[\,f(x)] + p\{u_0[\,f(x)]\} \\ &= 1 + u_0(x) + p[1 + u_0(x)] \\ &= 1 + u_0(x) + p[u_0(x)] \\ &= 1 + u_p(x) \end{aligned}$$

Furthermore, it can be shown that if u and u^* are two solutions to Abel's equation, then there exists a periodic function p with period 1 such that

$$u(x) = u^*(x) + p[u^*(x)]$$

Thus, if we have any solution u_0 to our problem and if we choose p to be a differentiable periodic function with period 1, then $u_p = u_0 + p(u_0)$ is also differentiable and solves the problem.

In the case of Weber's law, we have $f(x) = kx$, $k > 1$, and the differentiable function

$$u_0(x) = \frac{\log x}{\log k}$$

is easily shown to satisfy the condition of equal sensation jnd's. Therefore,

$$\frac{\log x}{\log k} + p\left(\frac{\log x}{\log k}\right)$$

is also a solution if p is differentiable and periodic with period 1.

[2] Sometimes this equation is spoken of as the Abel-Schroder equation, but more often Abel's name is attached to this equation and Schroder's name to the equation $v[\,f(x)] = cv(x)$, which arises from Abel's equation through the substitution $v = c^u$.

[3] We are indebted to Richard Bellman of The Rand Corporation for directing us to the literature on the Abel equation.

There is an infinity of such functions p, and so an infinity of different solutions to the problem for any Weber function, including Weber's law. This, of course, is quite unsatisfactory; later on we will show that one of the properties that we usually attribute to jnd's, and which as yet we have not used, enables us to insure a unique solution. However, first it will be useful to present Koenigs's results on the existence of solutions to Abel's equation.

THE EXISTENCE OF SOLUTIONS
TO ABEL'S EQUATION

In psychophysical problems, there is always a threshold $R > 0$, such that $g(x)$ is not observable in the range $0 \leq x \leq R$. Thus, it is only a matter of convenience what we assume about the behavior of g near 0; we shall suppose that

$$g(0) = 0 \quad \text{and} \quad 0 < g'(0) < \infty$$

where

$$g'(x) = \frac{dg}{dx}.$$

It is known also from experimental work that g is never 0 and that on the whole it will increase with x, except for limited ranges of some stimuli, where it may decrease slowly. With little or no loss of generality, we may suppose it never decreases so rapidly as to have a slope less than -1. In other words, we also assume:

$$g(x) > 0 \quad \text{and} \quad g'(x) > -1 \quad \text{for} \quad x > 0$$

From these assumptions, it follows that $f(x) = x + g(x)$ has these properties:

f is strictly monotonic in x, i.e., if $x < y$, then $f(x) < f(y)$;
0 is the only fixed point of f (x is a fixed point if $f(x) = x$);
and $1 < f'(0) < \infty$.

The strict monotonicity of f implies that there exists an inverse function f^{-1}, i.e., a function such that

$$f^{-1}[f(x)] = x = f[f^{-1}(x)]$$

It is easy to show that:

f^{-1} is strictly monotonic increasing, x is a fixed point
of f^{-1} if and only if $x = 0$, $0 < f^{-1\prime}(0) < 1$.

Observe that if we know a solution v to the equation

$$v[f^{-1}(x)] = 1 + v(x) \tag{3}$$

then $u = -v$ is a solution to

$$u[f(x)] = 1 + u(x) \tag{4}$$

So it will suffice to deal with f^{-1}. If, in addition to the three properties mentioned, f^{-1} is analytic, i.e., if there exist constants a_i such that

$$f^{-1}(x) = \sum_{i=0}^{\infty} a_i x^i,$$

then Koenigs has shown that a differentiable solution exists to Abel's equation. In applications, analyticity is no real restriction. For simplicity of notation, let us denote f^{-1} by h; then Koenigs's theorem (which is not easy to prove) may be expressed as follows: Let $h^{(n)}$ denote the nth iterate of h (i.e., $h^{(n)}(x)$ is the result of n successive applications of h beginning at the point x), and let

$$\phi(x) = \lim_{n \to \infty} \frac{h^{(n)}(x)}{[h'(0)]^n}$$

then ϕ exists and is differentiable, and

$$v_0(x) = \frac{\log \phi(x)}{\log h'(0)}$$

is a solution to Abel's Equation 3. Therefore, since $h'(0) = 1/f'(0)$,

$$u_0(x) = \frac{\log \phi(x)}{\log f'(0)}$$

is a solution to Equation (4) and so to our problem.

The difficult part of the proof is to show that the limit exists. Assuming that it does, it is easy to show that $u_0(x)$ is a solution. Since $h[f(x)] = x$,

$$
\begin{aligned}
u_0[f(x)] &= \left\{ \log \lim_{n \to \infty} \frac{h^{(n)}[f(x)]}{[h'(0)]^n} \right\} \Big/ \log f'(0) \\
&= \left\{ \log \frac{1}{h'(0)} \lim_{n \to \infty} \frac{h^{(n-1)}(x)}{[h'(0)]^{n-1}} \right\} \Big/ \log f'(0) \\
&= \frac{\log f'(0) + \log \lim_{n \to \infty} \dfrac{h^{(n-1)}(x)}{[h'(0)]^{n-1}}}{\log f'(0)} \\
&= 1 + u_0(x)
\end{aligned}
$$

The evaluation of the above limit for ϕ is rarely a simple task. Furthermore, the conditions under which it has been shown to exist and to provide a solution to Abel's equation are only sufficient conditions — there are other circumstances in which solutions exist. For example, the function $f(x) = ax^b$, $b \neq 1$, fails to satisfy $1 < f'(0) < \infty$, yet by direct verification one can show that

$$u_0(x) = \frac{\log \log [a^{1/(b-1)}x]}{\log b}$$

satisfies $u_0(ax^b) = 1 + u_0(x)$. The function $f(x) = x + ax^b$ also fails to meet the same condition, but a solution probably exists in this case too. Presumably, other functions can be found which approximate empirical data and which meet the assumed conditions, but it remains to be seen whether the limit ϕ can be evaluated. The difficulty is, first, in inverting f, and second, in finding a simple expression for $h^{(n)}$. Since this is generally difficult, we doubt that the mathematics of this section will be useful to psychophysicists who want a nongraphic method for cumulating jnd's.

It should be pointed out again that for the empirically important Weber function $g(x) = kx + c$ the solution is known: it is

$$u_0(x) = \frac{\log (kx + c)}{\log (1 + k)}$$

A FURTHER DEFINITION
OF THE SENSATION CONTINUUM

So far we have examined two formulations of Fechner's problem, both of which are unsatisfactory. The first, that of Fechner, contains an internal contradiction. The second, the functional equation formulation, we have shown can be solved. Unfortunately, we have also shown that it has infinitely many families of different solutions, which is intolerable. In this section we shall propose an addition to the second formulation which amounts to a method of summating jnd's. We shall show that if we demand a particular form of invariance of distances measured in jnd units, then there is a unique (except for zero and unit) sensation scale for each of a wide variety of Weber functions, and for Weber's law this sensation scale is Fechner's law.

The common psychological custom for measuring distances in jnd's between two points is to use the size of the jnd at the lower point as the unit of measurement. Although it is rarely if ever explicitly stated, it is certainly implicitly assumed that if the distances *ab* and *cd* are both α stimulus jnd's in length, then they have an equal number, say $K(\alpha)$, of sensation jnd's. As a formal mathematical condition, this states that

$$u[x + \alpha g(x)] - u(x) = K(\alpha)$$

where K is some fixed, but unknown, function of α. It can be shown, first, that if u is a solution to this problem, then it must be the integral

$$\int \frac{dx}{g(x)}$$

given by Fechner, but, second, that there are no solutions except when $g(x) = cx$ (Weber's law). We will not present a proof of this result since it is a blind alley, but we believe that it suggests that this customary measurement of distances should be abandoned.

We must now consider how such distances really should be measured. If x and y are more than one jnd apart, we may expect the size of the jnd to change as we go from x to y. That fact should be taken into account in using jnd's as units of measurement; failure to take it into account is what makes Fechner's auxiliary principle and the standard measuring procedure unacceptable. We shall proceed to formulate this more sensible method of using jnd's as measuring units.

Let $f(x) = x + g(x)$; then the point $f(x)$ is one x-jnd larger than x. The point $f[f(x)] = f^{(2)}(x)$ is one $f(x)$-jnd larger than $f(x)$. In general $f^{(n)}(x)$ is one $f^{(n-1)}(x)$-jnd larger than the point $f^{(n-1)}(x)$. Clearly, for $y > x$, we can find some integer n such that

$$f^{(n)}(x) \leq y < f^{(n+1)}(x)$$

and it is reasonable to say that y is between n and $n + 1$ jnd's larger than x. For the moment, let us suppose that y was chosen so that $y = f^{(n)}(x)$, then we can say y is exactly n jnd's larger than x. It seems plausible to require that the same be true of the sensory continuum, i.e.,

$$u[f^{(n)}(x)] - u(x) = n$$

In words, we are saying that if point y is 20 stimulus jnd's higher than point x on the stimulus continuum, then it must also be 20 sensation jnd's higher than point x on the sensation continuum. If the above condition is met for $n = 1$ (in other words, if all sensation jnd's for a given sensory continuum are equal), then it must also be met for all larger values of n, since

$$u[f^{(n)}(x)] - u(x) = u\{f[f^{(n-1)}(x)]\} - u(x)$$
$$= 1 + u[f^{(n-1)}(x)] - u(x)$$
$$\cdots$$
$$= n$$

But this takes care of relatively few points, and does not allow us to say exactly how many jnd's y is from x unless the difference is a whole number of jnd's. We must find a definition which tells us how to subdivide a jnd into fractional parts. How to do this is not obvious, since the definition of distances given above involves iterates of f, and these are apparently defined only for integers. Fortunately, it is possible to generalize the notion of an iterate to arbitrary, rather than integral, indices. This problem is closely related to that of Abel's functional equation which Koenigs examined; we shall be able to use his results.

First, we can set up some properties that a generalized iterate $f^{(t)}(x)$, where t is any non-negative number, should meet. In essence, they amount to stipulating that $f^{(t)}(x)$ should coincide with the usual definition when t is an integer and that the same law of composition should hold. Formally, it is sufficient to require that

$$f^{(0)}(x) = x, f^{(1)}(x) = f(x)$$

and for every s and $t \geq 0$,

$$f^{(s+t)}(x) = f^{(s)}[f^{(t)}(x)]$$

For integers, the generalized iterate coincides with the usual notion, as you can see, by repeatedly applying the last condition to the second one.

We have already presented a result of Koenigs which showed that if f is strictly monotonic and analytic, $1 < f'(0) < \infty$, and 0 is the only fixed point of f, then there exists a function ϕ defined in terms of the iterates of f^{-1} such that

$$u_0(x) = \frac{\log \phi(x)}{\log f'(0)}$$

is a basic solution to Abel's equation. This means that ϕ is itself a solution to what is called Schroder's equation

$$v[f(x)] = f'(0)v(x)$$

which is obtained from Abel's by taking exponentials on both sides.

Using this fact and following Koenigs, it is easy to show that ϕ^{-1} exists and that the function

$$f^{(t)}(x) = \phi^{-1}\{[\,f'(0)]^t\phi(x)\}$$

satisfies the three conditions of a generalized iterate. We show the latter. First,

$$f^{(0)}(x) = \phi^{-1}[\phi(x)] = x$$

Second,

$$f^{(1)}(x) = \phi^{-1}[\,f'(0)\phi(x)]$$

And so, using the fact that ϕ satisfies Schroder's equation,

$$\phi[\,f^{(1)}(x)] = f'(0)\phi(x) = \phi[\,f(x)]$$

Hence,

$$f^{(1)}(x) = f(x)$$

Finally,

$$\begin{aligned}
f^{(s)}\,[\,f^{(t)}(x)] &= \phi^{-1}[[\,f'(0)]^s\phi(\phi^{-1}\{[\,f'(0)]^t\phi(x)\})] \\
&= \phi^{-1}\{[\,f'(0)]^s[\,f'(0)]^t\phi(x)\} \\
&= \phi^{-1}\{[\,f'(0)]^{s+t}\phi(x)\} \\
&= f^{(s+t)}(x)
\end{aligned}$$

So, with this definition of the generalized iterate we can generalize the above definition of distances in jnd's to prescribe how to deal with fractional jnd's.

We reformulate our major mathematical problem:

> Given a Weber function g which is analytic, $g'(x) > -1$ for all $x > 0$, $g'(0) > 0$, and $g(0) = 0$, to find those functions $u(x)$ such that $u[\,f^{(t)}(x)] - u(x) = t$, for all $x > 0$, and all $t > 0$, where $f^{(t)}$ is the generalized iterate of $f(x) = x + g(x)$.

Note that by setting $t = 1$, this condition implies the equality of sensation jnd's.

First, we show that:

$$u_0(x) = \frac{\log\phi(x)}{\log f'(0)}$$

solves the reformulated problem:

$$
\begin{aligned}
u_0[\,f^{(t)}(x)] - u_0(x) &= \frac{\log \phi[\,f^{(t)}(x)]}{\log f'(0)} - \frac{\log \phi(x)}{\log f'(0)} \\
&= \frac{\log \{[\,f'(0)]^t \phi(x)\} - \log \phi(x)}{\log f'(0)} \\
&= \frac{t \log f'(0)}{\log f'(0)} \\
&= t
\end{aligned}
$$

Second, from the results about Abel's equation, we know that if there are any other solutions to this problem, they must be of the form $u_p = u_0 + p(u_0)$, where p is periodic with period 1. For u_p actually to solve the reformulated problem, it is necessary that for every $t \geq 0$,

$$
\begin{aligned}
t &= u_p[\,f^{(t)}(x)] - u_p(x) \\
&= u_0[\,f^{(t)}(x)] + p\{u_0[\,f^{(t)}(x)]\} - u_0(x) - p[u_0(x)] \\
&= t + p[t + u_0(x)] - p[u_0(x)]
\end{aligned}
$$

Thus, for every $t \geq 0$,

$$
p[t + u_0(x)] = p[u_0(x)]
$$

That is, p must be periodic with every period t, and so p is a constant. Thus, up to an additive constant, u_0 is the unique function which solves our reformulated problem.

In nonmathematical language, introducing the method of measuring fractional jnd's has enabled us to eliminate all solutions to Abel's equation save u_0, thus cutting down the number of acceptable solutions from infinity to one.

We conclude, therefore, that the condition stated in the reformulated problem constitutes an acceptable definition of a psychophysical sensation continuum, in the sense that it yields a unique Fechner function for any reasonable Weber function. We also find that for Weber's law this condition yields Fechner's law. The solution of our reformulated problem may cause unhappiness because it is not the same as the integral "solution" proposed by Fechner, except in the special case of the linear generalization of Weber's law. However, we have already shown that the integral "solution" contradicts the definition of equal sensation jnd's.

It is sad that the integral is not the right solution, for its evaluation is often easy, and we fear that no working psychophysicist will find in our mathematics a tool for determining a summated jnd scale any better or more efficient than the simple graphic procedure of adding jnd's up one at a time.

THE STATISTICAL NATURE OF JND'S

So far we have sounded as though we were treating jnd's as fixed quantities, although every psychophysicist knows that jnd's are statistical fictions, defined by an arbitrarily chosen cutoff on a cumulative frequency curve. However, we now show that our method of reducing the infinity of solutions to Abel's equation to one is equivalent to treating jnd's as just such statistical fictions.

We start with the old, famous psychological rule of thumb: equally often noticed differences are equal, unless always or never noticed. We define $P(y,x)$ as the probability that y is discriminated as larger than x. Now, this rule of thumb simply means that on the sensation continuum the function $P(y,x)$ is transformed in such a way that it no longer depends on x and y separately, but only on the difference of their transformed values. Put another way, the subjective continuum u is a strictly monotonic transformation of the stimulus continuum such that the probability that a change of δ units on the sensation scale will be detected depends only upon δ, and not on the place at which δ begins or ends.

Formally, if we are at a point x of the stimulus continuum, and therefore at $u(x)$ on the sensation scale, and if a stimulus y is presented such that $u(y) = u(x) + \delta$, then the chance that y will be detected depends upon δ, but not on x. If we note that

$$y = u^{-1}[u(x) + \delta]$$

then the condition is that

$$P\{u^{-1}[u(x) + \delta], x\} = P(\delta)$$

Our problem is to decide under what conditions this problem has a solution and what that solution is. To this end, we make the assumption that for each x, $P(y,x)$ is a strictly monotonic increasing function of y.

We show the following: If the above problem has a solution, then there exists a function $f(x)$ such that $P[f^{(t)}(x), x]$ is independent of x, where $f^{(t)}(x)$ is the tth iterate of $f(x)$ previously defined. The function $f(x) - x$ is a Weber function naturally defined in terms of P. If there is a solution, it is unique and it is the solution u_0 to Abel's equation

$u[f(x)] - u(x) = 1$. In other words, if there is any solution to the problem of equally often noticed differences being equal, then it is unique and it is the solution to our proposed reformulation of Fechner's problem.

The proof is comparatively simple and runs as follows. Suppose there exists a solution u to the condition that $P\{u^{-1}[u(x) + \delta], x\}$ is independent of x for all $\delta \geq 0$. Since P is strictly montonic in y for all x, there is a unique solution to $P(y,x) = k$ for each k, $0 < k < 1$; call it $y = f_k(x)$. For any δ, let $k = P(\delta)$, and so by our assumption u must satisfy

$$u^{-1}[u(x) + \delta] = f_\delta(x)$$

where we have written f_δ for $f_{P(\delta)}$. Applying u to this, we have

$$u[f_\delta(x)] - u(x) = \delta$$

Let $f = f_1$. We observe that if $\delta = 0$, then $f_0(x) = x$. Suppose we choose any δ, $\epsilon \geq 0$ and let $y = f_\epsilon(x)$; then

$$\begin{aligned}
\delta &= u[f_\delta(y)] - u(y) \\
&= u\{f_\delta[f_\epsilon(x)]\} - u[f_\epsilon(x)] \\
&= u\{f_\delta[f_\epsilon(x)]\} - u(x) - \epsilon
\end{aligned}$$

Thus,

$$u\{f_\delta[f_\epsilon(x)]\} - u(x) = \delta + \epsilon$$

But, from above,

$$u[f_{\delta+\epsilon}(x)] - u(x) = \delta + \epsilon$$

so

$$u[f_{\delta+\epsilon}(x)] = u\{f_\delta[f_\epsilon(x)]\}$$

whence

$$f_{\delta+\epsilon}(x) = f_\delta[f_\epsilon(x)]$$

Thus, we have shown that f_δ must satisfy the three conditions of a generalized iterate of f, i.e., $f_\delta = f^{(\delta)}$ for all δ, so a necessary condition for a solution is that

$$P[f^{(\delta)}(x), x]$$

shall be independent of x. From the fact that $u[f_\delta(x)] - u(x) = \delta =$

$u[f^{(\delta)}(x)] - u(x)$, it follows that the solution is unique and that it is the same as that given for our reformulation of Fechner's problem.

It probably is not obvious, but the point of this section extends beyond sensory psychophysics into the scaling procedures based on Thurstone's law of comparative judgment. Case V of that law is based on the assumption that equally often noticed differences are equal unless always or never noticed. This fact has two interesting implications. The first and more obvious one is that these two apparently different branches of psychological measurements are actually doing the same thing (namely, using a measure of confusion as a unit of measurement by assuming that confusion is equal at all places on the subjective scale). The second, less obvious implication is that perhaps sensory psychophysics can profit by considering, as Thurstone and his followers have, scaling methods with less rigid assumptions which nevertheless are based on confusability data. One of us (Luce) will pursue this possibility further in a forthcoming book (7).

GRAPHIC METHODS FOR CUMULATING JND'S

Psychophysical data do not come in mathematical form. In order to apply our method for cumulating jnd's (or Fechner's, for that matter), it is necessary either to put the Weber function into equation form, or else to develop a graphic equivalent of the appropriate mathematical operations. The graphical equivalent of Fechner's technique is well known, although rarely used (see, e.g., 15, pp. 94 and 147–148). It is, of course, wrong, since Fechner's technique is wrong. If our technique is to be of greatest applicability, we should provide a graphic equivalent also. Unfortunately, it seems difficult to find a truly convenient one. The only method we know of is to go back to the basic idea of adding up jnd's — the idea that one jnd plus one jnd is two jnd's. The method of applying this basic idea is given in Figure 1, and was discussed earlier in the paper. Its error characteristics are about the same as those of the graphic techniques of integration which have been used in the past. Unfortunately, the method is tedious; if there are 170 jnd's between absolute threshold and the upper limit of discrimination, then 170 separate operations are required to determine the cumulated-jnd scale. The errors in these successive operations do not multiply, however.

PRACTICAL EFFECTS OF THE NEW PROCEDURE

No doubt it is important to understand Fechner's logical error and to know how to avoid it, but the burning question for working psycho-

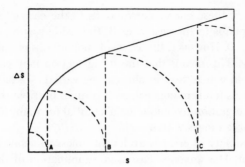

FIGURE 1   *How to cumulate jnd's. The size of the jnd at the origin is marked off on the x axis to find point A, the size of the jnd at A is marked off to find point B, and so on. The stimulus values A, B, C, . . . correspond to the points 1, 2, 3, . . . on the cumulated jnd scale.*

physicists is: What, if anything, does this do to the currently accepted conclusions about the uselessness of adding up jnd's?

First, it is easy to show that under some circumstances the difference between integration and the functional-equation solution is substantial. Consider the class of Weber functions $g(x) = ax^{1+e}$: if e is greater than zero, the asymptotic error of the integral solution as x approaches infinity is infinite; while if e is less than zero, the asymptotic error is zero. Of course, if e equals zero (Weber's law), the two procedures give identical results. The order of magnitude of the error for small numbers of jnd's depends on the constants in the equation; it can be of significant size even if e is less than zero. One way of looking at it is that the integral solution is the approximation given by the first two terms of a Taylor series expansion of the functional equation; all square and higher power terms of the expansion are omitted:

$$u[x + g(x)] - u(x) = 1$$
$$= u(x) + u'(x)g(x) + u''(x)\frac{g(x)^2}{2!} + \ldots - u(x)$$
$$= u'(x)g(x) + \left\{ u''(x)\frac{g(x)^2}{2!} + \ldots \right\}$$

A number of experimental determinations of jnd's, particularly for intensive continua, produce a curve of $g(x)/x$ that first falls and then is flat — a function often well approximated by $g(x) = kx + c$. However, for some continua the picture is less simple. There are some (pitch, for example) where the curve appears to rise again at the high end. The falling section of these curves corresponds to the case $e < 0$; the flat section corresponds to the case $e = 0$; the rising section corresponds to the case $e > 0$. However, the x axis of such graphs is usually plotted logarithmically. This means that the rising section may cover most of the range within which the stimulus can be varied — a fact which the logarithmic x axis tends to conceal. So it is quite possible that the error in using the integration technique is substantial for many sense modalities and for large ranges within each.

But the possibility of error is irrelevant unless someone has actually made the error. Has anyone? Extensive examination of the literature suggests that the answer is that not very many such errors have occurred. Some authors are quite unclear about how they added up jnd's, but many of them have preferred the step-by-step method which corresponds to the functional-equation solution because it was very simple to do. How simple it is, of course, depends on the number of jnd's to be added; we doubt very much if the jnd's for pitch will ever be added this way, since there are several thousand of them. We have found only one clear instance (15) in which the graphic equivalent of integration has been used (to cumulate pitch jnd's, as it happens), though it has been vigorously recommended. The general avoidance of the graphic equivalent of integration may be caused by shrewd intuition that something is wrong with Fechner's mathematical auxiliary principle. Or it may simply be a rare instance in which the fear of mathematical complexity has benefited science.

DO CUMULATED JND'S AGREE
WITH OTHER SCALES?

The results of cumulating jnd's have often been compared with the results of other psychophysical procedures (4). The most common finding has been that the cumulated jnd scales do not agree with scales determined by fractionation or direct magnitude estimation, at least for such continua as loudness. A review of this literature might seem appropriate here, but it is quite unnecessary, since the relation between scales based on confusion data (like cumulated jnd scales) and those based on fractionation or magnitude estimation has been extensively and excellently discussed in recent studies by Stevens (14), Stevens and Galanter (16), and Piéron (8, 9, 10).

The controversy over the relation between cumulated jnd scales and scales determined by other methods is embedded in a larger, sometimes acrimonious controversy about the relationships among various methods of sensory scaling. To some extent we shall have to enter the fray.

The first and most important question is this: Do the different scaling procedures, if properly used, lead to different scales? Unless we reject a great many experiments as improperly performed, we must answer "Yes." But the issue is not as simple or unambiguous as that answer. For example, Garner (3) has developed a loudness scale based on both fractionation and multisection judgments that fits a large number of experimental results in auditory psychophysics better than does the old sone scale (his paper was written prior to the development of the new sone scale [13]). Figure 2 shows the relationship between that scale and a cumulated jnd scale for loudness prepared by us from Riesz's data (11, 12). The two scales seem to be roughly linearly related — but does it mean anything for the controversy? Riesz's procedure has often been criticized, and his data are almost 30 years old. The form of Garner's scale (which is all that matters for this argument) is based primarily on his multisection rather than his fractionation data. Scales based upon multisection data usually agree with those constructed by confusability methods; the explanation proposed by critics of these methods is that the adjustment of five or six stimuli in a multisection experiment may produce confusion among the tones being adjusted. If this argument is correct, and if the form of Garner's scale is based upon multisection data, it is not surprising that the two agree. Our reason for so extensive a discussion of Garner's scale is that loudness is the central battleground of this controversy. If the verdict of

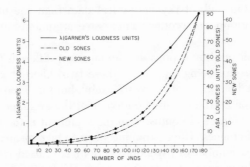

FIGURE 2 *The relation between Garner's loudness scale and Riesz's cumulated jnd scale. The old sone scale (ASA loudness scale) and Stevens's recent revision of it are included for comparison.*

psychophysical history is that confusability and multisection scales give results different from fractionation results for loudness, then psychologists will almost certainly assume that the two procedures yield different results in other intensive (or, as Stevens calls them, Class I or prothetic) continua. Unfortunately, even in psychophysics, not enough universally accepted data are available to settle the argument.

If confusability scales and scales based upon fractionation or direct magnitude estimation agree, no problem arises. If not (and we suspect they will not), psychophysicists must still evaluate each kind of procedure and its resulting scale. Some psychophysicists feel that fractionation and magnitude estimation have great face validity, and that confusability scales are distortions of the scales obtained by these procedures. They say that fractionation and estimation scales correspond to what Ss say they feel, they are obtained by straightforward procedures rather than indirect ones, and, after all, what logic is there in basing a measure of magnitude on variance or "noise."

Other psychophysicists feel that confusability scaling is the better method. They say that fractionation and estimation data are unreliable, variable, and, as a rule, at least fractionation data cannot be turned into scales unless obtained from a "good," which means extensively trained, subject. The estimation techniques have not been used enough times in enough places to indicate clearly what effect, if any, training may have on the results. Confusability scales can be obtained from untrained Ss who have no idea what form of scale is wanted from them; they can even be obtained from animals.

Each group asserts that its preferred scales are more nearly consistent with the bulk of psychophysical data than the other kind of scales; each group can produce impressive arguments to buttress its claim.

Still another position is possible: perhaps two different kinds of sensory processes are being tapped by these two different kinds of procedures. If so, both kinds of scales are useful, but for different purposes. This could well be the eventual endpoint of the argument.

Yet another source of confusion in the argument is the treatment of individual differences. The custom has been to take means or medians, and recently a number of psychophysicists have raised vigorous questions about the appropriateness of doing so. W. J. McGill [4] is currently attempting to find a better way of respecting individual differences

[4] W. J. McGill, Personal communication, 1957.

while still obtaining a "universal" scale. It will be interesting to see what light serious attempts to do justice to individual differences shed on the differences between the two classes of scales.

The status of cumulated jnd's has been controversial for more than a hundred years, and this paper is not intended as an attempt to settle the controversy. Our main point is that Fechner's problem has been improperly formulated and that the integral usually offered as a solution is not in fact a solution when the Weber function differs from $g(x) = kx + c$. We have also developed what appears to be the correct solution, only to find that in computational work it has usually been used in spite of its disagreement with the integral solution. This means that our clarification of the logical issues underlying Fechner's formulation does little to change the status of the present, primarily empirical, controversy about scaling methods. However, one of us (Luce [7]) has recently developed a way of dealing with confusability data based on a simple axiom which, if it works out successfully, may resolve the difficulty by changing our ideas about the meaning of confusability scales; this development will be described in another publication.

SUMMARY

Fechner's method for adding up just noticeable differences (jnd's) to obtain sensory scales is based on a mathematical error: he used a differential equation approximation to a functional equation instead of the functional equation itself. The functional equation can, however, be solved directly. The solution coincides with the differential equation solution only in the special case in which the linear generalization of Weber's law holds exactly. The mathematical properties of the formal solution are such that it probably will not be very useful for practical computation, but the extremely simple graphical procedure of adding up jnd's one at a time is the graphical equivalent of the mathematically correct solution. The amount of difference between the two procedures can be calculated for some special cases; its size depends on the form of the function relating size of jnd's to stimulus magnitude.

This error does not seem to have any significant impact upon the controversy over the relation between cumulated jnd scales and scales based on fractionation and direct estimation data because most psychophysicists have, in fact, ignored the recommended (incorrect) procedure and have stubbornly summated jnd's in the obvious and correct way.

REFERENCES

1. Boring, E. G. *A History of Experimental Psychology* (2nd ed.). New York: Appleton-Century-Crofts, 1950.

2. Fechner, G. T. *Elemente der Psychophysik*. (Reprint) Leipzig: Breitkopf und Härtel, 1889.

3. Garner, W. R. "A technique and a scale for loudness measurement." *J. Acoust. Soc. Amer.*, 1952, 24, 153–157.

4. Halsey, R. M. and Chapanis, A. "Luminance of equally bright colors." *J. Optical Soc. Amer.*, 1955, 45, 1–6.

5. Koenigs, M. G. "Recherches sur les intégrales de certaines équations fonctionnelles." *Ann. Scientifiques de l'École Normale Supérieure* (3), 1884, 1, Supplement, S1-S41.

6. Koenigs, M. G. "Nouvelles recherches sur les équations fonctionnelles." *Ann. Scientifiques de l'École Normale Supérieure* (3), 1885, 2, 385–404.

7. Luce, R. D. *Individual Choice Behavior: A Theoretical Analysis*. New York: Wiley, 1959.

8. Piéron, H. "L'évaluation des sensations." *Bull. Psychol., Univer. Paris*, 1950, 4, 3–38.

9. Piéron, H. *Les Problèmes Fondamentaux de la Psychophysique dans la Science Actuelle*. Paris: Hermann, 1951.

10. Piéron, H. *The Sensations, Their Functions, Processes and Mechanisms*. New Haven: Yale Univer. Press, 1952.

11. Riesz, R. R. "The differential intensity sensitivity of the ear for pure tones." *Physical Rev.*, 1928, 31, 867–875.

12. Riesz, R. R. "The relationship between loudness and minimum perceptible increment of intensity." *J. Acoust. Soc. Amer.*, 1933, 4, 211–216.

13. Stevens, S. S. "The measurement of loudness." *J. Acoust. Soc. Amer.*, 1955, 27, 815–829.

14. Stevens, S. S. "On the psychophysical law." *Psychol. Rev.*, 1957, 64, 153–181.

15. Stevens, S. S. and Davis, H. *Hearing: Its Psychology and Physiology*. New York: Wiley, 1938.

16. Stevens, S. S. and Galanter, E. H. "Ratio scales and category scales for a dozen perceptual continua." *J. Exp. Psychol.*, 1957, 54, 377–411.

STIMULUS-RANGE, NUMBER
OF CATEGORIES, AND FORM
OF THE CATEGORY-SCALE

Lawrence E. Marks

When Ss set about to partition a prothetic sensory continuum, a continuum that involves intensities of sensation such as brightness or loudness, they usually produce a scale not linearly related to the sensory scale produced by direct numeric (ratio-) estimates of sensory magnitudes.[1] The relation between partition-scales, of which the category-scale is an example, and magnitude- (ratio-) scales is typically a concave downward curve. In the experiment reported here, nine category-scales were obtained for brightness. The first aim of this study was to show that the form of the category-scale depends upon the two experimental parameters: the range of the stimuli and the number of categories available to S. The second aim was to show that the effects of these two parameters can be quantified by means of a simple equation relating the category-scale to stimulus-intensity. The same equation can be seen to apply to many other category-scales reported in the literature.

There is abundant evidence that the relationship between sensory magnitude (ψ) and stimulus-intensity (ϕ) is a power function of the form

$$\psi = k\phi^{\beta}, \tag{1}$$

where ψ is determined by one of the ratio-scaling procedures, k is a constant depending upon the units selected, and β is the exponent for the particular modality.[2] The present paper examines the possibility

From *American Journal of Psychology*, 1968, 81, 467–479. Reprinted with permission of the University of Illinois Press.

The research reported was supported by Contract F44620-67-C-0017 with the Air Force Office of Scientific Research. Reproduction for any purpose of the United States government is permitted.

[1] S. S. Stevens and E. Galanter, "Ratio scales and category scales for a dozen perceptual continua," *J. Exp. Psychol.*, 54, 1957, 377–411.

[2] S. S. Stevens, "The psychophysics of sensory function," in W. A. Rosenblith (ed.), *Sensory Communication*, 1961, 1–33.

that the category-scale, like the magnitude-scale, is a power function of stimulus-intensity, *i.e.*

$$C + C' = a\phi^{\alpha}. \tag{2}$$

Note that the category-scale is an interval-scale and has an arbitrary constant C' whose value must be estimated. It turns out that α is smaller than the exponent of the magnitude-function β. As the value of α approaches zero, the category-scale becomes more nearly a logarithmic function of stimulus-intensity.

This is not the first time that a power function has been proposed to describe the relationship between a category-scale and stimulus-intensity. For example, Garner used both an equisection procedure and ratio-scaling procedures to generate a scale for loudness.[3] He derived a power function with an exponent smaller than that found by direct ratio-scaling procedures alone. McGill found that a power function could describe interval-judgments of loudness for individual Ss.[4] All of the exponents were less than or equal to the exponent of the magnitude-function. Another example is the scale of Munsell value, determined by equating intervals of lightness of gray surfaces. Munsell value can be described quite well as the cube root of reflectance.[5] The exponent (0.33) is much smaller than the exponent β (about 1.2) of the magnitude-function for lightness of gray surfaces.[6] Finally, S. S. Stevens pointed out that the results of interval-scaling experiments often confirm a power function, although the exponents are smaller than those governing magnitude-functions.[7] The present proposal, however, goes beyond the statement that Equation 2 is able to describe the relationship between category-scales and stimulus-intensity. Many curvilinear functions can be rectified by means of an estimated parameter, such as C' in Equation (2). More significantly, it is proposed that the value of α can serve as an index of the extent to which various experimental parameters systematically affect the form of the category-

[3] W. R. Garner, "A technique and a scale for loudness measurement," *J. Acoust. Soc. Amer.*, 26, 1954, 73–88.

[4] W. J. McGill, "The slope of the loudness function: A puzzle," in H. Gulliksen and S. Messick (eds.), *Psychological Scaling: Theory and Applications*, 1960, 67–81.

[5] L. G. Glasser, A. H. McKenney, A. H. Reilly, and P. D. Schnelle, "Cube-root color coordinate system," *J. Opt. Soc. Amer.*, 48, 1958, 736–740; J. L. Saunderson and B. I. Milner, "A further study of ω space," *J. Opt. Soc. Amer.*, 34, 1944, 167–173; Stevens and Galanter. *op. cit.*, 399.

[6] Stevens and Galanter, *op. cit.*, 398–399.

[7] S. S. Stevens, "To honor Fechner and repeal his law," *Science*, 133, 1961, 81.

scale. It will be seen that the effects of stimulus-range and number of categories on the form of the category-scale for brightness can be expressed as a change in the value of α and that α is always greater than zero and less than 0.33, the exponent β of the brightness-function.[8]

METHOD

The white light from a 500 w. projector passed through a diffuser into a dark room. A circular aperture of 0.7 cm. diameter was placed in front of the diffuser. The angle subtended by the target was 1° with S 40 cm. from the aperture. The luminance of the unattenuated light was 114 db. re 10^{-10} Lam. This luminance could be attenuated by neutral-density filters in the path of the beam. After dark-adapting with red goggles for 10 min., S sat in the booth with his head in a chin rest. The viewing was binocular. The S was first shown the lowest luminance for the session (74, 64, or 59 db.) and told to call it 1; next, he was shown the highest luminance for the session (89, 94, or 104 db.) and told to call it 4 (or 20, or 100). Then each of six stimuli (74–89 db. in 3 db. steps, 64–94 db. in 6 db. steps, or 59–104 db. in 9 db. steps) was shown in an irregular order, twice each in the course of the session. Each stimulus lasted 1 sec., and about 20 sec. separated presentations. Twelve undergraduate and medical students served as Ss, each in all nine experiments. The order of participation in the nine experiments was varied from S to S according to a counterbalanced design. Each S participated in three experiments on each of three different days. Ten minutes of rest were given between experiments run on the same day.

RESULTS

The average category assigned to each stimulus is plotted as a function of log luminance in Fig. 1 for each of the nine experiments. If the category-scale were a logarithmic function of luminance, as some researchers have claimed,[9] then each set of points should approximate

[8] J. C. Stevens and S. S. Stevens, "Brightness function: Effects of adaptation," *J. Opt. Soc. Amer.*, 53, 1963, 375–385; L. E. Marks and J. C. Stevens, "Individual brightness functions," *Percept. & Psychophys.*, 1, 1966, 17–24.

[9] E. Galanter, "Contemporary psychophysics," in *New Directions in Psychology*, 1962, 141–153; W. R. Thurlow and L. E. Melamed, "Some new hypotheses on the mediation of loudness judgments," *Percept. and Psychophys.*, 2, 1967, 77–80; W. S. Torgerson, "Distances and ratios in psychological scaling," *Acta Psychol.*, 19, 1961, 201–205.

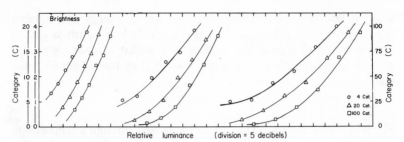

FIGURE 1   *Arithmetic averages of brightness-categories* (C) *assigned to each stimulus as a function of log luminance for nine experiments. (The three groups of functions are, from left to right, for a 15-db. stimulus-range [74-89 db.], for a 30-db. stimulus-range [64-94 db.], and for a 45-db. stimulus-range [59-104 db.]. Each point is the average of 24 judgments.)*

a straight line in these semilog coordinates. Nevertheless, the functions are clearly concave upward, their exact shape depending on both the stimulus-range and number of categories. Note, however, that it is not possible to decide whether the effects are due to stimulus-range or to stimulus-separation for these experiments.

All nine category-scales also appear in Fig. 2. Here the data have been fitted by the equation

$$\log (C + C') = \alpha \log B + \log a, \tag{3}$$

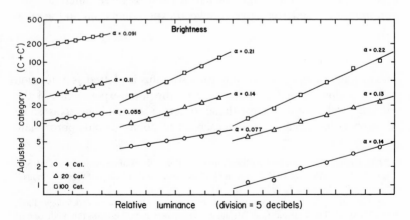

FIGURE 2   *Category-estimates* (C) *from Fig. 1 plotted as* C + C' *vs. log luminance, a value of* C' *estimated for each category-scale.*

which is the logarithmic form of Equation (2) (where B is luminance). The values of C' were estimated by the following procedure. For each category-scale a large number of values of C' were entered in Equation (3). For each value of C' a straight line was fitted to the data by the method of least squares in order to generate a value of α and a value of $\log a$. In addition, a Pearson correlation coefficient (r) was computed between $\log (C + C')$ and $\log B$. Finally, the value of C' was selected that maximized the value of r. The upper section of Table I contains, for each category-scale, the maximum values of the correlation coefficient r and the associated values of C' and α. Equation (3) fits the data quite well. Note that the slopes (values of the exponent α) tend to increase both with increasing stimulus-range and with increasing number of categories. The smallest slope ($\alpha = 0.055$ for four categories and a 15 db. range) is ⅙ the value of the brightness-exponent β (0.33), whereas the largest slope ($\alpha = 0.22$ for 100 categories and a 45 db. range) is ⅔ the value of the brightness-exponent.

DISCUSSION

Number of Categories and Scales for Loudness

The effect of the number of available categories is also seen in data of H. Rubin.[10] Five category-scales for loudness were plotted as a function of the magnitude-scale for loudness (sones); the differences in curvature produced by varying the number of categories are not easy to judge in such plots. The differences become prominent, however, in Fig. 3, which is a log-log plot of category-ratings *vs.* sound-pressure. Values of C' were estimated by the same procedure used for the brightness-scales (see Table I). Functions 1–5 were obtained for 3, 7, 20, 100, and an unlimited number of categories, respectively. As the number of categories increased, the exponent of the best-fitting power function also increased. The value of α was always less than 0.6, the value of the exponent β of the sone-function.[11] Although the largest exponent was obtained when the range of categories was unlimited, the range of categories used by the average S in that condition was typically less than 100. Thus the maximum number of categories available may not be the critical factor involved.

[10] Reported in Stevens and Galanter, *op. cit.*, 391.

[11] S. S. Stevens, "The direct estimation of sensory magnitudes: Loudness," this journal, 69, 1956, 1–25.

TABLE I

Values of C' That Give Best Fit to the Equation log $(C+C')=\alpha \log \phi + \log a$

(where C is a value on a category-scale and ϕ is stimulus-magnitude. Also entered are the associated values of r and α, and of β, the exponent of the corresponding magnitude-scale.)

Modality	Investigator	Parameters		C'	r	α	β
Brightness	Marks	Number of categories	Range in db.				
		4	15	10.5	.999	0.055	
		4	30	3.25	.991	0.077	
		4	45	0.1	.990	0.14	
		20	15	27.0	.999+	0.11	
		20	30	8.8	.997	0.14	0.33
		20	45	4.7	.999+	0.13	
		100	15	185.0	.991	0.091	
		100	30	25.0	.997	0.21	
		100	45	10.4	.997	0.22	
Loudness	H. Rubin[b]	Number of categories					
		3		0.4	.991	0.15	
		7		1.3	.997	0.18	
		20		1.5	.998	0.25	0.60
		100		13.0	.996	0.25	
		Unlimited		2.1	.997	0.29	

Continuum	Reference	Description				
Loudness	Garner[c]		2.7	.994	0.16	←
	S. S. Stevens and Guirao[d]	Softness[a]	9.1	.999	0.14	
		Loudness	1.1	.998	0.30	
		Equisection	−0.56	.999+	0.50	
	S. S. Stevens and Galanter[e]	"Pure" scale	0.5	.999	0.26	0.60
	J. C. Stevens[f]	Equal db.-spacing	6.0	.997	0.13	→
		Equal sone-spacing	0.3	.998	0.33	
Repetition-rate	J. C. Stevens and Shickman[g]	Log spacing	18.0	.997	0.066	1.0
		Linear spacing	0.4	.999+	0.41	1.0
Point-brightness	S. S. Stevens and Galanter[h]		3.75	.998	0.11	0.47
Vibration	S. S. Stevens[i]		0.7	.999	0.42	0.95
Number	J. C. Stevens[j]		0.5	.997	0.54	1.0
Finger span	S. S. Stevens and Stone[k]		0.5	.996	0.75	1.3
Saturation	Panek and S. S. Stevens[l]	Paleness[a]	7.3	.999+	1.2	1.7
		Redness	−0.15	.999+	1.2	1.7

[a] Fit to the equation: $\log (C'-C) = \alpha \log \phi + \log a$.   [b] Reported in Stevens and Galanter, *op. cit.*, 391.
[c] *Ibid.*
[d] S. S. Stevens and M. Guirao, "Loudness, reciprocality, and partition scales," *J. Acoust. Soc. Amer.*, 34, 1962, 1469.
[e] Stevens and Galanter, *op. cit.*, 392.
[f] J. C. Stevens, "Stimulus spacing and the judgment of loudness," *J. Exp. Psychol.*, 56, 1958, 248.
[g] J. C. Stevens and G. M. Shickman, "The perception of repetition rate," *J. Exp. Psychol.*, 59, 1959, 438.
[h] Stevens and Galanter, *op. cit.*, 396.
[i] S. S. Stevens, "Tactile vibration: Dynamics of sensory intensity," *J. Exp. Psychol.*, 57, 1959, 212.
[j] Unpublished.
[k] S. S. Stevens and G. Stone, "Finger span: Ratio scale, category scale, and jnd scale," *J. Exp. Psychol.*, 57, 1959, 92.
[l] D. W. Panek and S. S. Stevens, "Saturation of red: A prothetic continuum," *Percept. & Psychophys.*, 1, 1966, 63.

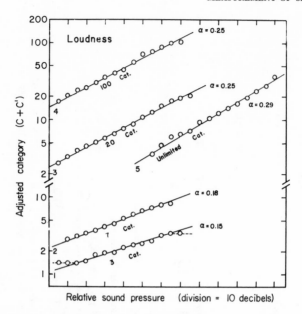

FIGURE 3 *Five category-scales for loudness* (C) *as a function of log sound-pressure.* (C + C' *is plotted on the ordinate for each scale. Data are from H. Rubin, read from graphs given by S. S. Stevens and Galanter, 1957.*)

Other Category-Scales for Loudness

Figure 4 contains seven other previously published category-scales for loudness. For these, too, the power function is able to describe quite well the relation between the category-scale and stimulus-intensity. The exponents of the functions in Fig. 4 are again all smaller than 0.6; the smallest is about ⅕ the size of the loudness-exponent, the largest about ⅝ (see Table I). The data for Functions 2–4 were reported by S. S. Stevens and Guirao.[12] Functions 2 and 3 were obtained by category-production rather than category-estimation. For Function 2 the Ss were asked to adjust softness, rather than loudness, so the category-values had to be subtracted from C'. The plotted function has the formula

$$C' - C = a\phi^{\alpha}. \tag{4}$$

[12] S. S. Stevens and M. Guirao, "Loudness, reciprocality, and partition scales," *J. Acoust. Soc. Amer.*, 34, 1962, 1469.

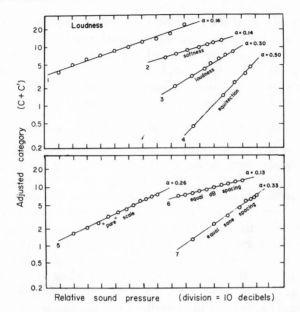

FIGURE 4   *Seven category-scales for loudness* (C) *as a function of log sound-pressure.* (C + C' *is plotted on the ordinate for each scale. Data for the functions are: 1 from Garner, read from a graph given by S. S. Stevens and Galanter, 1957; 2–4 read from graphs from S. S. Stevens and Guirao, 1962; 5 read from a graph from S. S. Stevens and Galanter, 1957; 6 and 7 from J. C. Stevens, 1958.*)

Function 4, which has the largest exponent of the three, was determined by equisection. Stevens and Guirao point out that the Ss' freedom to sample the upper and lower stimuli frequently may help to explain why their equisection scale is almost a linear function of the sone-scale.[13] Function 5 was an attempt to approximate a "pure" category-scale, *i.e.* one not affected by the particular way in which the stimuli are spaced relative to one another.[14] The data were obtained by a short-cut approximation to the iterative procedure that Stevens and Galanter suggest.[15] This function has an exponent of 0.26, a little less than half the value of the exponent of the sone-function. Functions 6 and 7 show category-scales measured by J. C. Stevens.[16]

[13] *Ibid.*, 1471.
[14] Stevens and Galanter, *op. cit.*, 392.
[15] *Loc. cit.*
[16] J. C. Stevens, "Stimulus spacing and the judgment of loudness," *J. Exp. Psychol.*, 56, 1958, 248.

The slope of Function 6 is smaller than that of Function 7. For Function 6 the stimuli were spaced by equal number of decibels; for Function 7 the stimuli were spaced to give equal intervals of loudness in sones. Since the total range of stimulation and the number of categories were the same for both functions, the difference in the exponents must have resulted from the difference in spacing alone.

Category-Scales for Other Perceptual Continua

Category-scales for a variety of perceptual continua were examined and the power function was found to describe these scales quite well. A sample appears in Fig. 5. The last section of Table I shows that the value of α was always smaller than the corresponding value of β. The large difference between the exponents for auditory repetition rate appeared to be the result of stimulus-spacing: equal logarithmic steps for Function 1 and equal linear steps for Function 2. The category-scale for numbers was obtained by presenting numbers one at a time to Ss, who rated them on a category-scale according to their apparent "largeness." [17] The exponent α was 0.54, about half the value of 1.0 that, hopefully, governs the growth of the magnitude-scale for num-

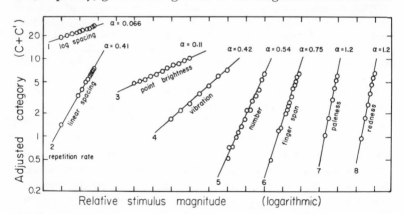

FIGURE 5   *Eight category-scales* (C) *as a function of log stimulus-magnitude.* (C + C' *is plotted on the ordinate for each scale. Data for the functions are: 1 and 2 from J. C. Stevens and Shickman, 1959; 3 read from a graph from S. S. Stevens and Galanter, 1957; 4 read from a graph from S. S. Stevens, 1959; 5 from J. C. Stevens [unpublished]; 6 read from a graph from S. S. Stevens and Stone, 1959; 7 and 8 read from graphs from Panek and S. S. Stevens, 1966.)*

[17] Unpublished data from J. C. Stevens.

ber. The last two functions of Fig. 5 relate apparent saturation of red to percentage purity.[18] Function 7 was derived from a scale for paleness (using Equation (4)), Function 8 from a scale for redness (using Equation (2)). The exponent α for both functions was about 1.2, nearly ¾ the exponent β of the magnitude-function (1.7).

"Opposite" Attributes and Category-Scales

Since use has been made of scales of "opposite" attributes (softness and paleness) to test the applicability of the power function, a discussion of the scaling of "opposite"attributes may be in order. Magnitude-scales for "opposite" attributes are usually related reciprocally to the magnitude-scales for the attributes themselves. It follows from this reciprocal relationship, and from the psychophysical power law, that if the exponent β governs the rate of growth of an attribute, then $-\beta$ governs the rate of growth of the "opposite" attribute. Examples of reciprocity are: softness and loudness,[19] darkness and lightness,[20] smoothness and roughness,[21] softness and hardness,[22] apparent fluidity and viscosity,[23] smallness and largeness of areas,[24] and shortness and longness of lines.[25]

If the category-scale and the magnitude-scale for an attribute both grow as power functions of stimulus-intensity (Equations 1 and 2), then the category-scale must be a power function of the magnitude-scale

$$C + C' = (a/k^{\alpha/\beta})\,\psi^{\alpha/\beta}. \tag{5}$$

[18] D. W. Panek and S. S. Stevens, "Saturation of red: A prothetic continuum," *Percept. & Psychophys.*, 1, 1966, 63.

[19] S. S. Stevens and Guirao, *op. cit.*, 1466–1471; B. Schneider and H. Lane, "Ratio scales, category scales, and variability in the production of loudness and softness." *J. Acoust. Soc. Amer.*, 35, 1963, 1953–1961.

[20] Torgerson, "Quantitative judgment scales," in H. Gulliksen and S. Messick (eds.), *Psychological Scaling: Theory and Applications*, 1960, 21–31.

[21] G. Ekman, J. Hosman, and B. Lindström, "Roughness, smoothness, and preference: A study of quantitative relations in individual subjects," Report No. 173, University of Stockholm, 1964; S. S. Stevens and J. R. Harris, "The scaling of subjective roughness and smoothness," *J. Exp. Psychol.*, 64, 1962, 489–494.

[22] R. Harper and S. S. Stevens, "Subjective hardness of compliant materials," *Quart. J. Exp. Psychol.*, 16, 1964, 204–215.

[23] S. S. Stevens and Guirao, "Scaling of apparent viscosity," *Science*, 144, 1964, 1157–1158.

[24] S. S. Stevens and Guirao, "Subjective scaling of length and area and the matching of length to loudness and brightness," *J. Exp. Psychol.*, 66, 1963, 177–186.

[25] *Ibid.*

If the category-scale for an "opposite" attribute grew as the $-\alpha$ power of stimulus-intensity, then Equation (5) would be equally valid for an attribute and its "opposite," and the category-scales for an attribute and its "opposite" would be reciprocally related. It has been discovered, however, that category-scales for "opposite" attributes are usually related as complements, not reciprocals.[26] It was for this reason that the negatives of the category-scales for softness and paleness were plotted as a function of stimulus-intensity in order to test the power function. Thus only for an attribute itself is the category-scale proportional to the magnitude-scale raised to the α/β power (Equation (5)). For an "opposite" attribute, the category-scale is proportional to the negative of the magnitude-scale raised to the $-\alpha/\beta$ power:

$$C + C' = -(a/k^{-\alpha/\beta})\,\psi^{-\alpha/\beta}. \tag{6}$$

What inference may be drawn from these relations with regard to the way in which Ss usually deal with "opposite" attributes? It may be that when Ss are asked to make categorical judgments of an "opposite" attribute, they merely reverse the scale that they use. For example, when asked to judge softness on a scale from 1 to 7, they may in fact judge loudness on a scale from 7 to 1. If this is so, it supports the contention that "opposite" attributes are psychologically derivative from the basic primary attributes. At least one exception exists, however, to the rule that the category-scale for an "opposite" attribute is the reverse of the category-scale for the attribute itself. Jastrow compiled data on stellar magnitude.[27] The lowest point on his scale represents the brightest stars, the highest point the dimmest stars. Thus the scale has the nature of a category-scale for the dimness of small sources. When a category-scale for an "opposite" attribute is plotted vs. log stimulus-intensity, the resulting function is typically positively decelerated. Figure 6 shows that Jastrow's stellar-magnitude scale, plotted against the average log luminance producing each magnitude (squares), yields a negatively decelerated function. Plotted directly as the attribute "dimness" (circles), that is, log $(C + C')$ vs. log luminance, the relation is approximated very well by a power function with an exponent of -0.123. For this category-scale, which is based upon nearly

[26] Schneider and Lane, loc. cit.; S. S. Stevens and Guirao, op. cit., J. Exp. Psychol., 66, 1963, 177–186; Torgerson, loc. cit.

[27] J. Jastrow, "The psycho-physic law and star magnitudes," this journal, 1, 1887, 112–127.

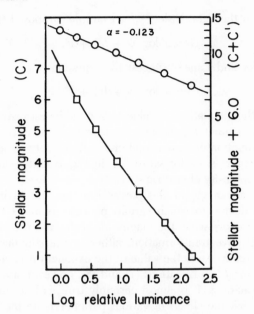

FIGURE 6   *Scale of stellar magnitude as a function of log luminance. (The squares are stellar magnitude [C]; the circles are stellar magnitude plus 6.0 [C + C']. Data from Jastrow, 1887.)*

20,000 observations, the correlation coefficient between $\log(C + C')$ and log luminance is .99996. It may be noted that the scale of stellar magnitude now in use is defined not as a power function but as a logarithmic function of luminance.

Advantage of the Power Function

Equation (2) seems to fit category-scales quite well, but are there systematic deviations? Figures 2–5 show that there are. A number of the functions are slightly sigmoid, *i.e.*, flattened at the ends, possibly due to "end effects." On a seven-point scale, for example, the S can never call the lowest stimulus anything less than 1 nor the highest stimulus anything greater than 7. This restriction could by itself impose curvature on the function. One might also object that Equation (2) is one of several functions that could describe the data equally well, especially given the freedom to introduce a constant (C') that is not represented in the data. Eisler,[28] for example, proposed the equation

$$C = a' \log (\psi + b') + c', \tag{7}$$

and Schneider and Lane [29] suggest the equation

$$C = a' \log (\phi + b') + c'. \tag{8}$$

For both of these equations, a value of b' must be estimated. Equation (8), however, cannot handle any category-scale that is a positively accelerated function of stimulus-intensity. At least two such examples exist: the category-scale for saturation in Fig. 5 and a category-scale for apparent intensity of electric shock.[30]

The main advantage of the power function lies in its ability to quantify the degree to which various parameters affect the relations among the category-scale, the magnitude-scale, and the original stimulus. Multiplicative transformation, either of the stimulus-scale or of the category-scale, leaves the value of the exponent α unchanged. The constants a' and b' in Equations (7) and (8), however, are changed by such transformations. It is almost certainly true, as Luce and Galanter have stated, that the effects of various parameters on the form of the category-scale will be fully understood only after a complete theory of category-scales has been developed.[31] The present study suggests, however, that the power function can provide at least a first-order empirical quantification of the changes in the shape of the category-scale that result from particular choices of experimental procedure.

SUMMARY

Nine category-scales were measured for brightness as a function of luminance. Their form varied with the stimulus-range and with the number of available categories. When adjusted by means of an additive constant, the category-scales can be described as power functions of stimulus-intensity. Their exponents are smaller than the exponent obtained by ratio-scaling procedures. The size of the exponent of the

[28] H. Eisler, "On the problem of category scales in psychophysics," *Scand. J. Psychol.*, 3, 1962, 81–87; Eisler, "Empirical test of a model relating magnitude and category scales," *Scand. J. Psychol.*, 3, 1962, 88–96.

[29] Schneider and Lane, *loc. cit.*

[30] S. S. Stevens, A. S. Carton, and G. M. Shickman, "A scale of apparent intensity of electric shock," *J. Exp. Psychol.*, 56, 1958, 328–334.

[31] R. D. Luce and Galanter, "Psychophysical scaling," in R. D. Luce, R. R. Bush, and E. Galanter (eds.), *Handbook of Mathematical Psychology*, 1, 1963, 268.

power function can serve as an index of how the stimulus-range and the number of categories affect the form of the category-scale. The power function is also able to describe other category-scales that have been reported for a variety of perceptual continua.

A QUANTITATIVE PRINCIPLE
OF QUALITATIVE SIMILARITY

Gösta Ekman, Trygg Engen, Teodor Künnapas,
and Ralf Lindman

Our general problem is to investigate subjective similarity between percepts as a function of the subjective attributes of the percepts that are being compared. We are not interested in stimulus properties in this context: stimuli will be used only for stimulation, i.e., for evoking certain subjective responses.

The independent variables of our experiments are the measurable subjective attributes of single percepts. The dependent variable is the measurable subjective similarity between these percepts when compared two at a time. What function is the subjective similarity between two percepts of the subjective attributes of the single percepts? How to describe the *psychological mechanism* at work?

This problem has been investigated previously for several unidimensional continua. The present investigation is a continuation and generalization of the work to multidimensional cases.

From *Journal of Experimental Psychology*, 1964, 68, 530–538. Reprinted with permission of the authors and the American Psychological Association.

The work reported in this paper was supported by research grants from the Bergvall Foundation and the Swedish Council for Social Science Research. Parts of the investigation were performed while Trygg Engen (Brown University) was a North Atlantic Treaty Organization Fellow and Ralf Lindman (University of Turku, Finland) was a research assistant at the University of Stockholm. Experimental and computational work was carried out by U. Gustafsson, I. Gustafsson, B. Lindström, C. O. Lindström, and B. Strömqvist. One experiment was performed at the Teachers College, Stockholm; the cooperation of J. Naeslund is gratefully acknowledged.

METHODS AND MODELS

A Multidimensional Ratio Scaling Method

A method for multidimensional ratio scaling has been developed by one of the present authors (Ekman, 1963). It may be characterized as a generalization of the direct unidimensional ratio scaling methods. The complete method is not necessary for the present purpose, but we shall have to make use of the kind of experimental data that are obtained in this method.

Consider Fig. 1. Two percepts, i and j, are represented by the two vectors. The relative lengths, h_i and h_j, of these vectors represent the subjective intensities of the percepts. If S were instructed to compare the subjective intensities (disregarding the qualitative difference that may exist), we should expect to obtain an estimate of the form h_i/h_j, which is a conventional ratio estimate.

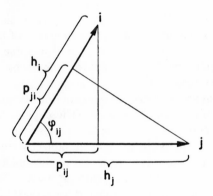

FIGURE 1   *The multidimensional ratio scaling model.*

If the two percepts differed only with regard to amount of a given subjective quality, both vectors would have the same direction. The angle φ_{ij} represents the qualitative difference between the percepts. The projection p_{ij} represents that part of percept j (e.g., a specified red) that is contained in i (e.g., a specified orange) and p_{ji} that part of i that is contained in j. In the experimental situation S is instructed to estimate, on a suitable scale, which portion of j is contained in i (e.g., "sixty-five percent of that red is present in this orange"), and vice versa. For each pair of percepts we thus obtain the two experimental estimates of the form

$$q_{ij} = p_{ij}/h_j, \tag{1}$$

$$q_{ji} = p_{ji}/h_i. \tag{2}$$

The experimental data are q_{ij} and q_{ji} for all pairs of percepts. From these data it is possible to proceed to scalar products, to which the methods of factor analysis may be applied. The final outcome of the complete analysis is a rotated factor matrix, the elements of which are the coordinates of the percepts on a set of reference axes that may represent primary subjective components (cf. Ekman, 1963). For the present purpose, however, the data may be used in a more direct way. It is seen from Fig. 1 that

$$p_{ij} = h_i \cos \varphi_{ij}, \tag{3}$$

$$p_{ji} = h_j \cos \varphi_{ij}. \tag{4}$$

From Equations (1–4) it follows that

$$\cos \varphi_{ij} = \sqrt{q_{ij}q_{ji}}. \tag{5}$$

Equation (5) will be used in the processing of our experimental data.

Models of Similarity Perception

THE UNIDIMENSIONAL SIMILARITY PRINCIPLE. In several previous experiments in this laboratory the similarity which an *O* perceives between two percepts, varying only in one dimension, was investigated as a function of the subjective properties of the percepts, i.e., their scale values on the unidimensional continuum. In the first experiment (Eisler and Ekman, 1959) the pitch of tones of constant loudness was scaled. In another part of the experiment, quantitative estimates of similarity were obtained for all pairs of different tones. It was found that the subjective similarity was a simple function of relative pitch. In the notation of this paper,

$$s_{ij} = \frac{h_i}{(h_i + h_j)/2}, (h_i \leq h_j) \tag{6}$$

where s_{ij} is the quantitative estimate of similarity on a scale from 0 to 1 (identity), and h_i, h_j are the subjective magnitudes of the percepts i, j on the unidimensional continuum.

The same relation has been verified for similarity on the unidimensional continua of brightness and visual area (Ekman, Goude, and Waern, 1961) as well as heaviness (Eisler, 1960). No exception to this rule has been observed. It is interesting to note the simplicity of th principle. One important aspect of this simplicity is the lack of empirical constants.

According to this equation, the degree of subjective similarity between two percepts, varying only in one dimension, is expressed by the ratio of the smallest subjective quantity and the arithmetic mean of the two subjective quantities.

A MODEL OF QUALITATIVE SIMILARITY. On the basis of the unidimensional similarity principle, a model has been constructed for the general case, in which percepts vary with regard to both subjective intensity and subjective quality. The theoretical part of the work will be omitted in the present context, because the general case has not yet been submitted to experimental test.

Our present multidimensional experiments have been restricted to the case, where the subjective intensity is approximately constant $(h_i = h_j)$ and only the subjective quality is varied. From the model of the general case, it is possible to derive for the special case of qualitative similarity the hypothetical equation

$$s_{ij} = \frac{\cos \varphi_{ij}}{\cos (\varphi_{ij}/2)} \cdot (h_i = h_j) \tag{7}$$

The rest of this paper is concerned with the applicability of Equation (7) to experimental data. The implications of the equation will be further discussed at the end of this paper.

PROCEDURE

Four experiments were performed in order to investigate the mechanism of similarity in a variety of situations: emotion (Exp. I), odor (Exp. II), color (Exp. III), and judgment of personality traits (Exp. IV). The selection of stimuli in Exp. I and III was partly based on previous work (Ekman, 1954a, 1954b, 1955).

EXPERIMENT I. Nine stimulus words were used, denoting various emotional states. In English translation the words were: HAPPY, PLEASED, CONTENT, SAD, GLOOMY, DEPRESSED, AGITATED, IMPATIENT, RESTLESS. The words were arranged in 12 pairs on each of six answer sheets so that each word occurred twice in combination with each of the other words, once in first position and once in second position. The order of word pairs was determined by random arrangement, and by varying the order of answer sheets the task order was rotated between Ss. The Ss were instructed to consider emotions of equal intensity and thus to make their judgments from a qualitative point of view.

EXPERIMENT II. Six odor stimuli were used, one consisting of pure amyl acetate and one of pure *n*-heptanal, the four additional stimuli being obtained by mixing these odorants in various proportions. In terms of amyl acetate concentration the stimuli were characterized by the percentages 100, 87.5, 75.0, 50.0, 25.0, and 0. One cubic centimeter of the various mixtures was kept in 11 × 80 mm. test tubes stopped with corks wrapped in aluminum foil. The *O* sniffed the odorant from cotton wool attached to the cork on a stainless steel rod 2 mm. in diameter. The cotton wool was saturated with and positioned just above the liquid in the test tube and was removed only for sniffing. The experiments were performed in a ventilated laboratory room at about 20° C. Fifteen pairs of test tubes, i.e., all different pairs of the six stimuli were presented together on a Plexiglas rack. The order of pairs was irregular. The differences between stimuli with regard to subjective intensity were small, and *Ss* were instructed to ignore such differences as might occur and to judge the quality of the odors.

EXPERIMENT III. Seven stimuli of constant brightness were chosen from the green-yellow zone of the spectrum. The spectral light was presented in two circular openings, 7 mm. in diameter and 12 mm. apart, in the front of an apparatus of a type that has been used in several previous investigations of color in this laboratory (e.g., Ekman, 1963). The stimuli were viewed from a distance of about 50 cm. Preliminary experiments were performed with the same group of *Ss* used in the main experiment in order to determine the stimulus intensities at which all wavelengths were perceived at constant brightness. Approximately monochromatic light was obtained by means of interference filters with transmission maxima at 522, 546, 560, 566, 570, 575, and 580 mμ. The experiments were performed in a dimly illuminated room. A prearranged random order of stimulus pairs was presented to each S.

EXPERIMENT IV. Ten stimulus words representing personality traits were used. In English translation the stimuli were: SHY, INHIBITED, RESERVED, UNCOMMUNICATIVE, TIMID, SELF-CENTERED, INDEPENDENT, SELF-SUFFICING, UNSOCIABLE, SILENT. The general arrangement and presentation of the stimulus words were similar to those of Exp. I. The *Ss* were instructed to disregard possible quantitative differences in the intensity of the personality traits and to base their judgments on qualitative characteristics.

Methods

RATIO ESTIMATION. The method will be described with reference to Exp. I. Each S was given the answer sheets and written instructions.

The Ss were instructed to regard the right-hand word in a word pair as a "standard" and to estimate how much of the "standard emotion" was part of the emotion denoted by the word on the left. Estimates were to be given on a percentage scale with 0 signifying that a word contained nothing of the standard emotion and 100 that all of the standard emotion was part of it. A similar procedure was adopted in the other experiments.

SIMILARITY ESTIMATION. This method will also be described with reference to Exp. I. The same answer sheets were used. The task was to estimate the similarity between the emotions represented by the words in each pair. Estimates were to be given according to a percentage scale with 0 representing "no similarity" and 100 "identity": this may, according to a previous methodological study (Ekman and Waern, 1959), be considered a ratio estimation method in which the similarity estimates are defined as percentages of identity. A similar procedure was followed in the other experiments.

In each experiment the two methods were used with different groups of Ss. (This is an essential requirement. From odor experiments not reported here, and, in particular, from special experiments performed with spectral light for a methodological purpose, it is evident that a confusion of instructions may take place in some Ss, if both methods are used with the same Ss in different sessions.)

Subjects

All Ss were students of psychology. Most of them had had some previous experience of "direct" scaling methods. In Exp. I ratio estimates were obtained from 38 Ss and similarity estimates from 41 Ss. In Exp. II the number was 10 in each condition, in Exp. III there were 15 Ss in each condition, and in Exp. IV the two groups consisted of 30 and 32 Ss, respectively.

RESULTS

The mean ratio estimates were computed separately for q_{ij} and q_{ji} as well as the mean similarity estimates for s_{ij} and s_{ji} (medians were computed in Exp. I and IV and arithmetic means in the other experiments). The experimental arrangements and the instructions given to Ss aimed at restricting the variation to the case of constant subjective intensity $(h_i = h_j)$. Plots of q_{ij} and q_{ji} showed a close linear agreement, indicating that subjective intensity was approximately constant (cf. Equations (1–4)). Estimates of cos φ_{ij} were obtained according to Equation

(5) by computing the geometric means of pairs of q_{ij} and q_{ji}. With regard to similarity estimates systematic differences between s_{ij} and s_{ji} were not to be expected and were not found. Geometric means were computed for all pairs of these means; they are our experimental estimates of similarity.

In the case of a purely qualitative variation, the hypothetical relation between subjective similarity and angular separation of the percept vectors in the subjective space is described by Equation (7). Theoretical values of similarity were computed from the cosines according to this equation. The hypothesis was tested by plotting the experimental similarity estimates against the theoretical values. The plots are shown in Fig. 2. It is seen that most points fall rather close to the line representing perfect agreement, the deviations show no systematic trend.

The data from all four experiments are summarized in Fig. 3. The least-square fit of a straight line to all data (altogether 117 points) yields

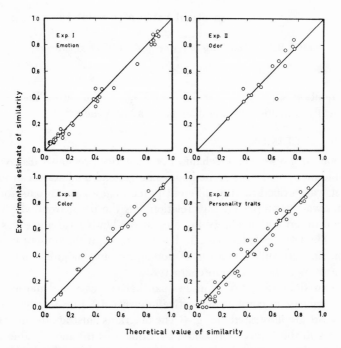

FIGURE 2 *Experimental estimates of similarity plotted against theoretical values computed according to Equation 7.*

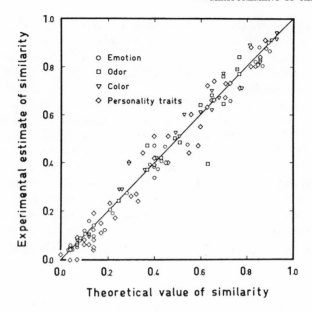

FIGURE 3   *Summary of results from all four experiments.*

the equation $s_{emp.} = -0.008 + 1.003s_{theor.}$. The fitted line would practically coincide with the diagonal drawn in the graph.

DISCUSSION

GENERAL REMARKS. The mechanism of similarity previously discovered for unidimensional cases turned out to be general in character in so far that it was verified in very different perceptual areas. An outstanding feature was its simplicity. This relation was the basis, from which the relation describing similarity in cases of qualitative variation was derived. The latter relation has also been verified, in the present investigation, in very different areas of perception and judgment and thus also appears to be general in character.

The unidimensional or "purely quantitative" case and the multidimensional case of constant subjective intensity, i.e. the "purely qualitative" case, are illustrated in Fig. 4. The diagrams illustrate the similarity relations in the forms represented by Equations (6) and (7); they also illustrate the common basic principle, in terms of which both cases can be interpreted.

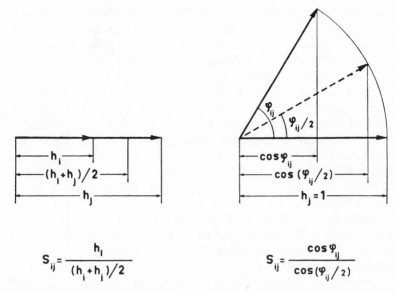

$$S_{ij} = \frac{h_i}{(h_i + h_j)/2} \qquad\qquad S_{ij} = \frac{\cos \varphi_{ij}}{\cos (\varphi_{ij}/2)}$$

FIGURE 4 *A comparison between the unidimensional and the present multidimensional similarity principles.*

In this interpretation the concept "mean percept" plays a central role.

1. In the purely quantitative case the subjective similarity is expressed by the ratio between the smallest quantity of the constant subjective quality and the mean of the two quantities.

2. In the purely qualitative case, the subjective similarity is given by the ratio between the projection (cos φ) of any of the percept vectors on the other (reference) vector, and the projection (cos ($\varphi/2$)) of the "mean percept" vector on the same reference vector.

Both principles are strikingly simple and appear basically identical. The "mean percept" entering into the present formulations of both principles may, possibly, be referred to the concept of adaptation level in its general form (Helson, 1947, 1948; cf. Eisler and Ekman, 1959).

It should be borne in mind that we have investigated the two extreme, although important, special cases of a purely quantitative and a purely qualitative variation. The generalization to the latter case was mediated by a hypothetical completely general relation that has not yet been submitted to experimental test. It remains to investigate experimentally the general case of simultaneous variation with regard to both subjective intensity and subjective quality. This is a self-suggesting line of further research.

The simplicity of the principles so far established may be an indication of a possible relative simplicity also of other psychological mechanisms. One essential feature of our work on similarity may be characterized thus: The psychological variable of similarity was studied as a function of other psychological variables — the study was "psychodynamic" (Guilford, 1939). We are rather convinced that we would not have found these simple principles if we had investigated subjective similarity as a function of stimulus variables — in so far as such variables can be defined (tonal frequency, amyl acetate concentration, wavelength) — because the simplicity of the intrasubjective, *purely psychological* mechanism would have been obscured by the psychophysical transformations.

ALTERNATIVE MODELS. The theory of the present study was developed, and the experiments were designed, with a view to homogeneous subjective states. Typical examples are percepts of color and odor as well as some emotional states. We do not expect the principle revealed in this study to apply to percepts or other psychological phenomena involving an obvious subjective structure. It is, for instance, to be expected that perception of form belongs to the latter category. Other models, possibly similar to the "city-block model" (Attneave, 1950), are more likely to apply to such cases. Work on problems of this type is now in progress.[1]

REFERENCES

Attneave, F. "Dimensions of similarity." *Amer. J. Psychol.*, 1950, 63, 516–556.
Eisler, H. "Similarity in the continuum of heaviness with some methodological and theoretical considerations." *Scand. J. Psychol.*, 1960, 1, 69–81.
Eisler, H. and Ekman, G. "A mechanism of subjective similarity." *Acta Psychol., Amsterdam*, 1959, 16, 1–10.
Ekman, G. "Dimensions of color vision." *J. Psychol.*, 1954, 38, 467–474.   (a)
Ekman, G. "Eine neue Methode zur Erlebnisanalyse." *Z. Exp. Angew. Psychol.*, 1954, 2, 167–174. (b)
Ekman, G. "Dimensions of emotion." *Acta Psychol., Amsterdam*, 1955, 11, 279–288.
Ekman, G. "A direct method for multidimensional ratio scaling." *Psychometrika*, 1963, 28, 33–41.

[1] H. Eisler, personal communication, 1963; see also Künnapas, 1964.

Ekman, G., Goude, G., and Waern, Y. "Subjective similarity in two perceptual continua." *J. Exp. Psychol.*, 1961, 61, 222–227.

Ekman, G. and Waern, Y. "A second-order ratio scale. *"Acta Psychol., Amsterdam,* 1959, 47, 343–352.

Guilford, J. P. "A study in psychodynamics." *Psychometrika*, 1939, 4, 1–23.

Helson, H. "Adaptation level as a frame of reference for prediction of psychophysical data." *Amer. J. Psychol.*, 1947, 60, 1–29.

Helson, H. "Adaptation as a basis for a quantitative theory of frame of reference." *Psychol. Rev.*, 1948, 55, 297–313.

Künnapas, T. "Multidimensional ratio scaling and multidimensional similarity of simple geometric figures." Report No. 166, 1964, University of Stockholm, Psychological Laboratory.

NAME INDEX

Page numbers in italics refer to bibliographic citations